Home Wiring

By Rex Cauldwell

Printed in 2012.

CREDITS

Dan Cary
Editor

Jen Weaverling
Managing Editor

Jenny Mahoney
Book Design and Production

SPECIAL THANKS
Steve Anderson, Kim Bailey, Craig Claeys, Brad Classon, Mario Ferro, Stephen Hutchings, Scott Jacobsen, Mark Johanson, Ralph Karlen, Bruce Kieffer, Mark Macemon, Chris Marshall, Jerry Miller courtesy of NSP, Milwaukee Electric Tool Corporation, John Nadeau, Bill Nelson, Northern States Power Company, Progress Lighting, Tad Saddoris, Tracy Walsh

ISBN 13: 978-1-58159-500-0

2 3 4 5 / 15 14 13 12

Handyman Club of America
12301 Whitewater Drive
Minnetonka, Minnesota 55343
www.handymanclub.com

Home Wiring

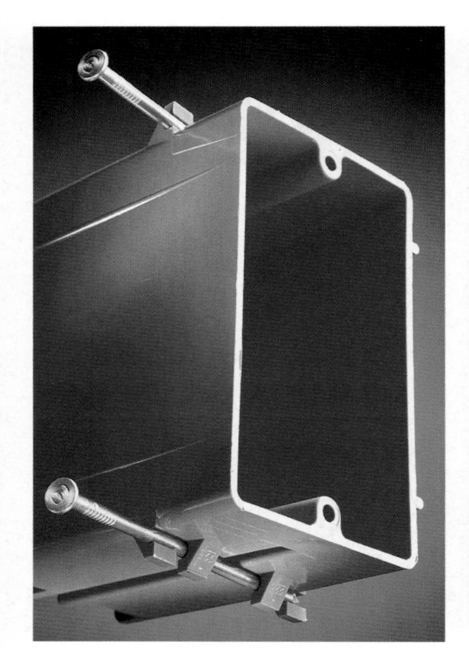

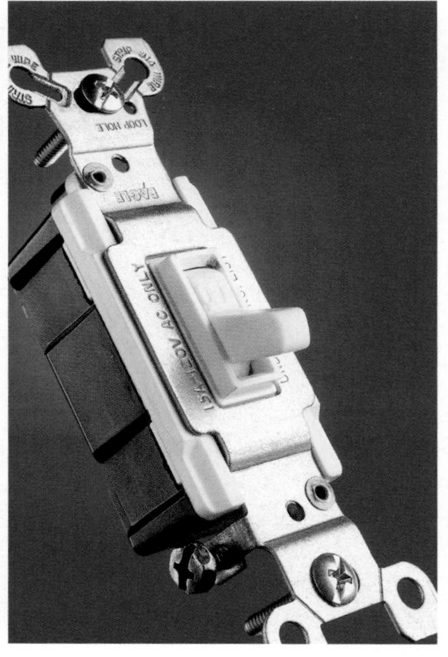

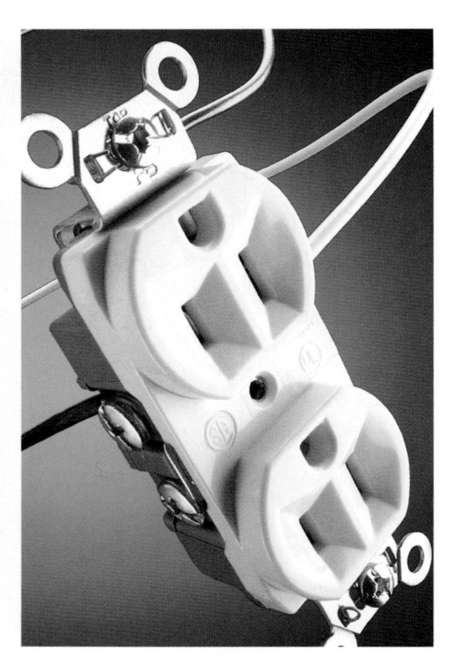

Rex Cauldwell

Handyman Club Library®

Handyman Club of America
Minnetonka, Minnesota

TABLE OF CONTENTS

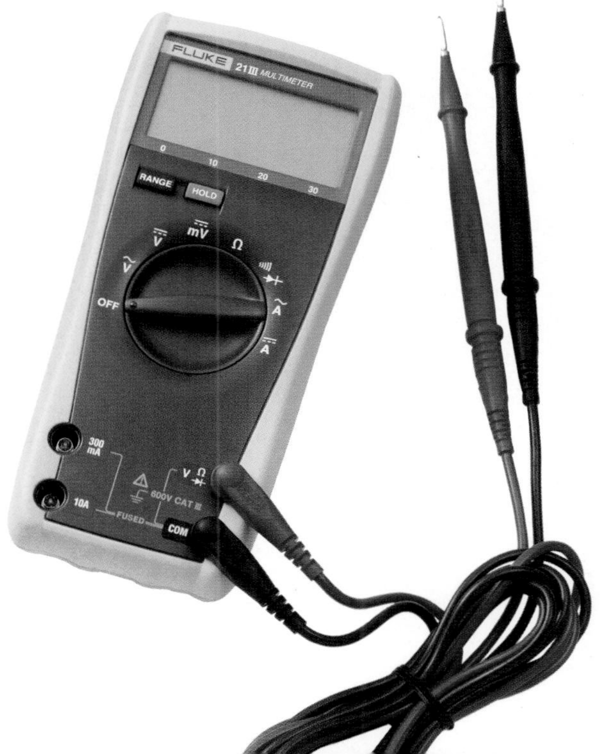

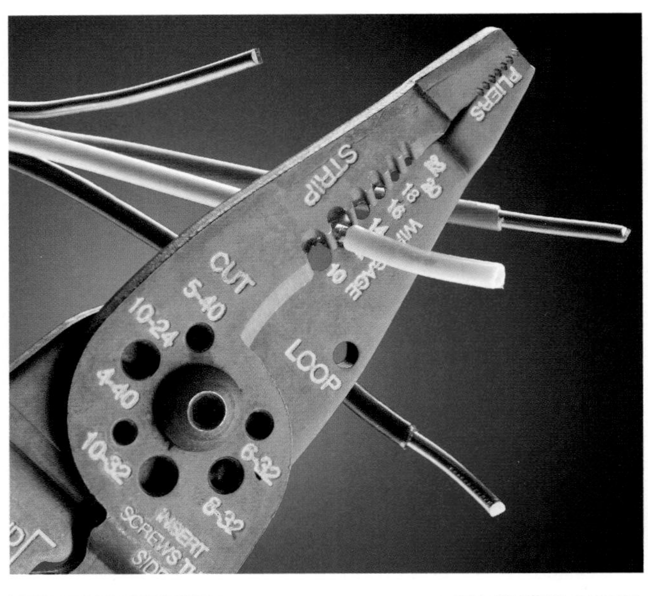
PLIERS
STRIP
CUT
10-24
5-40
4-40
10-32
LOOP
INSERT

MAIN
200
20
50

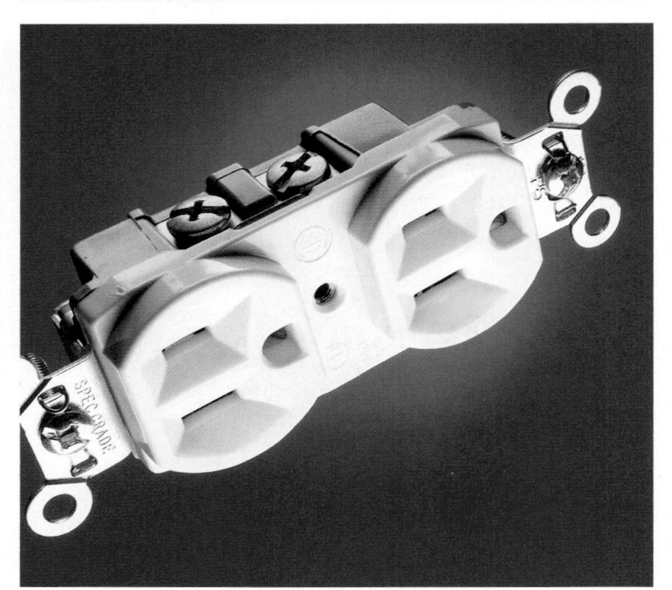
SPEC GRADE

Introduction

Home wiring is a different kind of skill from all the other building trades and do-it-yourself subjects. In many of these other pursuits, you can simply follow along, step-by-step, and if you're careful you'll end up with fabulous results. But in wiring, background information is absolutely critical to doing good work. You need to understand not only that the black wire connects to the brass screw, but what each part is doing and how it fits together with the rest of the electrical system. Electricity is all about flow, and any part of the system can affect any other part, even though they may be on opposite sides of the house and seemingly unrelated.

In *Home Wiring*, produced by and for the members of the Handyman Club of America, wiring professional and expert, Rex Cauldwell, does more than just teach which wire goes where. He explains the critical why and how of it. As a practicing professional electrician for decades, Rex is one of the country's most notable home wiring writers and authorities.

Did you ever wonder how a GFCI receptacle works? Rex explains it in thorough detail. Or have you been confused by the brimming smorgasbord of wiring equipment you see at even the most modest building center, when all you wanted was a new switch for the bedroom light? How do you know which among the dozens of switches you should buy? Rex will give you some terrific insight to make the decision-making process fast and painless.

This book is divided into four main sections. In *Home Wiring Basics*, you'll find some useful and interesting information on how electricity gets from the power plant to your home, along with some very important points on working safely with electricity. In *Tools & Materials for Home Wiring*, you'll find detailed, close-up photos of all the most important tools in the electrician's toolbox, together with information on how to buy them and how to use them. You'll also see examples of the most-used wire and cable (from the homeowner's perspective, not the commercial electric supplier's). In *Electrical Systems*, the major elements of the residential wiring system are broken down, dissected and discussed in detail. It's in this section that you'll find the information you need most to understand wiring. The main service panel, electrical boxes, switches and receptacles all are treated with the detail and clarity they demand. And you'll find many helpful step-by-step sequences so you can see for yourself exactly how the wiring is done.

Finally, *Home Wiring Projects* concludes with a section of popular wiring projects. A variety of lighting projects are presented in full-color, step-by-step format, along with common non-lighting projects such as installing baseboard heaters and ceiling fans, and supplying power to a garage or shed.

ELECTRICAL CODES

The information found on these pages conforms to the National Electrical Code (NEC) requirements. These requirements ensure safe, durable wiring installations that will best serve your needs. But your wiring project may have additional requirements not covered by the code. Also, the code requirements in your community may differ from those in the National Code. Local code always takes precedence in these situations. Always check with your local electrical inspector to make certain your project will comply with local standards. If your wiring project is part of a larger remodeling or building project that includes plumbing work, remember that plumbing has the right-of-way. Always do the plumbing installation before beginning any wiring work in that area.

IMPORTANT NOTICE

For your safety, caution and good judgment should be used when following instructions described in this book. Take into consideration your level of skill and the safety precautions related to the tools and materials shown. Neither the publisher, North American Membership Group Inc., nor any of its affiliates can assume responsibility for any damage to property or persons as a result of the misuse of the information provided. Consult your local building department for information on permits, codes, regulations and laws that may apply to your project.

HOME WIRING BASICS

Electricity comes from electrons—the supercharged, negative particles that fly around in atoms at astronomical speeds. When an electron breaks free of its orbit it is propelled away from the atom in a random direction. If enough electrons are propelled in the same direction, they create an electrical current flow.

Current that flows at a constant rate in one direction only is called DC for direct current. It is the type of electricity produced by batteries, from tiny AAA batteries to your car battery. All batteries have a negative terminal and a positive terminal. Current flows out of the negative terminal, through the load (whatever the battery is powering) and back to the positive battery terminal.

Current that flows back and forth (electrons that flow one way and then flow back again) is called AC or alternating current. It is the type of electricity we use in our houses. AC current is created by a mechanical device called an AC generator or an alternator. These contain turning mechanisms that create current when they spin.

Transmitting electricity. Once electricity is generated, it needs to be transmitted from the generator (usually a power plant) through thick power lines to our houses, sometimes over great distances. To make the journey, the electricity has to be raised in voltage to many thousand volts; the higher the voltage the lower the amount of electricity lost during transmission. These lines are called *high voltage transmission lines* and you see them high on metal towers. The high voltage lines go to various distribution stations called *substations* where the voltage level is stepped back down. The voltage, still a few thousand volts strong, is passed through cables hung from power poles lining roads (or in some cases the cables are buried). Generally, you'll see two cables running parallel to one another: the top cable is the "hot" primary service; the lower cable is a grounded neutral. Every house along the path of the cables taps into these power lines.

How electricity enters our homes. Immediately before entering a home, electrical voltage goes through a step-down *utility transformer*. This transformer can be mounted on a nearby power pole or it may be located on a concrete pad on the ground. Passing through the utility transformer reduces the electrical current from 7,500 volts down to 120/240 volts.

If you look closely at a utility transformer, you will see three terminals. All the electricity that comes into the house originates from, then returns to, these three terminals. The 240-volt service that supplies items like electric water heaters, electric ranges and baseboard heaters comes from both outer terminals. All 120-volt service comes from one of the two outer terminals and the center terminal. Many 240-volt appliances also use 120-volt service (for operating timers, clocks, buzzers, etc.) so they receive electricity from all three terminals.

Two wires and a heavy cable attach to the three utility transformer terminals to bring the power into the house. The center terminal on the transformer connects to a large, bare cable that swings over to the house. This wire is called a grounded neutral, or sometimes "the return." It is connected to a grounding wire that's bonded to the earth. But don't be fooled into thinking that there is no current flowing on this wire just because it is grounded. All current within the house starts at the utility transformer and must go back to it via the grounded neutral. Therefore, all

HOW ELECTRICITY IS TRANSMITTED

1 Electricity is generated by massive turbines at power plants fueled by coal, nuclear or hydroelectric sources (for the most part). Many thousands of volts strong, it leaves the power station through high voltage power lines and often travels through these lines for hundreds of miles.

2 The high voltage lines emanating from the power plant eventually reach power substations spotted throughout the service area. At the substation, transformers step the voltage down to just a few thousand volts (around 7,500) and distribute it into branch lines that bring service to whole neighborhoods. The power leaves the substation in heavy power line pairs supported by utility poles or, in some cases, it is buried underground.

3 From the substation, electricity runs to neighborhood utility transformers mounted on power poles (aerial service, left photo) or concrete pads (underground service, photo below). At the utility transformer, the current is stepped down again, this time to 120/240-volt service. One utility transformer usually feeds multiple homes. The power goes from the transformer directly to each home, generally through two hot cables and a neutral cable that are braided together.

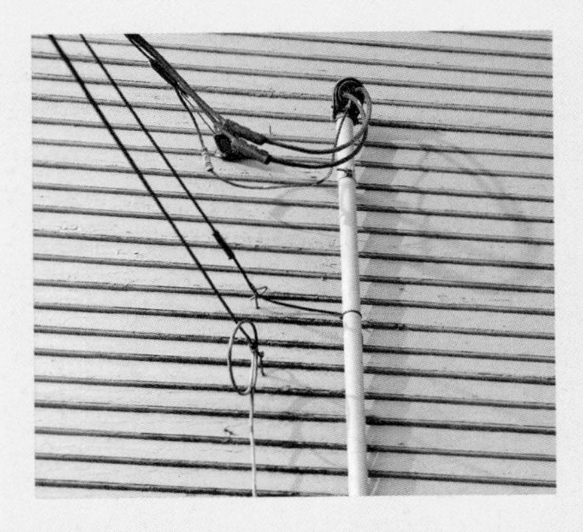

4 At the house, the cables from the utility transformer are separated and grounded to the earth. Called the utility drop, the cable is secured with a porcelain insulator to the home. From there, the power runs through an electric meter and into the home.

5 After the meter, the electrical service is brought to a main service panel via service entrance cable. At the panel the power is divided into many smaller circuits that feed different areas of the house.

6 Finally, household wiring brings the power, reduced to either 120 or 240 volts, along the circuit path. Through receptacles and switches the power reaches the lights, fixtures and appliances it is intended to run.

120-volt power that enters the house returns to the transformer via this wire, so it has a tremendous amount of current flowing through it. The grounded neutral is attached to the house at a porcelain insulator. Wrapped around the grounded neutral (and supported by it) are two insulated cables that carry the hot current. The two hot wires and the grounded neutral dip slightly before entering the house (called the *drip loop*). After the drip loop, they're spliced with cables (service entrance cables) that are installed by an electrician (not the utility company) to bring current to the main service panel via the electric meter. All these aerial cables should be high off the ground where no one can reach them. Standard heights are normally 18 ft. across roads, 12 ft. across a lawn, and 10 ft. for the drip loop. This aerial configuration can vary widely from area to area as local codes change. Power brought from the street through buried utility cables also uses a different connection configuration to get it to the meter.

ELECTRICAL TERMS & FORMULAS

When discussing electricity in general, there are four basic terms you'll need to be familiar with: *current, voltage, resistance and power.*

Current is the amount of flow of electrons. It is described in amperage (shortened to amps). *Voltage* (measured in volts) is the electrical pressure that pushes the current. The more voltage, the more pressure, and therefore the more electrons that get pushed out of orbit and sent down the wire. *Resistance* is the opposition to current flow and is measured in units called ohms. Because atomic structure varies for different materials, there are materials through which it is not easy for current flow to occur. These types of materials are called insulators and have a resistance measured in millions of ohms. They, obviously, are not used to conduct electricity. On the opposite end of the scale from insulators are conductors. Most metals are conductors, but the best conductors are copper and aluminum. The resistance of a conductor is measured in tenths or hundredths of an ohm.

Power is a term used to describe the amount of electricity consumed or created. It is simply a math product of voltage and current. To find the power rating, measured in watts or kilowatts, you simply multiply the current (in amps) times the voltage (in volts). You can use this formula to calculate electrical consumption and cost. For example, say your water heater operates at 4500 watts (it will say so on the packing box and usually on the label). You are going to use 240 volts to power the heater. If you divide the wattage by the voltage, you'll get the amperage: in this case, 18. Therefore, you know your water heater should pull 18 amps. Another example of using the formula is with baseboard heating. Most baseboard heaters designed for 240-volt service draw about 240 watts of power per foot of heater. How may amps per foot is this? Wattage (240) divided by voltage (240) equals one amp per foot. This now tells you how many feet of baseboard heater (16) you can put on a single 20-amp circuit breaker. In the case of baseboard heaters, which may be on for long periods of time, it is wise (and code in most areas) to limit the current draw to 80% of the amount allowed on the circuit. This keeps the wires from overheating and the breaker from tripping if the utility voltage changes slightly.

With the power formula you can also figure the cost of operating any appliance. At 10 cents per kilowatt (1000 watts) per hour, for example, how much does it cost to run a 4500-watt electric water heater? The 4500-watt reference means the appliance consumes 4500 watts of power per hour, when operating. If it costs you ten cents for each 1000 watts every hour, then 4.5 times 10 cents gives you out-of-pocket expense for using the heater every hour: 45 cents.

ELECTRICAL EQUATIONS & DATA

- Wattage divided by voltage = Amperage
- Wattage × 1000 = Kilowattage

HERE IS A SAMPLE CALCULATION OF CIRCUIT LOAD:

Circuit #3 (non-dedicated)
Circuit Information: Voltage = 120, Amperage = 20

APPLIANCE	WATTAGE/VOLTAGE	AMPERAGE
Microwave	800/120	= 6.7
Toaster	1050/120	= 8.75
Exhaust Fan	100/120	= .83

Total Load on Circuit #3 = 16.28 Amps

TYPICAL WATT/AMP RATINGS FOR HOUSEHOLD APPLIANCES:

Toaster: 1050/8.75	Microwave: 800/6.7
Refrigerator: 600/5	Dishwasher:1500/12.5
Air conditioner: 2000/8.3	Computer: 600/6
Circular saw: 1200/10	Table saw: 2160/18

Working Safely with Wiring

Even the most experienced handymen often draw the line at doing electrical work. It isn't the complexity or even the labor involved that gives us pause, it's usually fear. When working with electricity, a single slipup or error can have catastrophic results. If you are not comfortable working with wiring, the best advice is don't do it. If you want to develop your electrical understanding and your wiring skills, however, make sure you hold onto that fear. Never forget that each time you apply a tool to your electrical system you're taking a risk, and take all available precautions to minimize that risk.

Using the right tool for the job is a good start on the path to working safely with electricity, but being safe also requires taking precautions and paying attention. Knowing which wires or terminals are hot is another big step toward safety. One of the most important rules to follow when working with wiring is "Take your time." Most mistakes occur when the person working on the wiring, receptacle or switch is in a hurry and takes shortcuts he thinks he can get away with—like neglecting to turn off the power. Plan ahead and allow enough time when working on electrical circuits to work safely. And if you don't feel comfortable performing any part of the wiring task, stop and call a professional. In addition to these indispensable safety rules, you'll find many safety-related tips in the chapters that follow that have specific application to the subject being discussed.

Turn off the power. By far, the safest way to work around electricity is to have all power removed from the area you are working in. This can be done by throwing the main breaker or pulling the main fuses. In some cases, it is wise to have the power company shut off service to your home while you work. When shutting off the power, be sure to do it in the daytime whenever possible and always have a flashlight ready for emergency light.

A more convenient (and arguably safer) way to remove power is to throw off the specific breaker or unscrew the specific fuse that regulates the circuit you are working on. However, determining which breaker or fuse controls the circuit you plan to work on is not always easy—even if a panel index or circuit map has been provided on the inside cover of the service panel. Typically, people who don't know which breaker or fuse controls the circuit they want to work on use trial-and-error to find out, turning off circuits one at a time, then running upstairs to see if the light is still on or if the refrigerator is still

Shutting off the main breaker or breakers in your service panel is the safest way to ensure that there is no power in the wiring you're planning to work on. The downside is that you'll have no available AC power for operating tools and lights, so try to time the shutoff during the day and have a few cordless tools on hand.

SAFETY TIPS

- When unscrewing a fuse to remove power from a circuit, never loosen the fuse and leave it in the screw-in holder. It is possible for the fuse to vibrate back in and make contact, re-energizing the circuit. Instead, remove the fuse completely from its holder and set it aside (photo, above).
- If you have thrown the breaker off to work on a circuit and are afraid that someone might accidentally throw the circuit back on again, lock-outs (using a padlock) are available to lock the breaker in the OFF position. Lockouts can be found at most large electrical distributors.

Power to a specific circuit can be removed by simply turning off (or removing) the overcurrent protection device for that circuit (be it a circuit breaker or fuse).

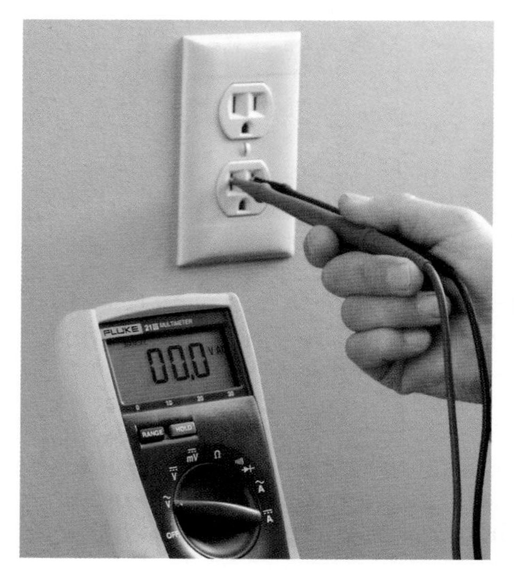

Always check the receptacle or switch with a multimeter to confirm that power has been shut off completely before you begin handling or working near the wires (See page 26).

running. This will eventually work, but a better way to locate the circuit is to use a radio. Simply plug a radio into a power outlet on the circuit you're planning to work on and turn up the volume. At the service panel, throw breakers or unscrew fuses until the radio stops playing, and you will have identified the circuit (naturally, this trick can't be used on lighting circuits or on 240/250 volt circuits). Then, label the circuit at the service panel so you can locate it again. Also, mark the outlet cover itself. On the inside of the cover plate, write the slot number of the breaker or fuse that controls power to that circuit.

Avoid touching bare wires at all times. If you must touch one, wait until you have verified that power has been removed. Use a multimeter to check the circuit for current flow (See pages 26 to 28).

Plug-in testers (also called neon circuit testers) and other bulb-type measuring devices do not measure voltage, they simply light up if the voltage is high enough. Avoid using cheap, two-lead, single-bulb plug-in testers. In addition to the device's inability to detect low current flow, the small size and tiny probes require you to put your fingers too close to the hot terminals of the receptacle or switch (See photo, top right, page 11). If the voltage is below 53 volts or so, the bulb will not illuminate. Such low voltage likely is caused by loose or corroded connections, but it can turn into high voltage very quickly when you start moving the wires. This is why you need to use a multimeter to detect any current flow. There will be other times when you need to verify that a specific wire or splice is not hot before you work on it. Here again, use a multimeter.

Know which wires are likely to be hot. When you open a light, receptacle or switch outlet box, or even the main service panel, you will see wires of many different colors. Knowing which wires are potentially hot and which probably are not is mandatory to working safely. Technically, any insulation color other than green is likely to be hot. However, within a residence, black and red wires are the two insulation colors that are almost always used as hot. These are the two wires that bring power from the breakers and fuses into the outlet boxes and to the load. Once they enter the outlet box, they connect to the small slot within the receptacle or power the switches that power the lights.

Power wires, once they enter the outlet box, will either connect directly to the receptacle or switch or go to a splice in the back of the box. Out of this splice you will find several hot feeds (more black and red wires) that go to additional receptacles and switches. Always assume these wires are hot until proven otherwise. Make two voltage checks to make sure the splices, receptacles, and switches are not hot. First, from neutral (the white wire) to the hot wire. Second, from the ground to the hot wire. Making two voltage checks allows for the possibility that the neutral might be broken. If the neutral is broken you will see a "0" volts reading, even though the red or black wire is hot. Making a second voltage check from the ground to the hot wire will give you a voltage reading even though the neutral is broken.

The wires on the brass-screw side of a receptacle (the side with the short slot on the receptacle front) are potentially hot because these wires (red or black) eventually go all the way back to the circuit breaker. The other side of the receptacle (the silver-screw side) is the neutral side. This side, though grounded, can sometimes shock you. If there is current flow upstream from the receptacle there may be current flow through the white wires at the receptacle. If you touch the silver screws or white wire, the current should, in theory, keep on going back to the panel via the wires because it is the path of least resistance. However, if for some reason there is a problem with these wires on their way back to the panel (a loose connection, for example) the current might see your fingers as a lower resistance way to get back to the panel. So treat both sides of the receptacle with the respect of a hot wire, bearing in mind that the person who installed the wiring might have wired the receptacle with the color-coded wires reversed.

The same logic applies to a switch. You don't know for certain which of the two terminals is hot. A good electrician could tell by looking at the colored wires. However, he or she would be assuming that the previous electrician wired according to code and sometimes that is a dangerous assumption to make. You also may find that both wires to the switch are the same color. So, unless you have used a multimeter to determine which screw is hot, treat both screws as hot.

On a switch, the way to tell which screw the power comes in on is to make a voltage measurement from ground to each screw with the switch set to OFF. One measurement should read approximately 120 volts—this is the hot screw. The other should register no voltage—this is the side that takes the power to the load. It won't be hot until you throw the switch to ON.

White insulation normally means the wire is a neutral. This wire is energized after the power has passed through the load. It brings the current back to the panel. All current is in series so the current in the white wire is equal to the current in the black wire, making them both just as dangerous when current is flowing through the load. So don't think that just because a wire is a neutral it cannot shock you—it can. A voltage measurement from the neutral to the black or red wire should always be approximately 120 volts.

There are a few exceptions when the white wire is not a grounded neutral. This occurs primarily where the white wire is used as a hot feeder in switching circuits and as a traveler (a wire with intermittent hot power in a three-way switch circuit). By code, a white wire that is put into service as a feeder line should be taped with black electrical tape, but that may not have been done, in which case there is no way of telling if the white wire is being used as a switched feeder or not. Always assume any wire is hot until all power is removed from the circuit and checked with a multimeter.

A green insulated wire or bare copper wire is a ground wire. This wire goes back to the main panel grounding bus and is connected directly to the earth. There should never be any current flowing on this wire. When properly grounded, the ground wire will drain any surges instead of letting them build up, as when a hot wire touches an appliance frame (called a ground fault). The fault current flows back to the panel allowing the breaker to kick. A voltage measurement from the ground wire to the red or black wire should be approximately 120 volts. A voltage measurement from

DANGER A small, bulb-type circuit tester requires that your fingers get too close to potentially hot terminals and wires when checking for current. Use a full-size multimeter instead.

HOW TO FIND THE HOT TERMINAL ON A SWITCH

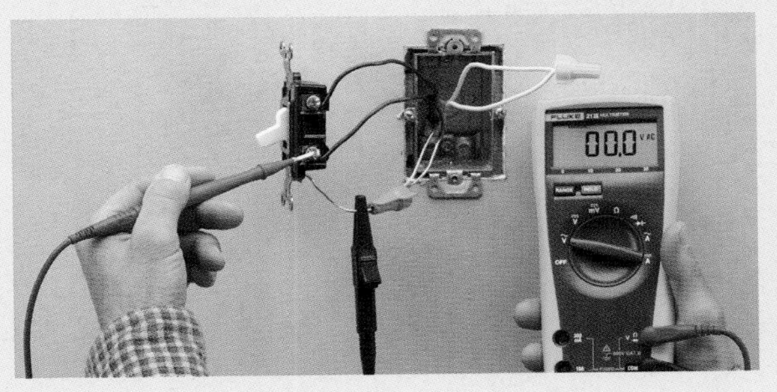

Switches, in particular, are subject to unconventional wiring practices so it is often hard to know for certain which terminal is hot (and consequently receiving power even if the load being switched is off). To confirm which switch terminal is hot, use a multimeter. With the switch on OFF, apply one probe to the ground and the other to each screw terminal in turn. The hot terminal will read between 110 and 120 volts with the switch on OFF (top photo) and the wire leading to the load will read 0 volts (bottom photo).

ANTICIPATING HOT SPOTS

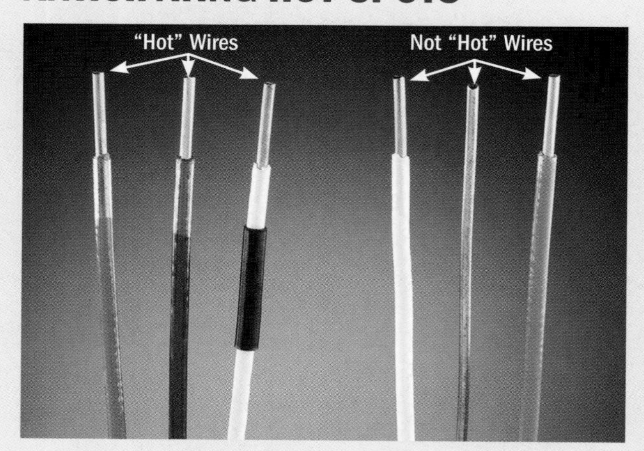

Insulated wires that are black, red or any color but white or green probably are hot. White wires with black tape are "coded hot." Note: Test all wires for current.

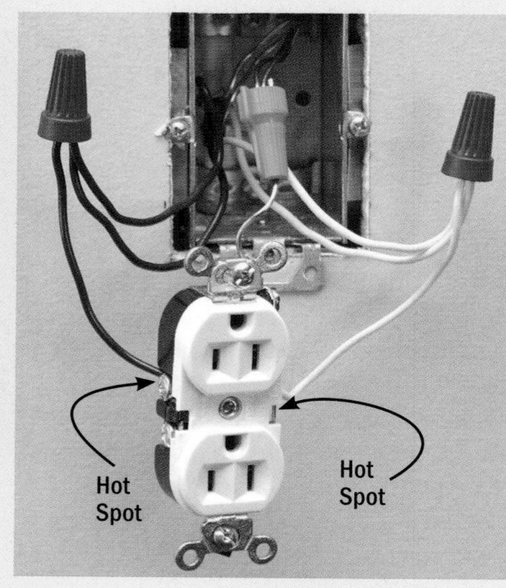

The brass screw side of a receptacle is hot (when installed correctly), but the silver screw side can have current flowing through it if there is a load upstream.

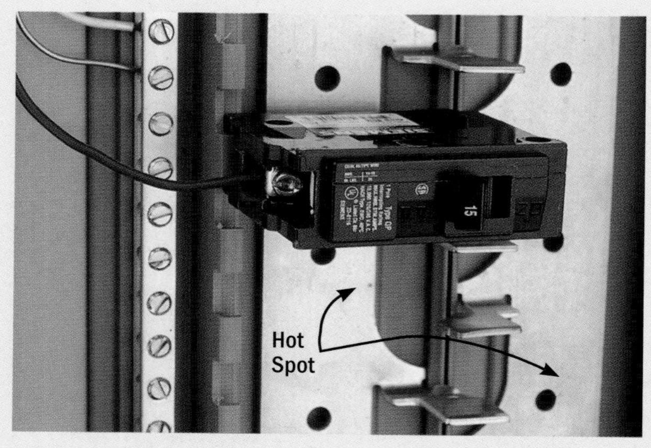

The copper buss bars are hot, even when the breaker is set to OFF.

Sometimes there is a hot wire exposed where the installer stripped too much insulation off the wire. This hot spot is very easy to touch by accident.

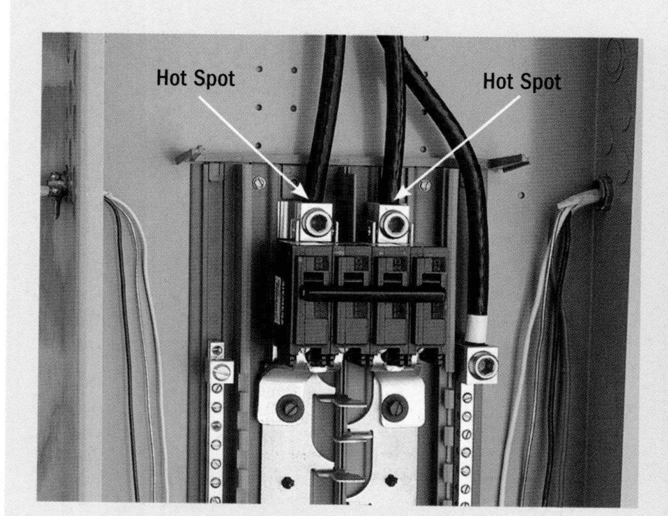

The lugs that connect the service entry cables to the service panel remain hot even when the main breakers are thrown to OFF.

In some cases, you may find that the bare ground wire is being incorrectly used as a hot wire. This is done in a three-way switch circuit when the installer forgot to install three-way switch cable. He/she is using the ground wire as a traveler.

ground to neutral should always read 0 volts. If you get any other reading, call an electrician.

In some cases, you may find that the bare ground wire is being incorrectly used as a hot wire. This is done in a three-way switch circuit when the installer forgot to install three-way switch cable. He/she is using the ground wire as a traveler.

The main service panel is always hot. To turn off all power in the house you can turn the main breaker in the service panel off. This removes the power to the breakers that are in the panel itself. However, if you are working in the panel, such as when adding or removing a breaker, beware. There is still hot power in the panel. The two large diameter cables that enter the panel and go to the main breaker lugs are still hot. These cables may have insulation missing where they enter the breaker, exposing the hot bare conductor and creating a hazard.

Watch out for unexpected hot spots. When a circuit breaker is in the ON position a circuit breaker is hot at the points where the wires are attached to the breaker. Sometimes there is hot wire exposed where the installer stripped too much insulation off the wire. This hot spot is very easy to touch by accident.

Be very careful when you pull a receptacle out of the wall. The black or red wires under the brass-colored screws can be hot. If you grab the receptacle by its sides to remove it, you will be touching the hot wires. Always make sure the power is off and also make a habit of grabbing the receptacle by its yoke—the metal flanges that secure the receptacle to the box (See photo, right). The same logic goes with switches. Never touch the side of the switch containing the screw terminals—they could be hot. Pull the switch out of the box via the yoke after you remove the two attachment screws. When pulling switches and receptacles out of boxes, always be aware of what is happening within the box. Sometimes splices pull apart and wire caps come loose. If the switch or outlet is connected with "push-in" wires that are inserted into holes in the back, use extra caution—these wires have a tendency to disengage.

Avoid assumptions. As a rule of practice, never assume that the person who installed your home wiring did it correctly. Mistakes can happen, but even wiring that meets code can contain hidden hazards. For example, there may be more than one hot feed in an outlet box. If you cut the power off to the most obvious feed wire, you would still have hot wires hiding somewhere in the box. This often occurs in kitchen outlet boxes, where one circuit feeds a receptacle outlet and another feeds an overhead light.

Watch out for metal boxes. Metal boxes, especially when they're too small, are a major wiring hazard. When pushing a receptacle or switch into a metal outlet box, it is a good idea to cover the screw terminals with electrical tape (you might also put some tape on the box interior sides). You will also have a problem with the wires being nicked and cut as they fold back against the sharp edges of the back of the metal box. Put some electrical tape on the back of the box to prevent this. Or use plastic boxes instead. Another danger around metal outlet boxes is shorting the multimeter probe against the side of the box as it touches the switch or receptacle screw. Even pros have a problem with this. When this happens, sparks will fly (you do have your safety glasses on, right?) and you will melt the end and sides of the probe, ruining it. It's always best to have the power off, but if you have to have power on (for example, when you want to measure voltage), one trick you can do is to tape the probe tips with some electrical tape so only the tip is exposed. This way, if you accidentally touch the metal box with the side of the probe, all that touches it is the electrical tape.

Shallow or undersized boxes (including the common handy box—See page 48) also present safety hazards, especially if they are made of metal. Most, being only 1½ in. deep, are too small to legally hold a

HANDLING SWITCHES & RECEPTACLES

When handling receptacles and switches, always grab them by the yoke (the metal flanges at the top and bottom). Do not handle the sides or back of the receptacle or switch until you have confirmed that none of the wires or screw terminals are receiving current flow.

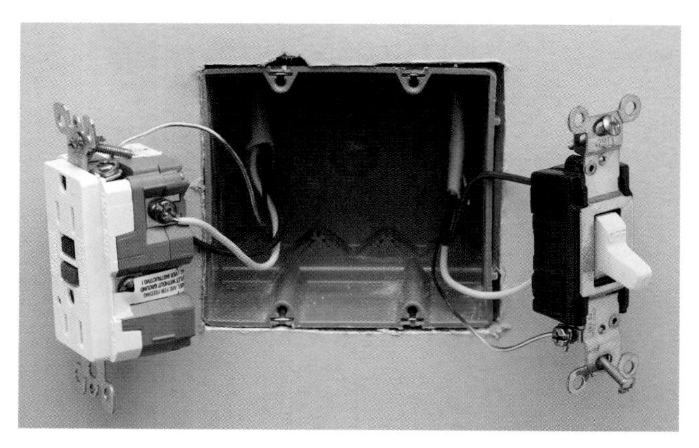

DANGER Be on the lookout for outlet boxes with multiple hot wires. This often occurs in kitchen outlet boxes, where one circuit feeds a receptacle outlet and another feeds an overhead light.

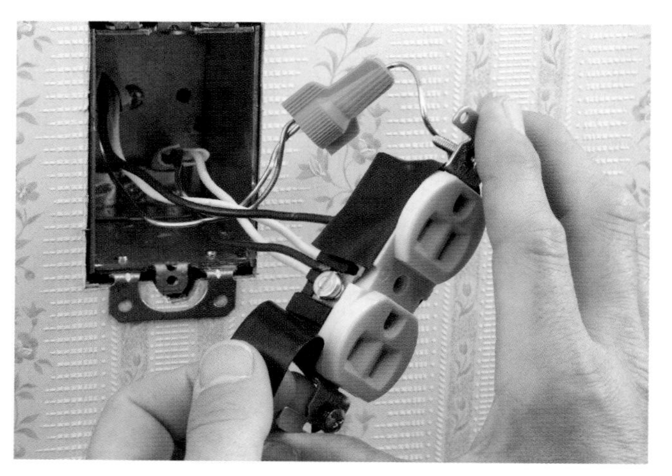

Before pushing a receptacle or switch into a metal outlet box, it is a good idea to wrap the side screw terminals with electrical tape.

Watch out for loose wires. Some receptacles and switches are made with push-in terminals on the back so the installer can simply insert wires into the terminal, which is faster to do than twisting the stripped wire around a screw terminal. But just as push-in connections are easier to make, they're also easier to "unmake." A high percentage of receptacle and switch failures are the result of push-in connections that come loose.

receptacle, switch or even a splice. Avoid using handy boxes in new installations, and replace them with larger boxes whenever you encounter them. Handy boxes are always a safety problem.

Never use an adapter (cheater plug). The purpose of a cheater plug adapter is to connect a three-wire cord into a two wire receptacle. There are many problems doing this. First, you may not be grounding the appliance—all you are probably doing is allowing it to operate. Ungrounded, the frame of the appliance could become energized and electrocute anyone touching it. Second, the appliance manufacturer wants the appliance to be grounded—that's why they supplied the three-wire cord. Third, it is a violation of the electrical code to hook up an appliance against the manufacturer's recommendations. That is, without adequate grounding.

Avoid multiple plug-in adapters. These are the little plug-in units that can change a single receptacle into a multiple receptacle. They plug into a single receptacle and give you access to several receptacle plug-ins. These are quite easy to overload and have been known to catch fire. Instead, if you have a large number of low-wattage items to plug into a single receptacle, use a power strip with surge protection. These are much heavier-duty and many come with internal breakers.

Always wear protective safety glasses. If a hot wire touches a ground wire, neutral wire, or a metal box, there will be sparks. A single spark hitting your eye can blind you. This accident can happen when a hot wire has part of its insulation missing and gets shoved against the side or back of a metal box.

GFCI LIMITATIONS

The use of GFCI (ground-fault circuit interrupter) devices is not a replacement for using common sense. Just because you have your tool powered through a GFCI receptacle or GFCI-protected extension cord doesn't mean you can do dangerous things with the tool. It is possible to have your AC-operated tool powered through a GFCI and still get electrocuted. GFCIs only operate when they sense a ground fault (short through to ground). If the operator puts himself between the hot wire and neutral without any current flowing to earth, the GFCI will not open the circuit (see the chapter on GFCIs). As a rule, do not use any AC-powered tool while you are standing in water. Never use any electrical tool if you or the tool are wet.

METAL PROBES & METAL BOXES DON'T MIX

DANGER: Be careful not to touch the metal probe of a multimeter or analyzer against the edge of a metal box as you make a measurement from a switch or receptacle terminal. This will cause a short circuit and sparking.

SOLUTION: One trick that will help prevent a metal probe from contacting the edge of a box is to wrap the probe with electrical tape so only the tip of the probe is exposed.

Another potential hazard is created by clipped wire ends that can fly into the eye, scratching the lens. Also, when drilling overhead it is imperative to wear safety glasses to prevent debris from falling into your eyes as you look up. Make sure the glasses you buy are comfortable and resistant to scratching and fogging.

Consider wearing rubber gloves when working around electricity. Dishwashing gloves are thin enough to allow you to work with thin wires—but never assume they will give you enough protection to handle a hot wire. They are just a protective measure in case you accidentally touch a hot wire. Professional electricians wear heavy rubber gloves intended specifically for this purpose when they handle hot wires.

Always use nonconductive ladders such as wood or fiberglass. When you cut into a hot wire, you want to be insulated from the ground, not connected to it. Make sure the ladder is stable and well anchored before you climb it.

DANGER Do not use a three-prong adapter (sometimes called a "cheater plug") to plug a grounded appliance into an ungrounded, two-slot receptacle. Appliances with a grounded, three-prong plug must be connected to a properly grounded receptacle with the correct slot configuration.

Power tool use. Never plug any AC powered tool into an electrical circuit that is not ground-fault protected (See pages 98 to 110). GFCI protection will save your life if the tool malfunctions by shorting a hot wire to the frame while you are using it. A typical example might be while you are using a drill in the garage or out on the lawn. A 3-ft. pigtail (very short extension cord) with GFCI protection built into the cord is ideal and is available at most electrical distributors. Before operating the tool, verify that the GFCI device is working by pressing the TEST button.

SAFETY TIPS FOR HOME WIRING

WEAR SAFETY GLASSES

Three good reasons should convince you that eye protection is well worth the time and hassle. The first is cutting wire. If you snip a small piece of wire off the end of a wire, it shoots out like a rocket ship. It could (and it has happened) fly up and into an eye. Second, as you work overhead, dirt and debris can fall into your eyes. Third, an arc from a shorted wire could send a fiery brand into your eyes.

ALWAYS STAND ON AN INSULATOR

This helps prevent your body from making a complete circuit—without a complete circuit you cannot be shocked. If you accidentally touch a hot wire and you are insulated from any return conductor, such as a concrete floor or even bare earth, you should not get shocked. A thick rubber welcome mat works just fine as an insulator. And as added protection, always wear rubber-soled shoes—the thicker the soles the better.

TOOLS & MATERIALS FOR HOME WIRING

Most electrical tools are specialized. That is, they are designed for specific jobs in that specific trade. A few common garage tools are acceptable for use in wiring projects, but other than using ordinary screwdrivers and perhaps your favorite drill, use the appropriate wiring tool for the task. For example, everyone has some pliers in the shop or a kitchen drawer. But these types of pliers are not made for electrical work. If you were only going to use them one time, you might get away with it—but not for an entire project. Household pliers can't cut, twist or pull wire as well as electrical pliers designed for that type of job.

This chapter will show you the tools you need to conduct home wiring projects properly. If you are going to be doing your own electrical work, think of the additional tools as an investment that will help you do quality work and do it safely.

Materials needed for home wiring projects (other than boxes, receptacles, switches and wiring fixtures, which are discussed in later chapters) include electrical cable, cable connectors (wire caps), conduit and conduit fittings.

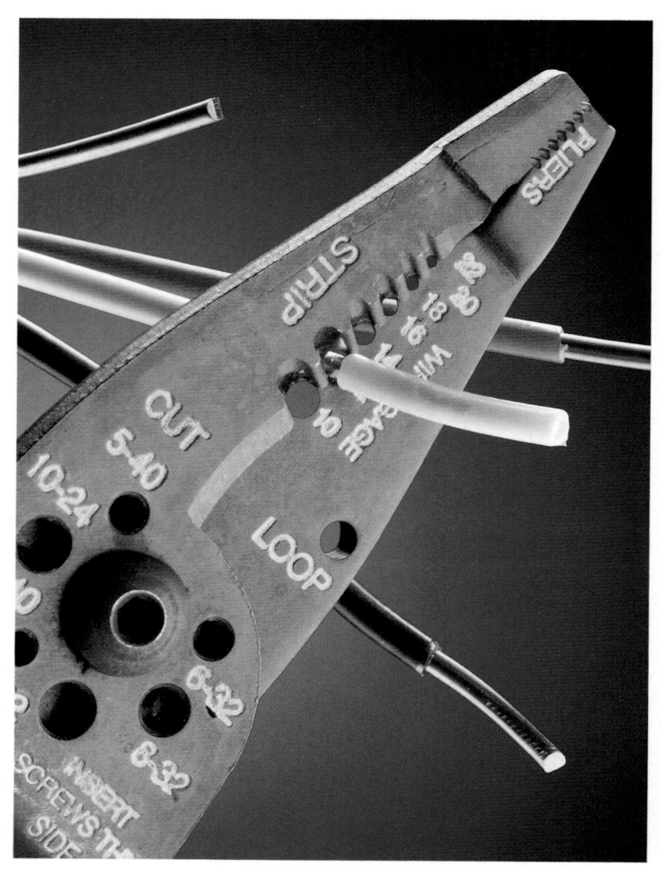

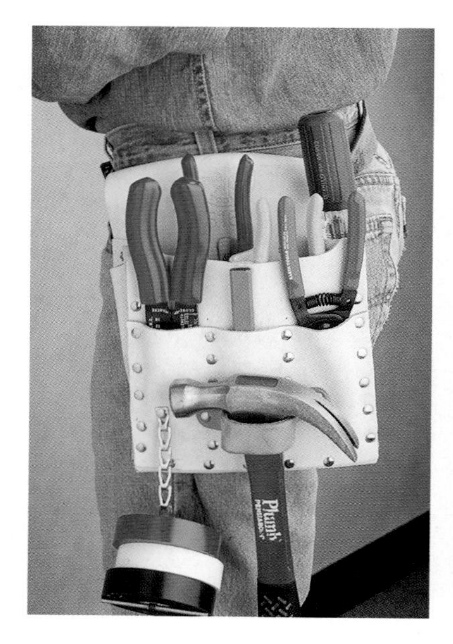

Once you start collecting electrical tools, you'll need somewhere to store and carry them. An electrician uses a tool belt. This places the most commonly used tools right at waist level, near the hands. If you don't want to spend money on a tool belt, carry tools in a toolbox or a carryall big enough to hold all your wiring tools. For example, a bucket that has a fabric drape around it with a series of pockets. The advantage of this method is that the bucket can double as a seat or stool, which is an especially nice thing to have when you're wiring a number of receptacles. They even make a special cushioned lid to fit the typical 5-gallon bucket. If you don't want to invest in anything, simply use an empty 5-gallon bucket. But remember, most tools are lost because they were not put back in a carrier.

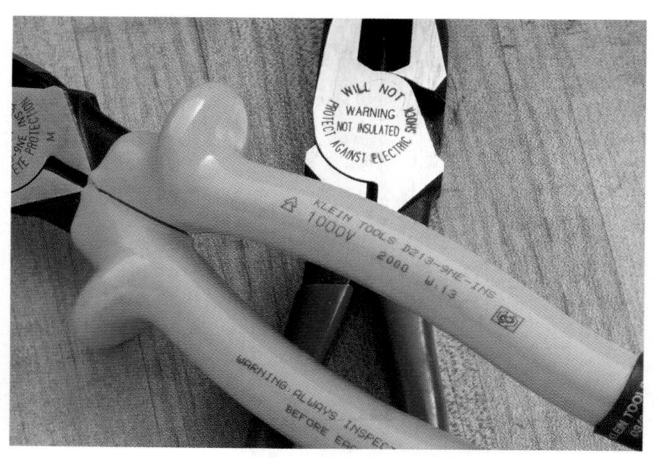

Super-insulated electrician's tools will protect you if they come in contact with a live wire. Ordinary plastic-dipped handles do not offer suitable shock protection by themselves. Super-insulated tools are marked with an overlapping triangle and the number "1000," which means the tool is rated at 1000 volts. You'll need to go to an electrical supply store to find them, and they are fairly expensive, but they can save your life.

Lineman's Pliers

Lineman's pliers (also called *side cutters*) will be your most-used electrical tool. Keep them close at hand at all times. They have a heavy-duty upper and lower cutter blade on one side of the pliers. This means they can only cut wire coming in from the side—not from the front. Don't short-change yourself here: you need a good, high-quality pair. Common handle length is 8 in., since you need this much length to have the leverage to cut larger-diameter wire. With its heavy construction and broad nose, you will find a multitude of uses for the side cutter. The most common, of course, will be for cutting and pulling wire. But you'll also find uses for side cutters when fastening or taking loose small nuts, twisting wires together before a wire connector goes on, and twisting out the metal knockouts on metal boxes and panels.

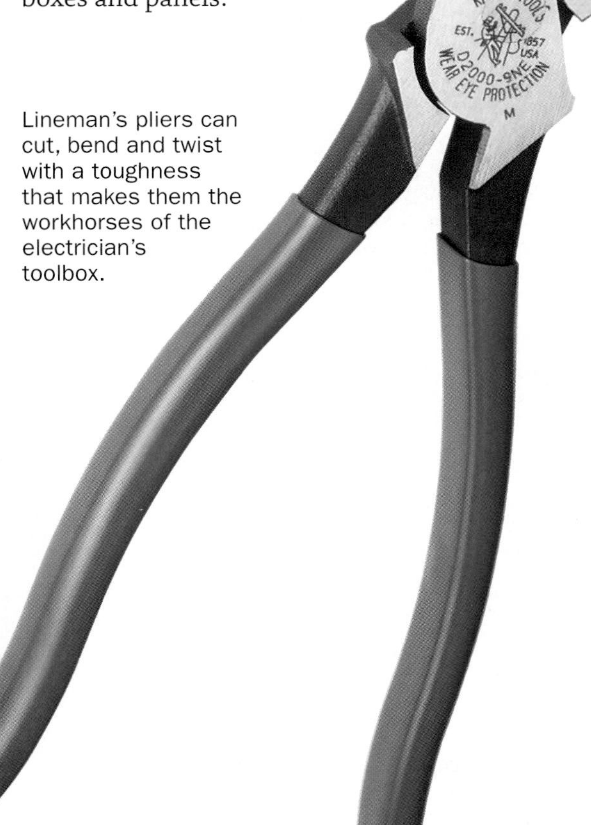

Lineman's pliers can cut, bend and twist with a toughness that makes them the workhorses of the electrician's toolbox.

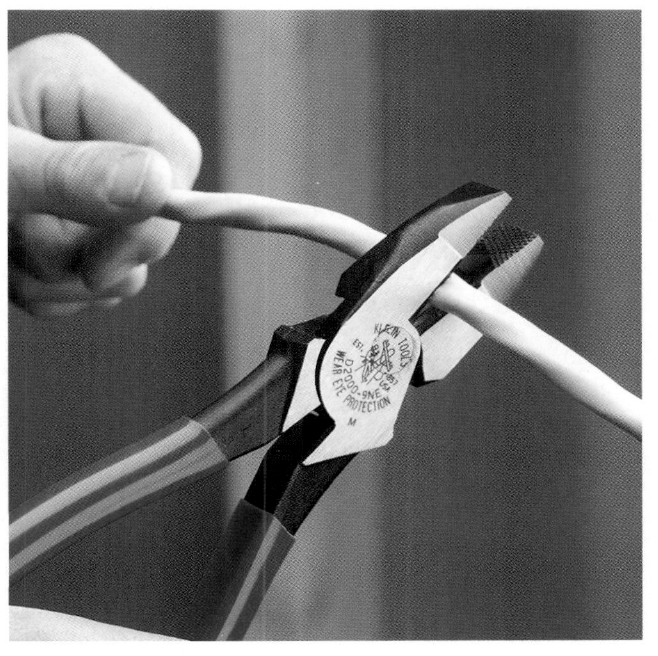

Lineman's pliers are also called "side cutters" because cable and wire are fed into the cutting blade through the side of the tool head.

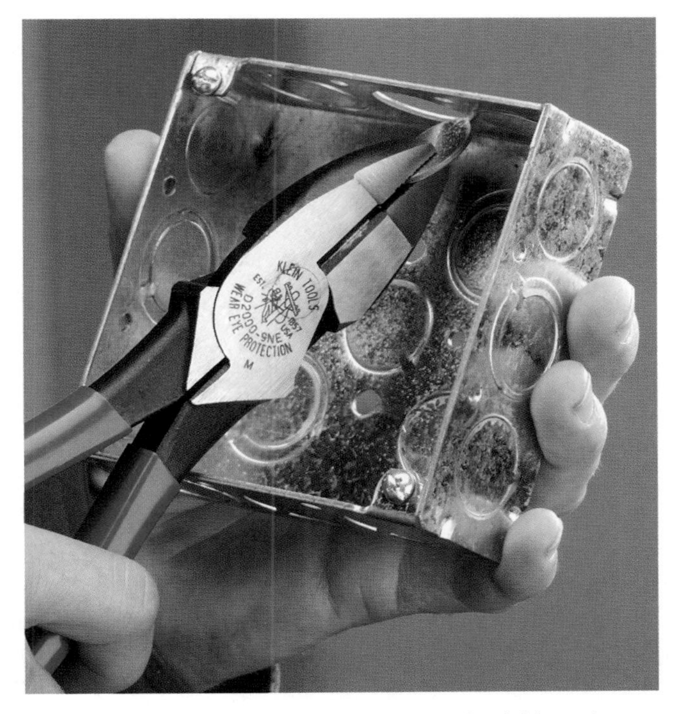

Knockouts in metal boxes can be removed quickly and easily with a pair of lineman's pliers. Plan ahead when installing a box: it's always easier to remove the knockouts before installing the box than to wait until it is mounted or, worse yet, packed with wires and connectors. The rugged jaws of a pair of lineman's pliers also make twisting wires together practically effortless.

Long-nosed Pliers

Long-nosed pliers (also called *needlenose pliers*) are the pliers you will use to reach into outlet boxes and pull out wires, as well as to bend wire ends into half loops to twist around screw terminals. Be sure to get a pair that can also cut lighter-gauge wire so you can avoid switching tools too often while you work. When you buy long-nosed pliers, choose the ones that fit best in your hands—not too small, not too big, but just right.

Long-nosed pliers (smaller models are typically called needlenose pliers) are used mainly for twisting wire loops and cutting conductor wires.

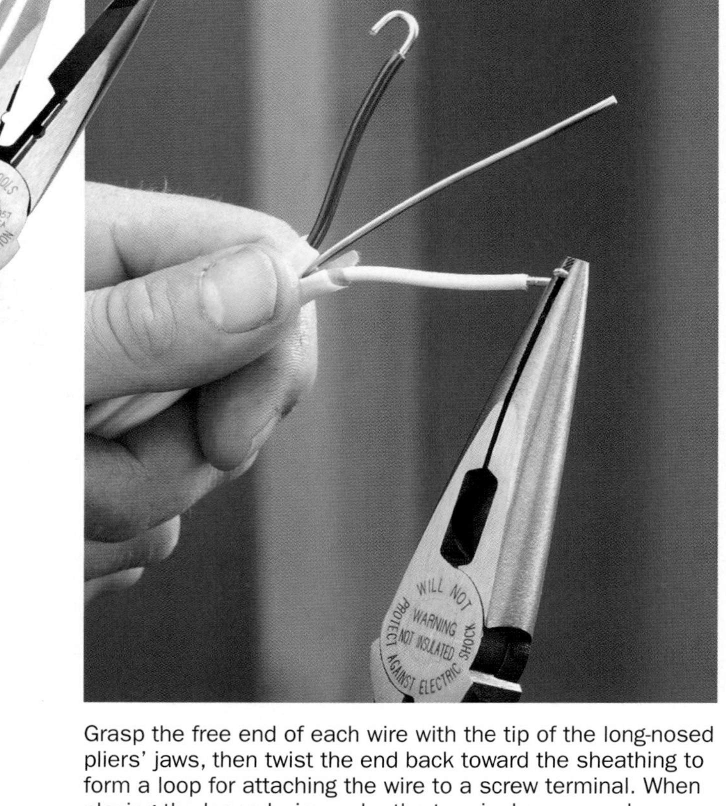

Grasp the free end of each wire with the tip of the long-nosed pliers' jaws, then twist the end back toward the sheathing to form a loop for attaching the wire to a screw terminal. When placing the looped wire under the terminal screw, make sure the open end faces clockwise so the wire will tighten around the screw terminal as the screw is tightened.

BENT LONG-NOSED PLIERS

Bent long-nosed or needlenose pliers aren't a mandatory tool for your wiring toolbox, but they can come in handy for pulling wire. The pair shown here is about 10 in. long, allowing it to reach into deeper, hard-to-access areas. The upturned jaws also help you get at wires that are tucked behind other cabling, and the fulcrum point created where the jaws turn up provides a bit of extra leverage. As with straight long-nosed and needlenose pliers, avoid using bent long-nosed pliers to turn screws or bolts—the sideways pressure will cause the jaws to become misaligned.

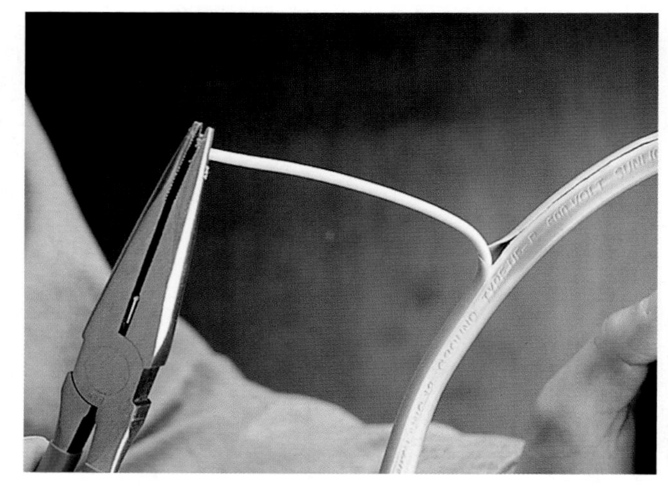

Use long-nosed pliers to separate tough cable sheathing, like the UF feeder cable shown here. Lightly score the sheathing first with a utility knife. Get a firm grip on the end of one of the conductors with one pair of pliers, then grasp the sheathing with another pair. Pull firmly on the conductor and it will tear the sheathing as it separates. This is much safer than trying to cut through tough sheathing with a utility knife or cable ripper. Trim off the empty sheathing with a utility knife or wire cutters.

Diagonal Cutters

A pair of diagonal cutters gives you the ability to work more easily than with side cutters in boxes containing multiple wires. Their low clearance also allows you to trim wires flush to a surface in cases where you want to preserve as much of the original wire as possible. And because you can see the wires and cutting jaws more clearly, they are an excellent choice for cuts that demand a high degree of precision.

Diagonal cutters are good for cutting wires in tight areas. They also give a better view of the wire for making more precise cuts.

Diagonal cutters are narrow and can reach into a box to make a cut more easily than lineman's pliers, which cut from the side of the head.

End-cutting Pliers

Although they might look like something you'd use to trim horses hooves, end-cutting pliers are very useful for pulling wire staples. They are often called "nippers" because they also can be used for their designed purpose of "nipping" or cutting a wire head-on.

End-cutting pliers, often called nippers, are used to trim off the ends of wires or cable and to pull out wire staples.

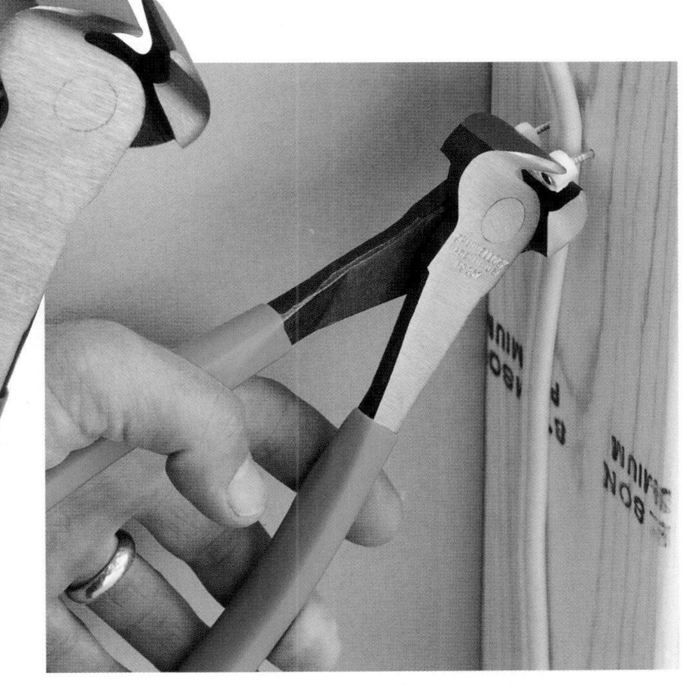

To pull out a wire staple, grab the staple leg with one end of a pair of end-cutting pliers, then rock the pliers back away from the cable. The staple will come right out, without damaging the cable.

Wire Strippers

Before a wire can be twisted around a screw terminal, you need to remove about ¾ in. of insulation to expose bare wire. Although you can use a utility knife or even a pocket knife to strip off the insulation, wire strippers are preferred because they will not nick the cable. If a cable is nicked, a weak spot is created that can cause the wire to snap when it is twisted. This normally happens right after you have wound the wire around a receptacle or switch screw.

There are many different types of wire strippers available on the market. Most are good, so it makes little difference which you pick. They all work in basically the same manner (See photo, right).

It is possible, however, to insert the wire you're working with into the wrong gauge notch and nick the wire or even cut through it. So take your time and make sure you know the gauge of the wire you are stripping. And always test the cut first on a scrap piece of the same type of wire you're stripping.

A basic wire stripper has calibrated holes for stripping insulation, along with a wire cutter.

A multi-use wire stripper (red handle) can strip and cut wire, and offers a couple of other bells and whistles as well. Typically, they include a bolt cutter and rethreader for trimming box cover bolts and switch or receptacle anchor bolts.

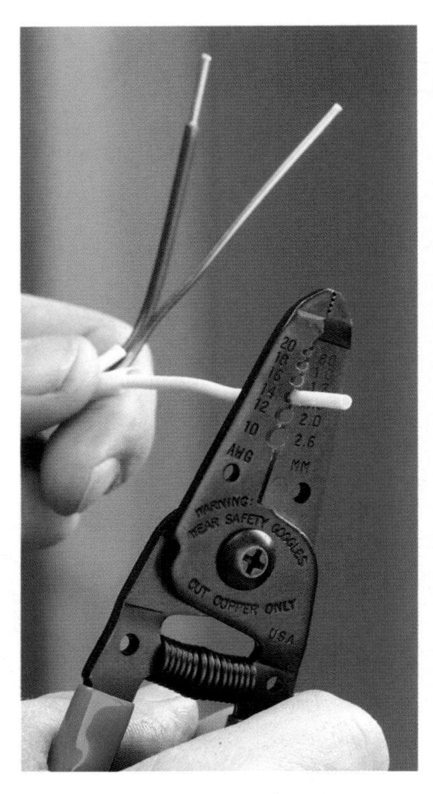

Wire strippers have notched jaws that, when closed, form precisely sized holes to match common wire gauges. You simply insert a 14-gauge wire, for example, into the 14-gauge notch, then clamp down the jaws of the stripper, spinning it slightly then drawing it toward the free end of the wire. The insulation will pull away easily, revealing a clean, straight cut in the insulation that does not nick the wire.

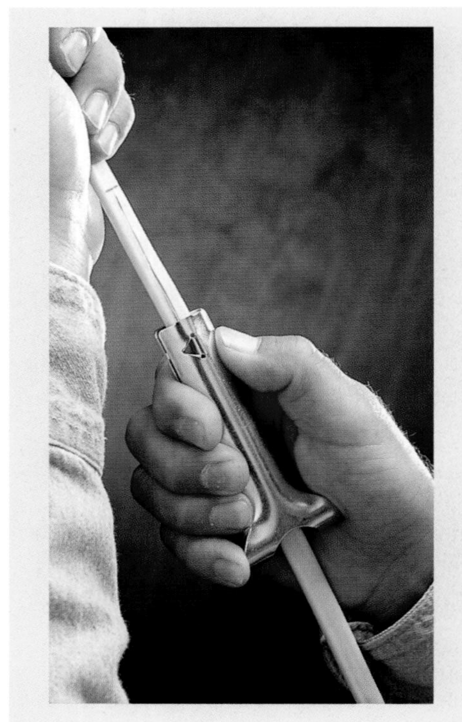

CABLE RIPPERS

A *cable ripper* is an inexpensive tool that has only one purpose: to make longitudinal cuts in nonmetallic (NM) sheathing. You feed the sheathed cable through the "T" end of the opening, then squeeze the free ends of the ripper together so the ripping tooth is centered on the cable, about 10 in. from the end. Squeezing, pull the ripper toward the cable end. For occasional ripping, these devices are quite handy. But professionals who rip a lot of sheathing generally use a utility knife, since the cutting tooth on the cable rippers becomes dull rather quickly.

Screwdrivers

Common, inexpensive screwdrivers with insulated handles are just fine for most home wiring projects. You will need a variety of both Phillips-head and slotted-head tools of different lengths and blade sizes. Some jig saws will only accept a very narrow, thin-bladed screwdriver for changing the blade, so you'll definitely want one of these. At the same time, only a wide blade, heavy-duty screwdriver will turn locked-down, rusted screws.

To keep from abusing the good screwdrivers, always carry an old, heavy-duty screwdriver that you don't mind scarring up a bit. This will be the one that you use to pop open the metal knockouts in a panel or a metal electrical box.

NOTE: It's very tempting to use a cordless screwdriver any time you have a screw to deal with. For carpentry-related chores, like attaching boxes to wall studs, these are fine. But because screw terminals and set screws require very little torque and can be driven quickly by hand, you're better off using hand screwdrivers to gain the extra control you want when working around wiring.

Decent screwdrivers are a must for performing wiring tasks neatly. The tools should have insulated plastic handles, preferably with rubber grips. You'll need a selection of blade sizes and shank lengths in both slotted and Phillips-head types. The screwdriver in the middle of the photo to the left has an offset shaft for enhanced speed (See photo, below).

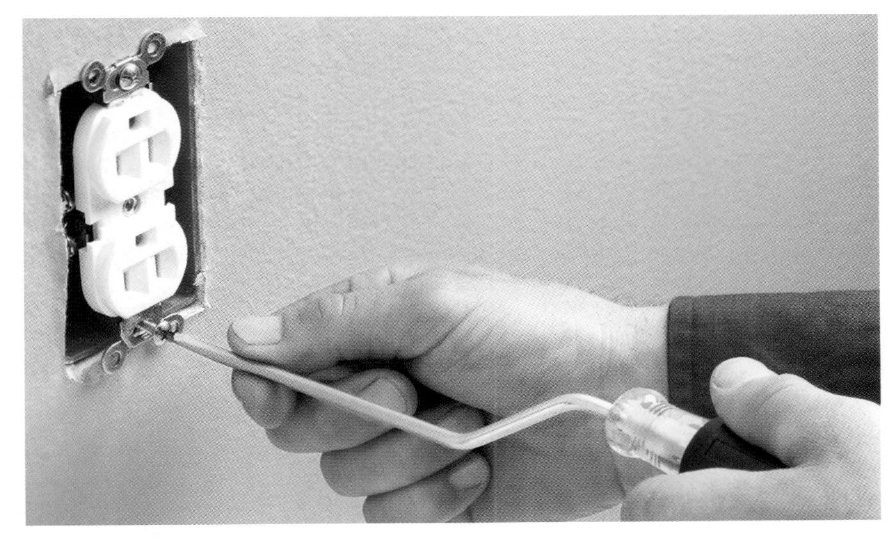

A useful specialty screwdriver with a swiveling, gooseneck shaft makes quick work of driving set screws. The shaft is not hard-set into the handle; it swivels. Twirl the screwdriver in a circle to drive the screw. Offset screwdrivers come with either slotted or Phillips heads.

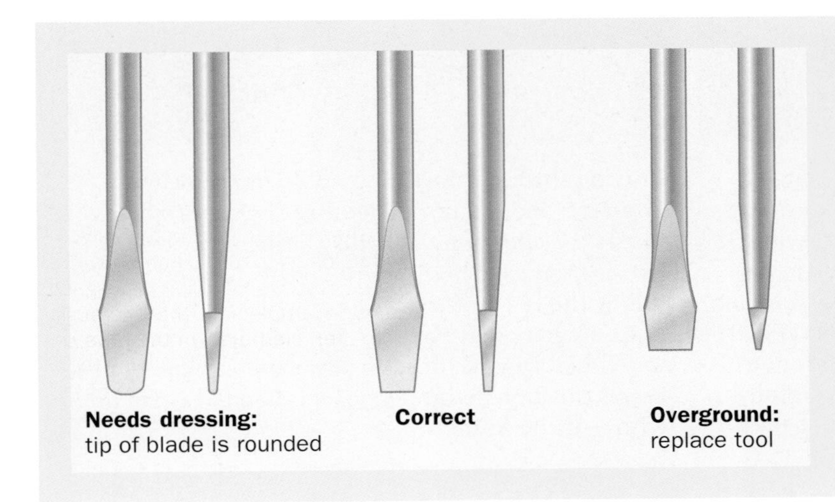

TIP FOR TIPS

Keeping your slotted screwdriver blades well dressed reduces the chances of stripping the slots, speeds up screwdriving and helps prevent accidents caused by the blade slipping out of the screw slot. Dressing can be done on a bench grinding wheel or with a flat file. The faces should not have a sharp, wedge-like angle, but should be nearly parallel. The tip should be straight across and square to the shaft so it fits snugly in the screw slot.

Utility Knives

Ordinary utility knives are perfect for working with cable sheathing because they have thin, rigid blades that are always sharp. Slender, inexpensive knives with breakaway blades, like the yellow-handled knife above, are ideal for wiring work.

The primary use for a utility knife when wiring is to cut the sheathing of the cable free from the wires. Always get a knife that has a retractable blade so it won't cut you when you're handling it or putting it away. A pocket knife does not work well as a substitute for a utility knife. The curved blade is rarely razor sharp and is too thick to easily split the sheathing. When stripping the sheathing from the cable, cut just hard enough to slice the sheathing but not the wires. Always keep the blade tip in the center of the sheathing. That way, if you cut in a little too far you'll only hit the ground wire with the blade, not the insulated conductors.

Be careful when using a utility knife to strip sheathing; many people have been severely cut doing it. Make sure the cable is flat, not twisted, and supported on an even surface, not part of your body. If you must cut cable sheathing in mid-air with the end held by hand, keep fingers clear of the blade.

Once the slice is made, peel the sheathing back and cut it away. If you're inclined, you can try using cable sheath cutters (sometimes called cable rippers, see page 20) but most of the time they don't work very well once they get dull.

If you need to use a knife to strip wire insulation, cut the insulation at a diagonal, like you're cutting shavings off a tree limb. Never circle the wire with a blade, it will cut a groove into the wire and the wire will snap. Large diameter multiconductor cables are the exception. For these, you normally have to cut around the cable—just do it lightly.

Inexpensive utility knives with breakaway blades are ideal for wiring work. They are small and thin, which allows them to reach into tight places such as a crowded receptacle or switch box.

STRIPPING CABLE WITH A UTILITY KNIFE

Once sheathed cable has been inserted through a cable clamp and into a box, tighten the clamp to secure the end of the cable. Holding the free end of the cable, position the utility knife blade in the center of the cable sheathing and carefully draw the blade toward the free end of the cable. Start the cut just inside the cable clamp (there should be about 10 in. of cable feeding through the box. Cut carefully to the end, keeping your fingers clear, then pull back the sheathing and trim it off with the knife.

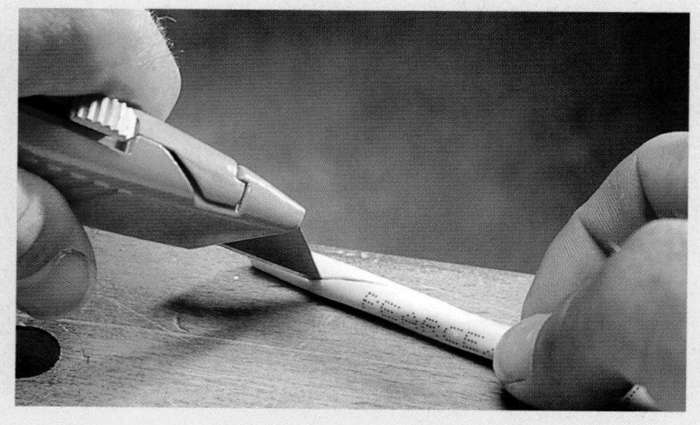

Cutting through sheathing on 3-wire cable with ground is more difficult because the wires spiral inside the sheathing. A utility knife may work better than a cable ripper to do this. You must follow the twist of the wires carefully with the knife so you don't damage the insulation on the individual wires. Once the sheathing is ripped, peel it and the paper wrappers back, then cut them off with a utility knife.

Saws

Just about any wiring project you'll take on will likely require some cutting: whether it's notching out a stud, cutting conduit to length or making a cutout for a receptacle box or to run new cable through a wall. The best type of saw to use will depend on your exact situation, but if you have a power jig saw, a wallboard or keyhole saw and a hacksaw in your toolbox there is little you won't be able to handle. A reciprocating saw is also a very useful tool for wiring work.

Almost as much as the type of saw, the jig saw or reciprocating saw blade you use will determine how long the cutting chore takes and how neat the final result is.

A reciprocating saw cuts wood, nails, steel, cast-iron pipe, rebar—practically anything.

A jig saw is used mostly for making cutouts in walls.

Jig saw blades. Use 6 to 8 teeth-per-inch, sturdy bi-metal blades, preferably with an *alternate set* tooth configuration.

Reciprocating saw blades. Blades for reciprocating saws come in *standard design*, *extra thick* and *bi-metal* type. Standard teeth generally are found on low-cost blades that tend to break easily and wander in the cut. Extra-thick blades will yield a straighter cut and are more durable. Bi-metal blades are the best for general wiring work because they can handle many materials, including nails, and they can flex without breaking. Bi-metal blades are slightly higher in price, but their longer life more than repays the investment.

A metal-cutting saw is needed if you're installing metal conduit. You can either use a reciprocating saw with a metal-cutting blade (top photo) or a hacksaw (bottom photo). Deburr the ends of the conduit with a file after making the cut.

The best saw for making cutouts for outlet boxes depends on the type of wall surface. In wallboard, use a utility knife or wallboard saw (top photo). On harder surfaces, like exterior siding, use a jig saw (bottom photo) or a reciprocating saw.

RECIP SAW BLADES

METAL CONDUIT

Use a thin, metal-cutting blade with 14 to 18 teeth-per-inch (*tpi*). When cutting threaded metal pipe, cut at the threads whenever you can.

PLASTIC CONDUIT AND PIPE

You can use a metal-cutting blade or one with slightly fewer *tpi*. But for best results, use a tubing cutter (See page 152).

COPPER TUBING

Tubing cutters work best, but a hacksaw or a recip saw with around 22 *tpi* will do the job.

CUTTING OUT A STUD

Use a thin, bi-metal, 14 to 18 *tpi* blade. Cut the nails holding the stud, not the stud itself, with the blade inserted between the bottom of the stud and the sole plate.

ROUGH-CUTTING WOOD

Use a 4 or 5 *tpi* blade that tapers toward the tip.

Drills

Most, if not all, drilling required in electrical work can be done with an everyday ⅜-in. electric drill and a set of sharp spade bits. The most common uses are to drill holes for running cable through wall framing members and to create starter holes for making cutouts in walls. Cordless drill/drivers also may be used for driving and removing screws, along with drilling holes.

If you're undertaking a large wiring project, such as wiring an addition, you should probably take a look at your drill or drills to decide if they're up to the task. If you're planning to drill dozens of cable holes through studs or joists, you might even consider renting a right-angle drill (See next page) so you can use auger-style drill bits (See next page). Avoid using auger bits with ordinary power or cordless drills, which don't have the torque such bits need to bore through wood. Half-inch power drills generally do have sufficient torque to drive auger bits, but it is very dangerous to use them for this purpose. If the bit sticks, the torque is so great that the body of the drill can rotate violently, causing any number of problems, including breaking your wrist.

A cordless drill/driver allows you to drill holes and drive screws without the hazard created by power cords and, perhaps more importantly, in areas where the electricity has been shut off.

Cordless tools are not required for wiring, but if you have one you'll find it convenient to use: especially if you need to shut off power at the main breaker while you work. Another big advantage of any cordless tool is that you don't need to drag extension cords up ladders when working in hard-to-reach areas. You will also feel safer in a damp environment like a crawlspace.

A hammer drill has plenty of power and torque, enhancing both speed and control. It is especially useful for drilling into masonry.

DRILLING POINTERS

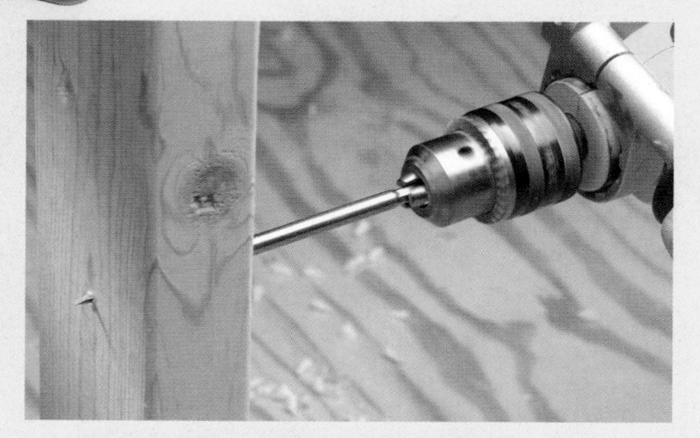

When you can see the tip of the bit break through the opposite face of the wood (top photo), stop and remove the bit. Then, start drilling from the other side (bottom photo) using the tip hole as your center reference. This eliminates "blow-out."

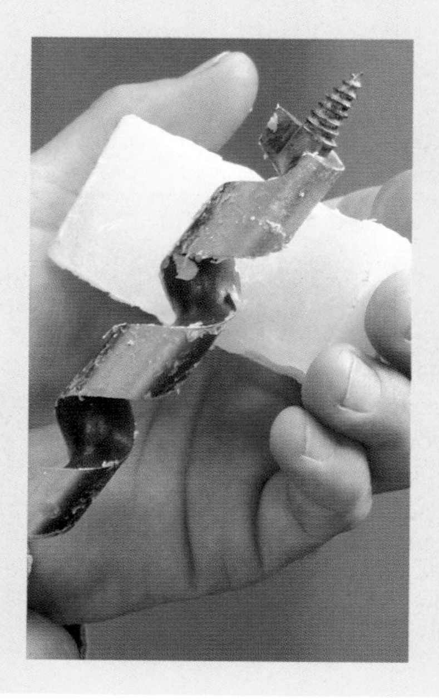

Lubricate auger bits with beeswax to reduce resistance so they can cut more easily. Unlike soap and other lubricants, beeswax will not promote rust or cause problems with the wood or the cable sheathing that runs through the hole.

RIGHT-ANGLE DRILLS

Right-angle drills are heavy-duty tools designed with the chuck and spindle at a right angle to the handle and motor shaft, lessening (but not eliminating) danger when using high-torque bits, such as auger bits. All right-angle drills must be held tightly, and used with sharp bits.

TYPICAL APPLICATIONS:

- When a long auger bit is needed to get through deep wood
- Large diameter holes
- Heavy-duty continuous drilling
- When a lot of torque is needed to get through hard wood.

Bit extenders

For drilling deep holes, as when drilling through a rim joist to run power cable out of the house, either buy a spade bit with a very long shank (some are as long as 16 in.), or insert a standard spade bit into a bit extender. The bit shank is secured into the bit extender with set screws tightened by an Allen wrench. Using the long-shank bit in combination with a bit extender, you can drill holes approaching 30 in. deep. The extra depth is most useful on older houses with wide foundation walls that support more than one joist.

Spade bits

Spade bits are the most commonly used bits for cutting wood, and ½- to 1-in. bits are the most-used size. If a 1-in. hole isn't large enough to allow for the number of cables coming through the stud, do not enlarge the hole. Instead, drill a second 1-in. hole directly above and at least 2-in. away from the first hole. This keeps the holes in the center of the stud and doesn't weaken it as much as increasing the hole size.

General-purpose spade bits range in size from ¼ to 1¼ in. A ½-in. bit will cut a large enough hole for running nonmetallic cable through wall studs, without weakening the stud.

You will note that spade bits come with either a flat blade or with two end spurs. Bits with spurs cut much faster. Shank length on spade bits also varies, from standard short shank bits like those shown above, to extra-long shanks (photo below) for drilling deep holes.

The weakness of the spade bit when compared to the auger bit is the shaft strength—the spade bit will snap under medium torque situations. That means that if you jam the bit when it breaks out of the hole, the head of the spade bit can break off. Also, if you hit a nail with a spade bit, the bit will very likely be ruined. If you find you have to apply a lot of pressure to drill with a spade bit, have it sharpened or replace it.

Auger bits

Originally called *ship auger bits*, these are the heavy-duty spiral bits that are used for fast, deep, heavy-duty hole cutting. Because they cut so fast they require tremendous torque from your drill. Use these only with a powerful right-angle drill. If you hit a nail, the bit will dull and cut slowly. Don't try to force it through the wood; resharpen the bit instead.

Auger bits, similar to the bits used with an old brace-and-bit hand drill, make quick work of drilling holes for running cable. Because they cut so aggressively, they should be used only with a powerful right-angle drill.

It takes some practice to get the hang of using auger bits. Due to their fast cutting, you can quickly get so deep into the wood that the bit gets stuck, potentially burning out the drill motor. When drilling very deep holes, drill a series of partial depth holes, starting with a large diameter bit and switching to increasingly smaller bits as you drill deeper.

When drilling with an auger bit, keep enough constant pressure on the bit so the cutting action doesn't stall. If the bit starts turning without going deeper into the wood, it will open up a hole around the screw tip and the auger will stop cutting. For this reason, auger bits cannot be used to enlarge an existing hole. The screw spiral on the tip of an auger bit needs to get its teeth into solid wood at all times—this is what pulls the cutting shank into the wood. If the spiral spins in a hole, the auger will also do nothing but spin.

Bit extenders and long-shank spade bits are used to drill access holes in deep stud or joist cavities.

Multimeters

Multimeters are electronic devices used to measure voltage, current (amperage) and resistance, and also to make continuity checks. This is the tool that tells you whether a wire is hot or not. Digital models come in both *autoranging* and *manual* versions. Manual models require that you know the approximate amount of what is being measured beforehand so you can turn the range knob to the proper scale. The autoranging versions are better in that you just put the probes on the testing points and it gives you an instant reading.

A multimeter will have two probes, but it makes no difference which probe goes where when using the AC voltmeter. Place the red probe on the positive terminal and black on the negative when the DC voltmeter part of the multimeter is used for your car battery. Place the two probes where you want to measure the voltage, say into the hot and neutral slots of a receptacle. This test is better and more accurate than using a plug-in analyzer (See page 29).

When using the continuity scale, always have the power removed from the circuit or you might damage the meter. A typical use is checking water heater elements and light bulbs to see if they are still good. One probe goes on each terminal. If the element is good you hear a buzz or see 000 on the display.

A multimeter can measure resistance, current and voltage. Most will also come with a continuity tester. There will be two probes attached to the multimeter. The upper part of the probe will have a plastic sleeve and this is where your fingers hold the probe. The lower part of the probe will be metal—never allow your fingers to slide down the probe's plastic sleeve and touch the metal end when taking a measurement. At best, you will get a false reading. At worst, you may get electrocuted.

Be careful where you put the probes. At all times, the metal probe ends must be isolated from any conductor other than the one you are measuring. The problem with shorting the probe against other metal

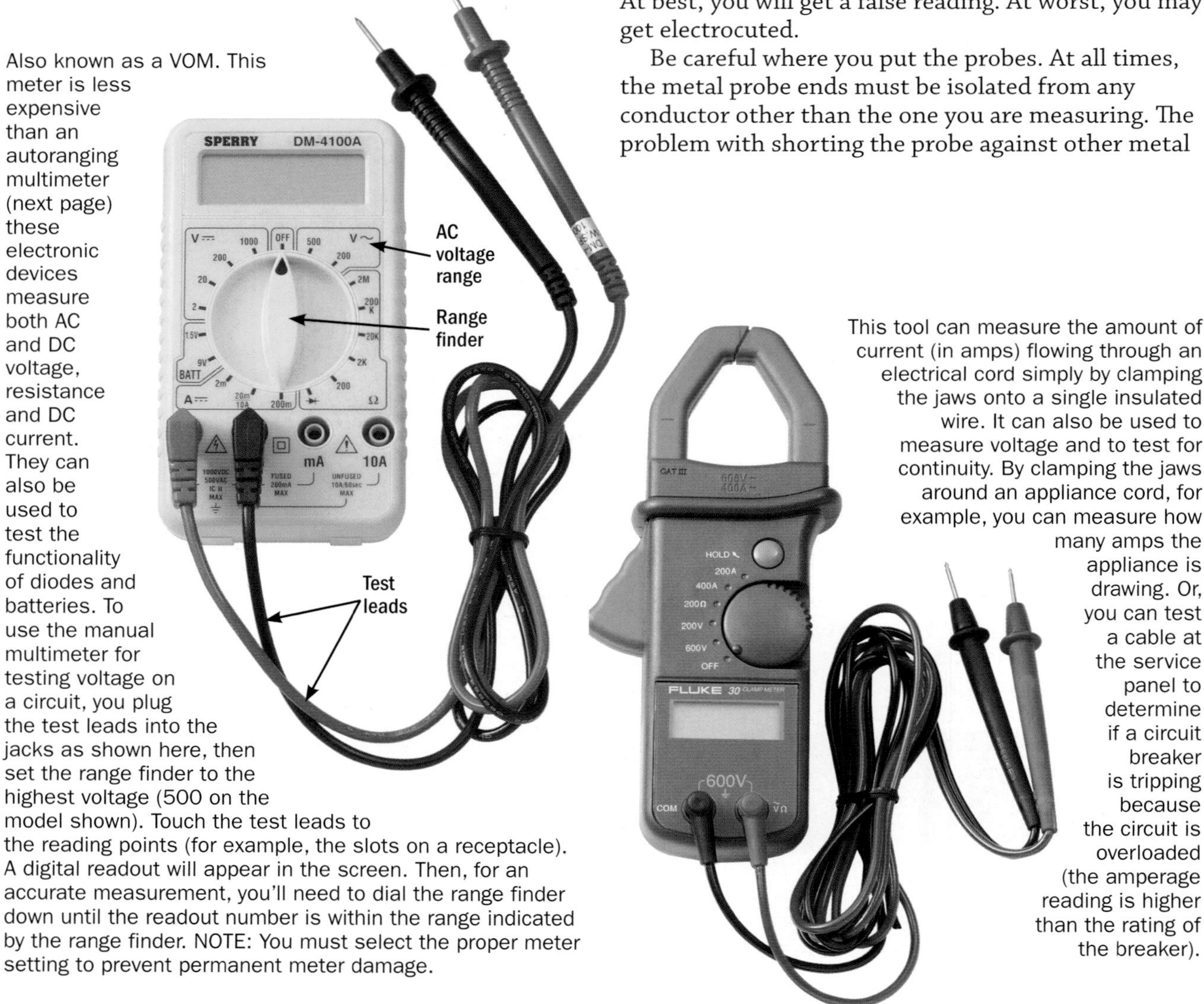

Also known as a VOM. This meter is less expensive than an autoranging multimeter (next page) these electronic devices measure both AC and DC voltage, resistance and DC current. They can also be used to test the functionality of diodes and batteries. To use the manual multimeter for testing voltage on a circuit, you plug the test leads into the jacks as shown here, then set the range finder to the highest voltage (500 on the model shown). Touch the test leads to the reading points (for example, the slots on a receptacle). A digital readout will appear in the screen. Then, for an accurate measurement, you'll need to dial the range finder down until the readout number is within the range indicated by the range finder. NOTE: You must select the proper meter setting to prevent permanent meter damage.

This tool can measure the amount of current (in amps) flowing through an electrical cord simply by clamping the jaws onto a single insulated wire. It can also be used to measure voltage and to test for continuity. By clamping the jaws around an appliance cord, for example, you can measure how many amps the appliance is drawing. Or, you can test a cable at the service panel to determine if a circuit breaker is tripping because the circuit is overloaded (the amperage reading is higher than the rating of the breaker).

can be solved the same way as discussed when using the probes around a metal box—tape the probes up except for the sharp tip (See page 15).

Here are other mistakes to avoid:

- Never measure current (amperage) with the probes of a multimeter—it is too dangerous. If current needs to be measured, use a clamp-around meter (See photo, below).
- Never measure resistance or take continuity measurements with power on the circuit: you may ruin the meter.
- If you need the probes to stay on the object being measured to free your hands, use probes with alligator clamps on the ends to latch around screws and wires.

Typical uses for a digital multimeter:

- Measure voltage or lack of voltage on a receptacle
- Verify that wires are not hot
- Verifying open neutral (no voltage detected wide slot to narrow slot, but voltage is detected ground slot to narrow slot)
- Verifying voltage is present at a light bulb socket
- Continuity check across a light bulb (open indicates a bad bulb)
- Continuity check across water heater elements (open indicates a bad element).

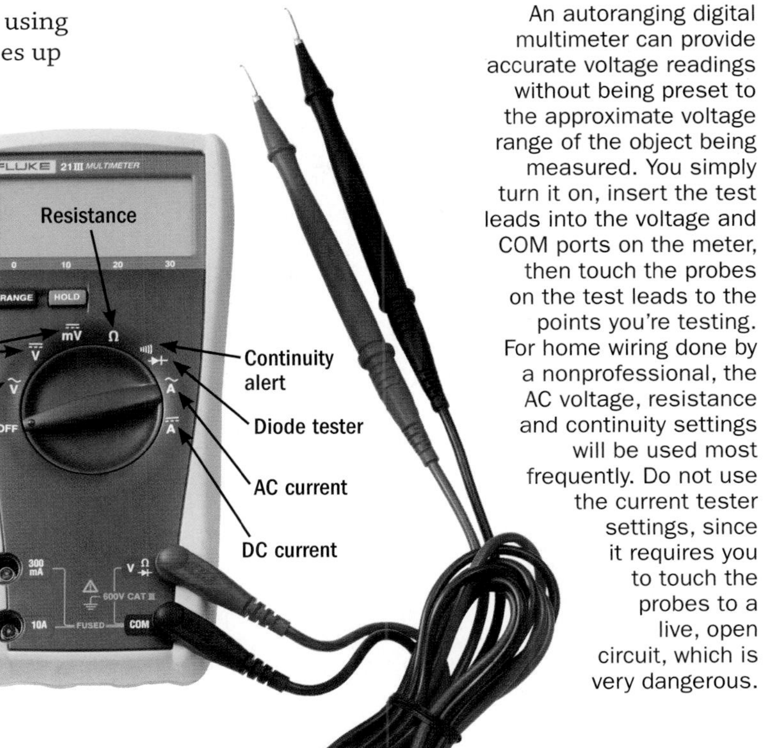

An autoranging digital multimeter can provide accurate voltage readings without being preset to the approximate voltage range of the object being measured. You simply turn it on, insert the test leads into the voltage and COM ports on the meter, then touch the probes on the test leads to the points you're testing. For home wiring done by a nonprofessional, the AC voltage, resistance and continuity settings will be used most frequently. Do not use the current tester settings, since it requires you to touch the probes to a live, open circuit, which is very dangerous.

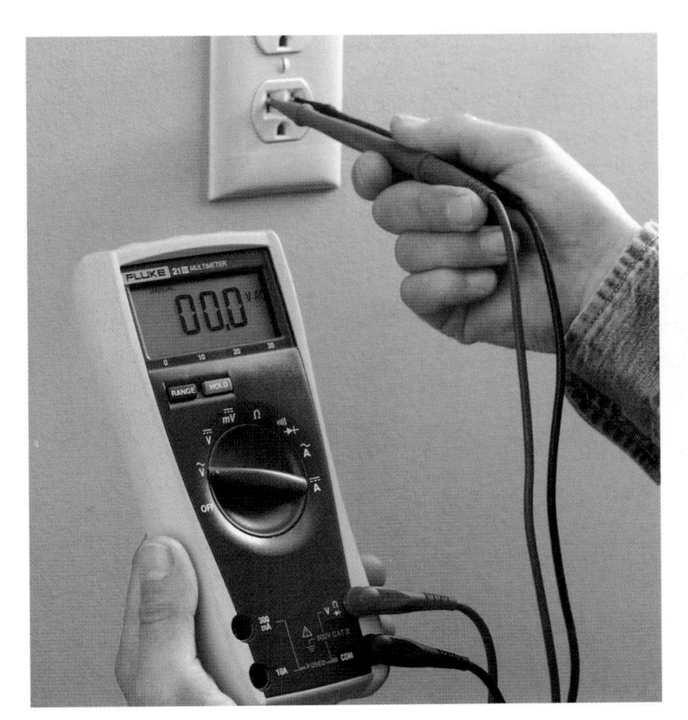

A clamp-around meter (above) offers the ability to measure current (amps) through single insulation wire's, so you can determine how much draw is being pulled on a line or appliance cord without exposing live, bare wires. The tool is fairly expensive, though.

A digital multimeter (left) is a reliable tool for testing to make sure power is not flowing in an outlet or line.

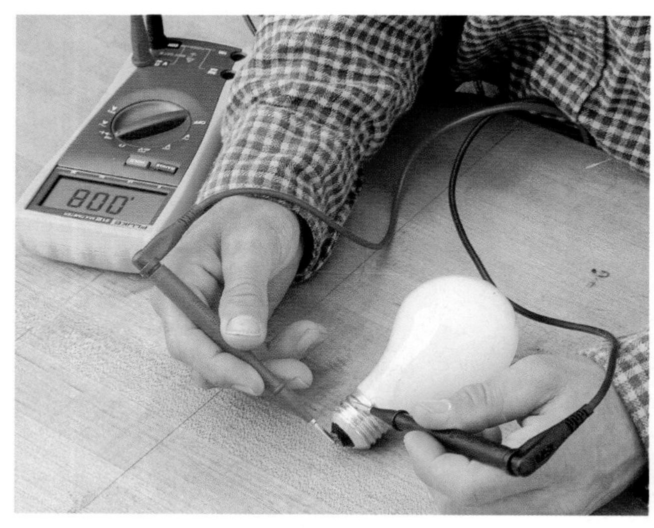

Testing for continuity with a digital multimeter is a quick way to find out if a light bulb is blown or if you have a more complicated lighting problem on your hands. Just set the multimeter to the continuity setting (See previous page), touch one probe to the socket and the other to the hot terminal at the base of the bulb. If the multimeter buzzes, the bulb is good and the problem is elsewhere.

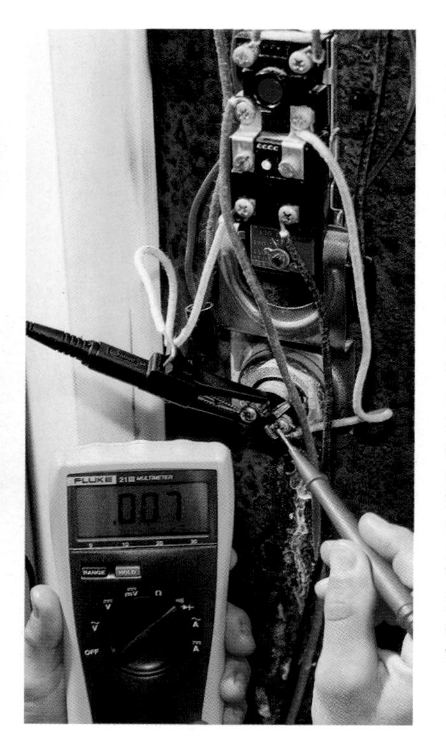

Electric water heater elements also can be tested for continuity to determine if they are the cause of a nonfunctional water heater. As with light bulbs, just touch the probes of a multimeter to the element terminals. Make sure the multimeter is set to determine continuity and be sure the power to the heater is off, otherwise you could ruin the meter. You'll hear a buzz if the water heater element is in good working order.

Electrical Tape

Anyone doing electrical work will find constant need for high-quality black electrical tape, as well as several different colored electrical tapes. Black is used for all the standard wrapping needs. Tapes of other colors are used for specific purposes in electrical work:

Green tape. Any wire that has green insulation (or has some other colored insulation but has green tape around it) is a ground wire. Green designates earth ground.

White. Any wire that has white insulation is normally a neutral wire—the wire that brings the power back to the service panel after it has gone through the load. However, if the wire is a color other than white but is taped white, it is by definition a neutral wire. A typical example would be the service entrance conductor coming into the main service panel.

Black and red. These are the two typical colors that designate hot wires. But hot can also be blue, purple or any other such color (except green).

Other colored tape. Tape colored anything other than green, white, black or red is used to label and identify cables. For example, you have a multitude of cables coming into the panel from all over the house, how do you know which cable goes where? By using tape to band each end. The purple tape on the cable in the bath receptacle box, as an example, is matched to the purple band on the cable in the main service panel.

You will be tempted to use the cheap tape found in grocery and hardware stores. Don't do it. Such tape will not have the insulating capability of high-quality electrical tape. Look for 3M-brand Super 33+ or Super 88. Both are good tapes that are effective between 0°F and 260°F. They also resist UV rays and are UL-listed. The Super 33+ product is 7 mil thick and the Super 88 is 8.5 mil thick.

Plug-in Analyzers

These little devices have taken the wiring world by storm over the last few years because they are inexpensive and very easy to use and understand. You simply push the tester into a receptacle outlet that has power, and lights on the analyzer will glow to indicate how the receptacle is wired. Prospective homebuyers use them to test existing outlets in a house. Do-it-yourselfers use them to check their wiring work. But be aware of the limitations of plug-in testers. Some are not *UL*-approved for testing receptacles, wiring or even the circuit. And the consumer models cannot detect if your electrical system contains a bootleg ground (that's where someone has jumped the neutral over to the ground screw in a very dangerous attempt to bring a ground into the system). They are also prone to giving false readings, so most pros who use them carry at least two so they can confirm the information.

When using a plug-in analyzer, be sure to read the printing on the analyzer carefully—they have differing systems for indicating what is wired right or wrong. If the display lights on the tester flash randomly and intermittently, it is normally because the receptacle female prongs aren't making good contact with the male prongs of the tester. Or, the wires in or around the receptacle may be loose.

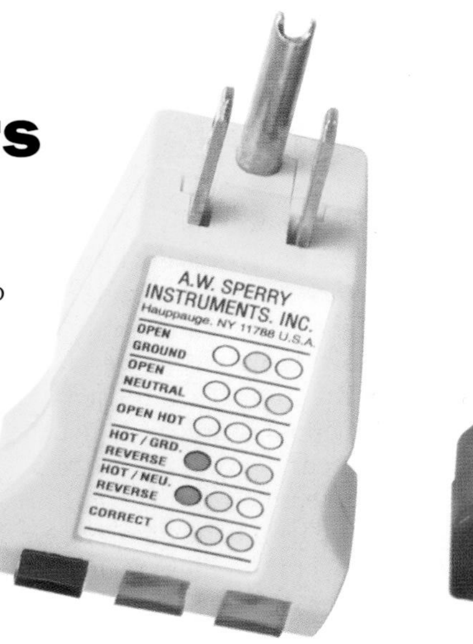

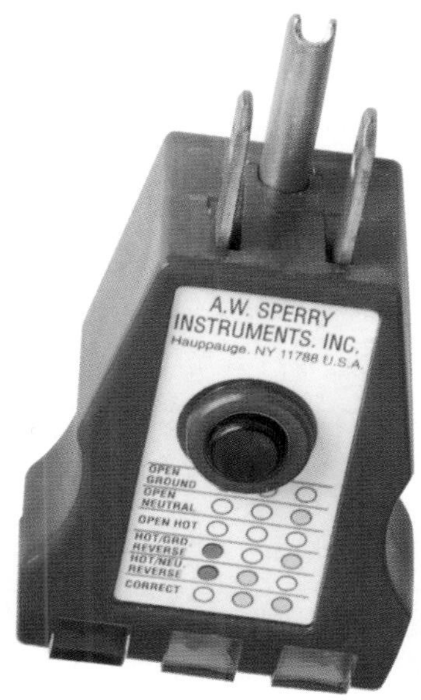

Plug-in analyzers can be useful for making a quick check to see if a receptacle is wired correctly. Just plug it into the slots and compare the way the lights illuminate with the key printed on the analyzer. Some models, like the one to the left above, simply give a readout of their finding. Others, like the tester on the right, also can be used to test GFCI-protected receptacles by simulating a ground fault (See photo, below left).

To use a plug-in analyzer, simply insert the tester prongs into the receptacle (test both the top and bottom receptacle). Glowing lights indicate whether the receptacle is properly grounded and if the hot and neutral wires are attached to the correct terminals. If the analyzer has a little button, it can be used to test GFCIs. When you push the button it creates a simulated ground fault on the line to test if the GFCI will trip.

NEON CIRCUIT TESTERS

The smallest and cheapest of the plug-in analyzers are *neon circuit testers*. Comprised of a neon bulb and two test probes, these devices light up when the probes detect current flow, so they're used frequently to test circuits for power. If the bulb doesn't light up when the probes are inserted it is assumed that power is not present. While cost and ease of use work in the neon tester's favor, they do have a significant and potentially dangerous drawback: the bulbs on many of these testers will only glow if the power they detect is in excess of 50 volts. On occasion, a loose connection may be creating enough resistance to reduce the current to less than 50 volts, but the power isn't actually off. And the 50-volt charge that goes undetected is more than enough to give you a potentially harmful shock. For maximum safety, use a digital multimeter (See pages 26 to 28) rather than a neon tester to check for power.

NM CABLE

14-2 w/g

12-2 w/g

14-3 w/g

12-3 w/g

10-2 w/g

10-3 w/g

6-3 w/g

UF CABLE

14-2 w/g

12-2 w/g

Wire & Cable

What we normally call wire and cable are technically known as *conductors*. Usually, a single conductor is called a wire and group of them is called cable. However, large conductors are composed of many individual conductors, usually twisted together, so the terms are interchanged quite often.

The larger the diameter of the conductor, the less resistance it creates. Less resistance is good since resistance opposes the current and inhibits voltage getting to the load. If more than 10% of the household voltage doesn't make it to the load due to too much resistance, motors and fixtures can burn out. So why not just use very large diameter wire everywhere and don't worry about it? Cost.

The diameter of a wire is described by its *gauge*. The larger the gauge number, the smaller the wire. Most 120-volt home wiring circuits are wired with 14 or 12-gauge conductors. Small appliances or lamps may contain 18 or 20-gauge wire. On the bigger end, you can find wire as thick as 2/0 and even up to 4/0 in a home.

How do you tell the two gauge cables apart? It is normally written on the sheathing of the cable. For example, the aforementioned 12-gauge cable is labeled on its sheath, *12-2 w/g NMB*. The 12 is the gauge, the 2 means there are two insulated conductors, and *w/g* simply means "with ground." The *NMB* means nonmetallic sheath with a 90° Centigrade temperature rating. Almost all interior wiring today is done using NM cable (popularly called *Romex*).

When purchased in 50 or 100-foot rolls, cable is relatively inexpensive, even if it's heavier 12-gauge cable. If the cable will be exposed instead of covered by a wall in a stud or joist cavity, it should be run through conduit to protect it from damage (See pages 36 to 37). Some

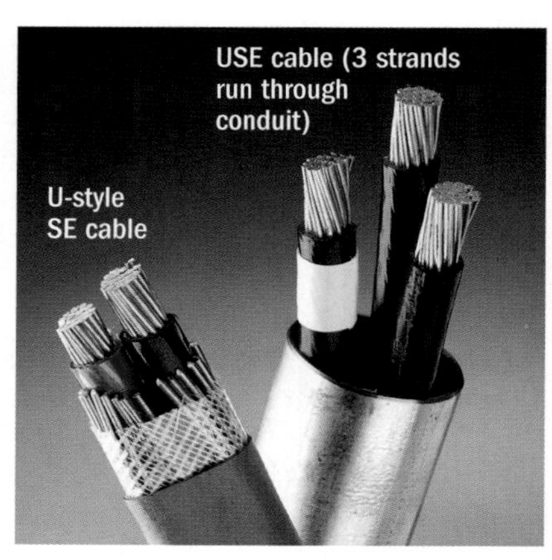

Two common types of copper service entrance cable (SEC) are: the U-style, with two hot conductors wrapped in a braided wire neutral and bound by thermoplastic sheathing (left); and USE cable (right), which is created by running strands of insulated 1/0 conductor through conduit. One USE strand is taped white for neutral and the other two strands are hot.

codes still allow armored cable to be used in interior situations. Armored cable is manufactured with flexible metal coil sheathing. But generally, you'll find it easier to work with nonmetallic cable fed through conduit than to handle and cut armored cable. And the cables will also be better protected.

Exterior wiring is normally done with underground feeder cable (UF), which is constructed like NM cable except the sheathing is made of a much more rugged material and wraps around all conductors individually. In certain situations, UF cable should be run through exterior-rated conduit (See pages 151 to 153).

Types of wire

Household receptacle and switch wiring. Here your choice is simply 14 or 12-gauge cable. If you are not on a tight budget, always opt for the heavier 12-gauge. Be wary of low-bid jobs, as the installer may use mostly 14-gauge simply because it is the smallest diameter

ALUMINUM WIRE

From approximately 1965 to 1972, 2 to 3 million homes were constructed with single-strand branch circuit aluminum wiring. Unfortunately, the homeowners soon learned that aluminum wiring exposed to air will produce a surface barrier chemical reaction that can act as an insulator, destroying wiring connections and increasing resistance. In addition, the screws that held the wires down would become loose after a period of time. As a result, codes today restrict the installation of new aluminum wire. Exceptions are made for large diameter wire, like the service entry cable shown here.

But even large diameter aluminum wiring can be problematic unless the exposed conductors have been coated with a noncorrosion compound and the terminals are kept tight.

If you have single strand aluminum wiring feeding the receptacles and switches in your home, you have a major problem. In addition to its tendency to corrode, it is difficult to splice and breaks easily. Also, most electrical fixtures are UL-approved for copper wire only. The best solution is to simply rewire the house. If that is not an option, some companies do manufacture wire connectors they say will splice copper to aluminum. Switches and receptacles for aluminum wire are sold at large electrical supply houses.

Aluminum service entry cable

4/0-gauge

2/0-gauge

gauge allowed by the NEC. As you might think, 14-gauge conductors can create problems, so they must be used only where there is low current draw. Because home builders usually don't know where you will be using your heavy electrical items, it's common to find 14-gauge cable almost everywhere in newer homes, except the kitchen area, bath and utility room, where the NEC requires 12-gauge.

TIP: Since 12 and 14-gauge cables look almost identical when they are lying in rolls on the floor, it is easy to get the two mixed up. To solve this problem, simply spray paint the sides of the 14-gauge cable.

Common cable for household wiring includes: 14/2 NM, 12/2

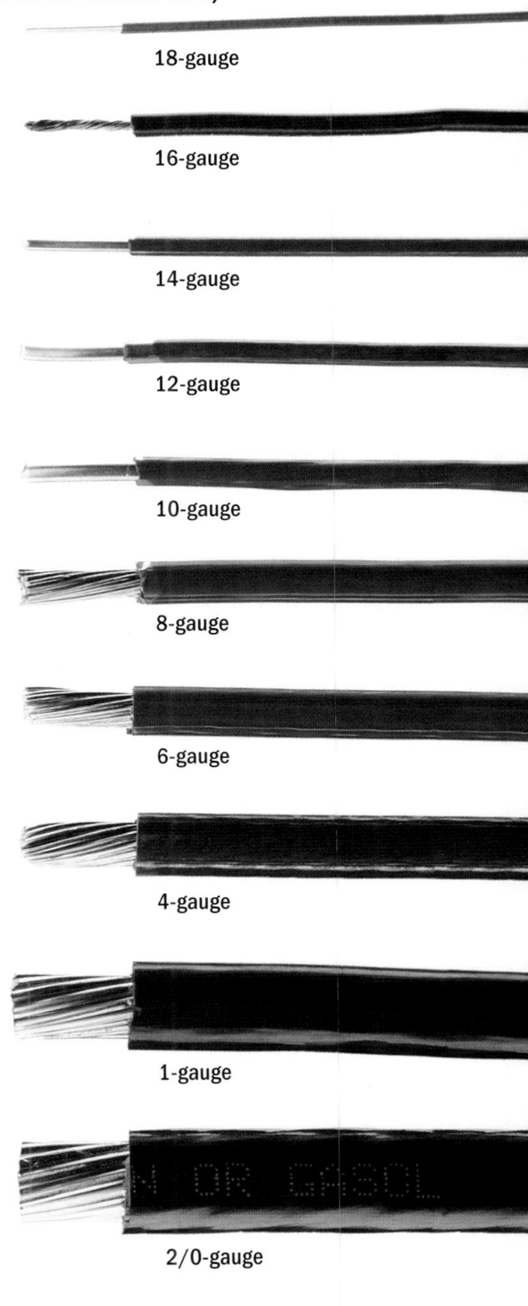

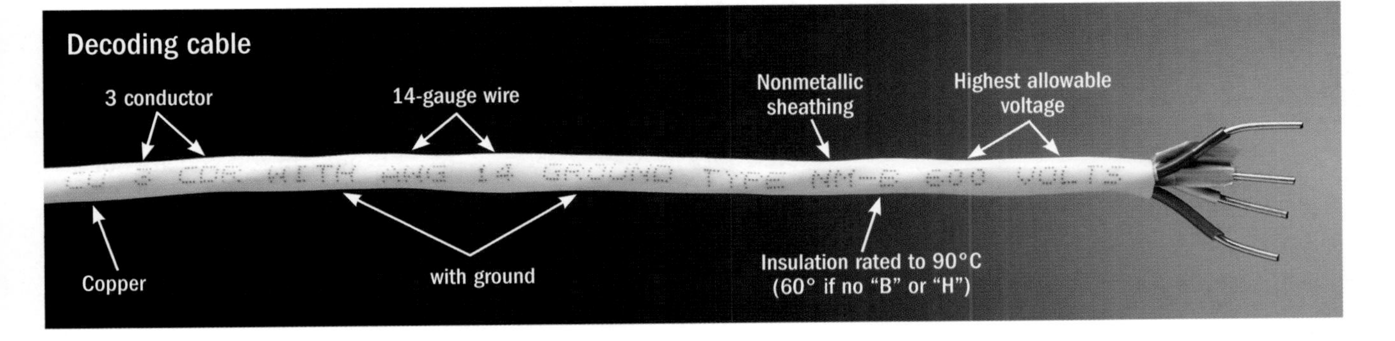

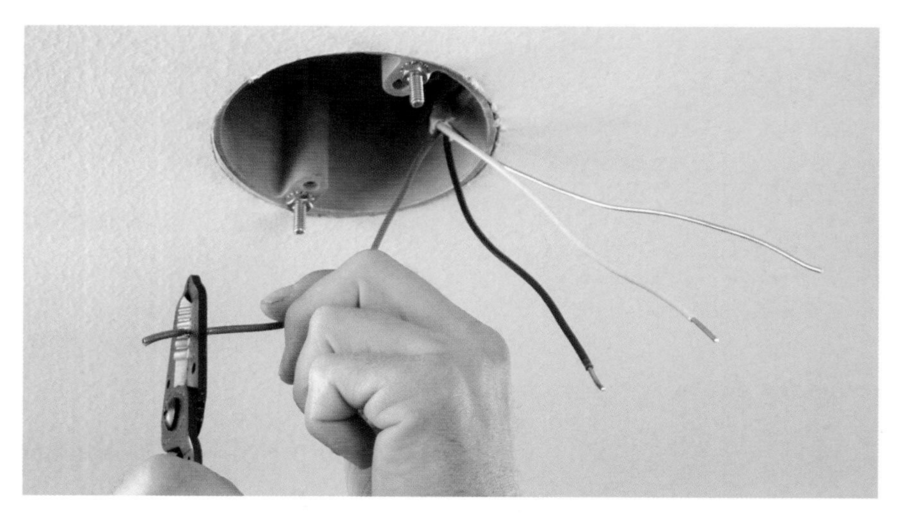

Prepare insulated wires for making connections by stripping insulation from each wire, using a wire stripper (See page 20).

HOW TO SPLICE CABLE IN A JUNCTION BOX

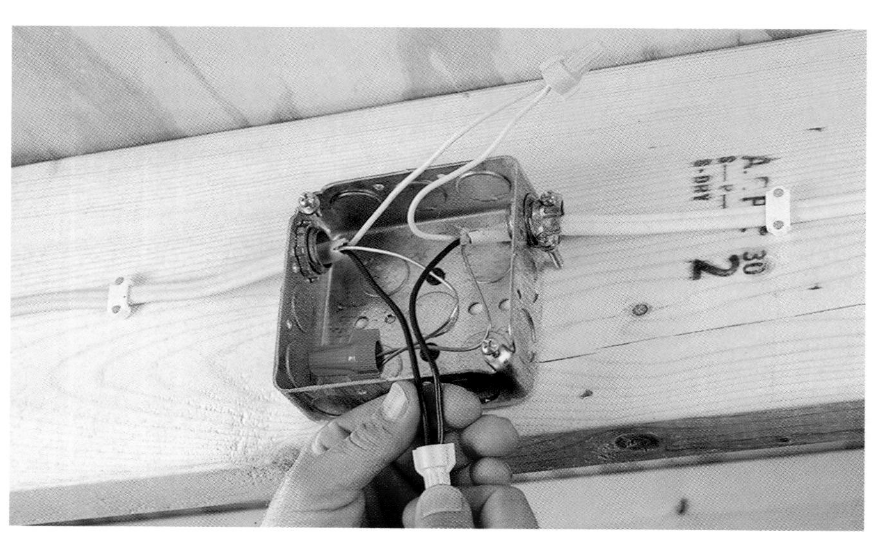

1 Any time a run of cable is interrupted, you can splice new cable to the old to lengthen the run. But the splice must be made with wire connectors and sealed in a junction box. Attach the junction box to a joist or wall stud and knock out entry holes for both cables (if using a metal junction box). Feed both cables into the box, securing them at the knockouts with cable clamps. You'll need a good 6 to 10 in. of cable entering the box from each side. Strip the cable sheathing and wire insulation (See page 34) then connect the like-colored wires with wire connectors (See page 35). Fold the wires into the box, starting with the ground wires.

2 Check to make sure all the connections are intact and secure, then cover the junction box with a box cover plate.

SIZE REQUIREMENTS FOR SERVICE ENTRY CABLE

SERVICE	COPPER	ALUMINUM
200-amp	2/0 gauge	4/0 gauge
150-amp	1 gauge	2/0 gauge
100-amp	4 gauge	2 gauge

NM, 14/2 NM w/g, 12/2 NM w/g, 14/3 NM, 12/3 NM, 14/3 NM w/g and 12/3 NM w/g.

Service entrance cable. In most cases, the largest wire in a residence will be the service entrance cable (SEC)—the very thick wires that bring power from the transformer connection to the service panel in your home. If you're working with SEC, copper wire generally is a better choice than aluminum because it's smaller in diameter so it is easier to bend and fits better into conduit.

Electric stove wire. Copper stove wire is normally 6 or 8-gauge, making it the heaviest wire coming out of most main service panels. Aluminum could be used here (6 or 4-gauge) but many local codes forbid it because it is susceptible to corrosion.

Electric dryer wire and electric water heater wire. Both typically need to carry 4000 to 5500 watts, so they are a hefty 10-gauge copper in most cases.

Wire connectors

In the old days, wires were twisted and soldered then wrapped with rubber tape for insulation. This system worked well but did not allow new wires to be added or wires to be taken out of the splice very easily. Today, using wire connectors, also called *wire nuts* or *wire caps* from the original design from *Ideal*, is the common way of splicing two or more wires (copper wire of 10-gauge and smaller) together. These connectors make splicing fast and easy. Most connectors consist of a thermoplastic shell with an expanding wire spring within. The wire spring cuts into the wire's outside surface slightly to make a tight connection.

Most wire connectors are color coded. The common wire connectors you will use, starting with the smallest, are orange, yellow, red, and blue or gray (although this system is not applied uniformly by all manufacturers). The number of wires each connector is designed to contain (See photo, right) is written on the bag or box the connectors are packed in.

An occasional problem with wire connectors occurs when moisture gets into the connector and causes the wires to corrode. At least one manufacturer now makes connectors that contain a silicone lining inside to inhibit moisture penetration.

Preparing the cable

Certain basic material handling skills will be required when you undertake any wiring project. Running cable into a junction box and stripping off sheathing and insulation will almost certainly be necessary. Most common mistakes made by do-it-yourselfers have their root in improper preparation of the cable: too much wire can be left in the box, causing a space crunch that creates pressure on the connections and leads to failure; too much wire insulation can be stripped off, leaving bare conductors exposed in the box after wire connectors are twisted on; cable clamps that secure the incoming and outgoing cable can be left out or improperly attached, leading to contact between the sharp edges of a knockout hole and the cable sheathing, which in turn can cause short circuiting.

Whether you're running all new wiring or simply replacing a switch, taking the care to correctly handle the wire and make the connections carefully is critical to the success of your wiring project. See the photo sequence on the following pages for a demonstration of preparing cable and conductors for making wiring connections.

USE THE CORRECT CONNECTOR

Wire connectors are color-coded to indicate the number of wires of various gauges they can connect so you can easily choose a connector that is neither too large nor too small for your job. An orange connector handles up to two 14-gauge wires. Yellow accepts three 14-gauge or two to three 12-gauge wires. Red connects four to five 14-gauge or four 12-gauge wires. Gray or blue connects six 14-gauge or five 12-gauge wires. Green wire connectors are used with grounding wires. They can handle two to four 14-gauge or 12-gauge wires. Some green connectors have a hole in the tip allowing one grounding wire to pass through and connect to a grounding screw terminal, so an extra pigtail isn't needed. Wire connector packages should list the number of all wire gauge sizes and combinations they can safely connect.

MAKING SCREW TERMINAL CONNECTIONS

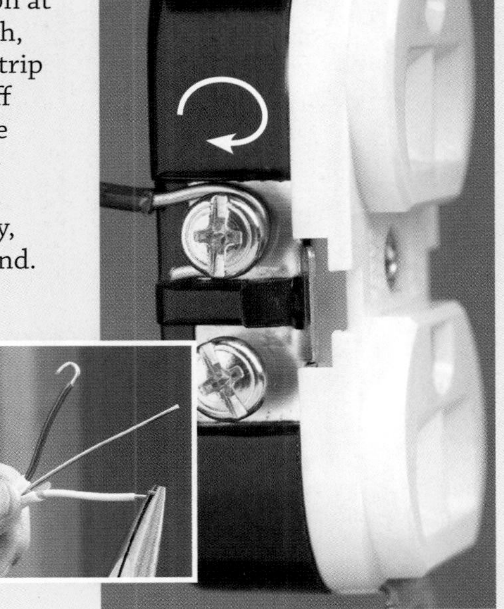

To make a secure connection at a screw terminal on a switch, receptacle or fixture, first strip about ¾ in. of insulation off each conductor using a wire stripper. Then, with a long-nosed or needlenose pliers, grasp each conductor firmly, just short of the stripped end. Rotate the pliers while holding the conductor steady to form a loop. When you attach the wire, be sure to orient it so the loop is clockwise. Then, when you tighten the screw, the screw will work with the loop, not against it.

HOW TO PREPARE NM CABLE FOR MAKING CONNECTIONS

1 After running cable from the load and power source, it must be inserted into the junction box through the holes in the box. If you are using a new metal box, a plug or covering will need to be knocked out (See page 50). Pull the cable(s) into the box so you'll have plenty available to work with. If you're using a metal box with cable clamps, tighten the clamps enough to hold the cable, but don't clamp them all the way down.

2 Once all cables have been inserted into the box, the sheathing on each cable must be stripped off to expose 4 to 6 in. of wire. Using a utility knife or a cable ripper, reach into the box and split the insulation down the center of the cable to its cut end. Cut just deep enough to slice through the sheathing. Once the cut is made, separate the sheathing from the cable and slice it off at the base of the cut.

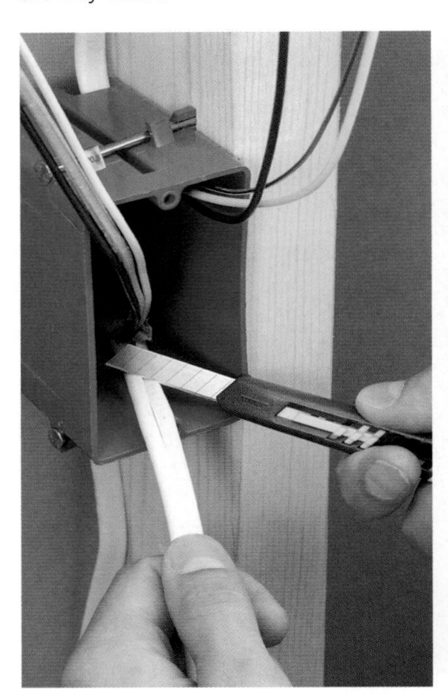

3 Feed the cable back through the entry opening into the box until only about ½ in. of sheathing is exposed in the box. Tighten the clamp, if present. Strip, push back and secure all cables.

4 Separate the individual conductors in each cable then trim to length. All like-colored conductors should be the same length when pulled together to the side of the box.

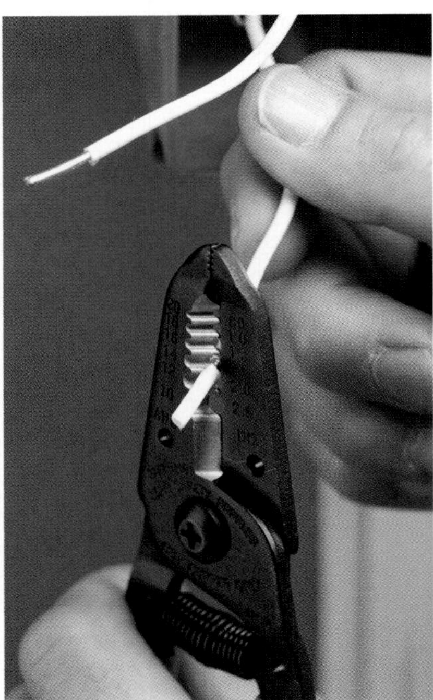

5 Select the correct wire gauge on your wire stripper and strip the insulation off each conductor. If you'll be connecting the wires to screw terminals, strip off about ¾ in. of insulation. If twisting them together with a wire connector, strip off about ½ in.

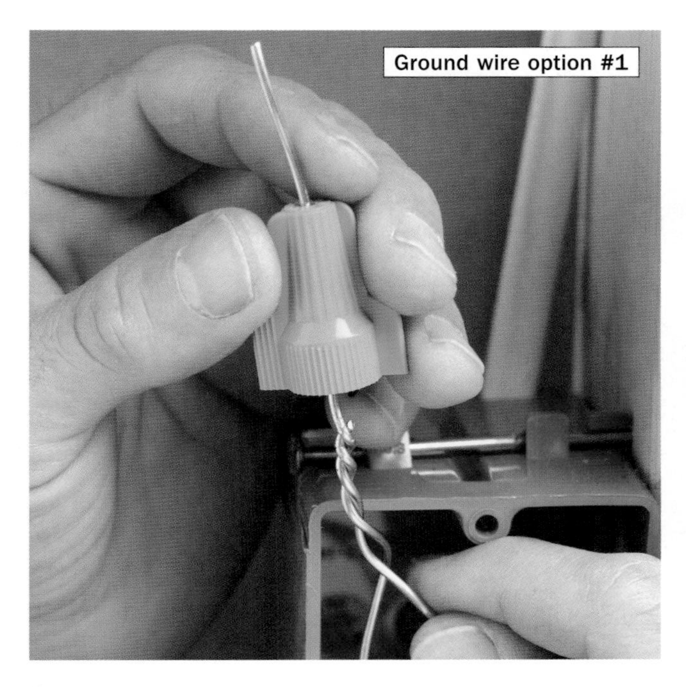

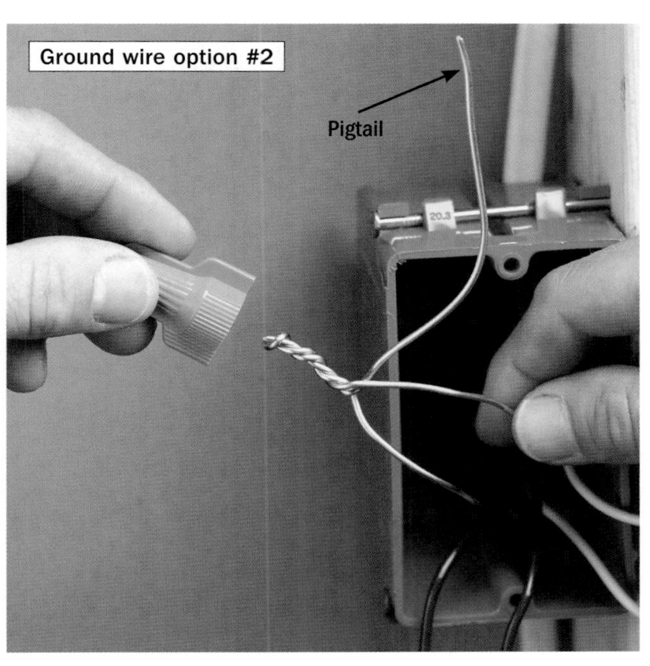

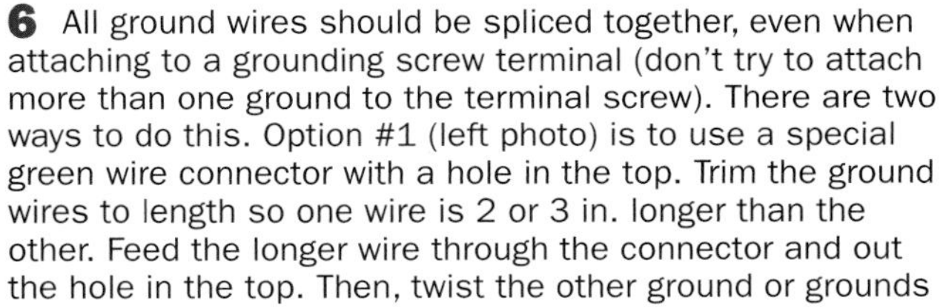

6 All ground wires should be spliced together, even when attaching to a grounding screw terminal (don't try to attach more than one ground to the terminal screw). There are two ways to do this. Option #1 (left photo) is to use a special green wire connector with a hole in the top. Trim the ground wires to length so one wire is 2 or 3 in. longer than the other. Feed the longer wire through the connector and out the hole in the top. Then, twist the other ground or grounds to the long wire, a couple of inches down from the end. Twist the connector around the wires until tight, then attach the free end of the long wire to the grounding terminal. Option #2 (right photo) is simply to twist a short pigtail into the connector with the ground wires, then attach the end of the pigtail to the grounding terminal. **NOTE:** If you're using a metal box, another ground wire must be run from the wire connector to the grounding screw on the box.

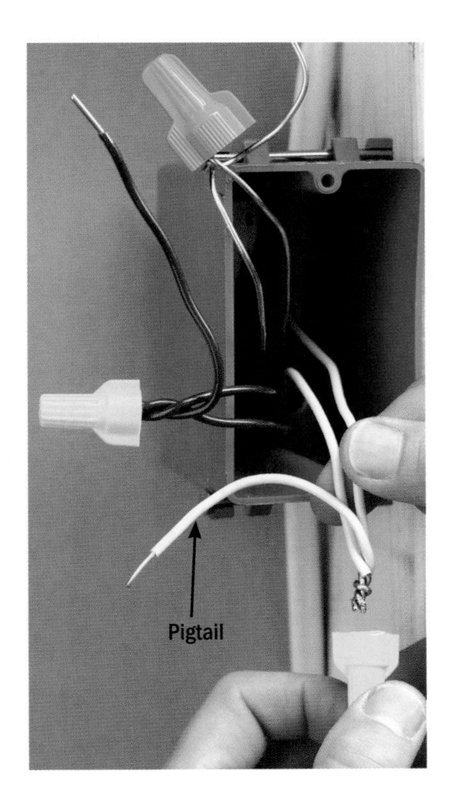

7 If the wires are to be spliced together, all like-colored wires are to be twisted together with a wire connector on the bare ends. Before attaching the connector, hold all wires to be connected in a tight group with the ends even. Grasp the wires (as a group) in the jaws of a pair of pliers and make a couple of clockwise rotations with the pliers to twist the wire ends into a neat spiral. Twist on the wire connector, being careful not to over-twist and strip the wires.

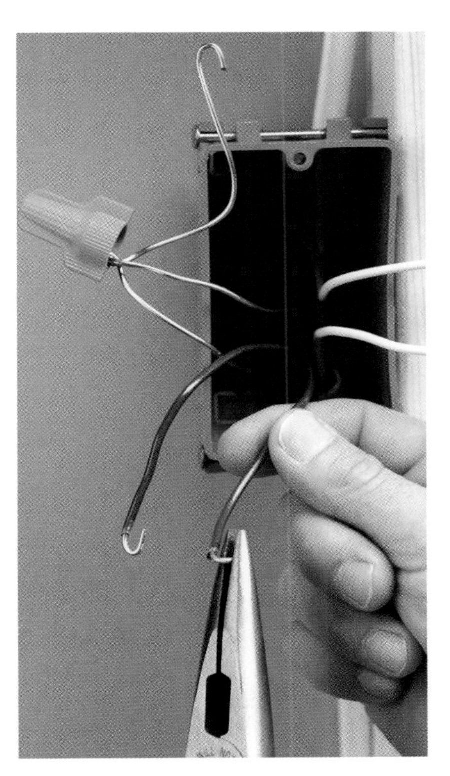

8 The ground (bare copper) wires in this case are to be spliced together with one wire connecting the entire splice to a receptacle, a 6-in. pigtail wire with both ends stripped is added into the splice and the free end is connected to the receptacle. Bend the free end of any wire or pigtail wire into a hook so it can connect to a screw terminal (See page 18). Use long-nosed pliers to form the wire-end loops.

Metal conduit is the most familiar conduit material. The lightest gauge metal conduit (EMT) is still used extensively in exposed interior wiring locations, such as basements and garages. But it is not allowed for exterior work. IMC and rigid metal conduit, when used with watertight connectors, may be used outdoors. But they are seldom used anymore, in favor of lighter and more workable PVC conduit.

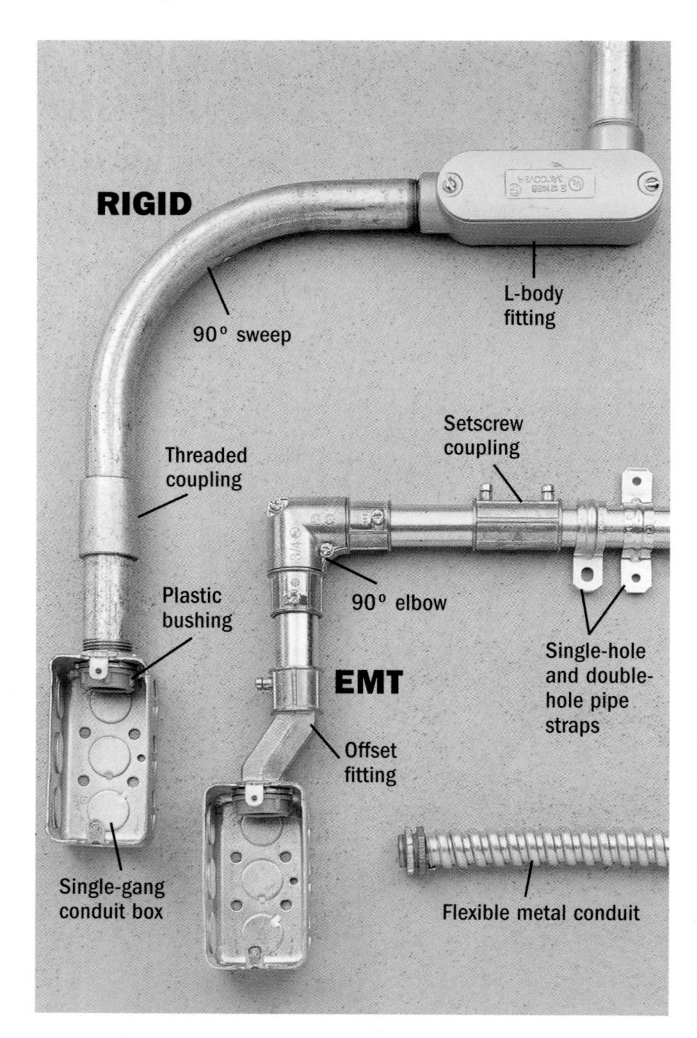

Metal conduit and fitting types used in home wiring are **Rigid** for exterior use and **EMT** (Electrical Metal Tubing) for interior, dry locations.

Conduit

Conduit is used to protect wires in exposed locations, such as on masonry surfaces in a basement. Conduit rated for exterior use can be used to install circuits outdoors. Check with your local electrical inspector to determine the type of conduit your project requires.

Metal conduit

Metal conduit is available in three types. EMT (Electrical Metallic Tubing) is lightweight and easy to work with, but because of its thinner tubing, EMT shouldn't be installed where it could easily be damaged. IMC (Intermediate Metallic Conduit) has thicker, galvanized walls to withstand rougher treatment. It also is a good choice for outdoor installations when used with weatherproof fittings. Rigid metal conduit provides heavy-duty protection, but it is the most expensive and also requires threaded fittings. IMC or EMT should be adequate for most of your projects. PVC conduit (See next page) is increasing in popularity because it is lighter in weight, inexpensive and easy to work with, but check your local building department first: PVC isn't approved for some applications and in some geographic areas.

Metal conduit fittings

Metal fittings are available to make the installation of metal conduit quite easy. Rather than bend the conduit yourself with special tools, you can purchase these connectors premade to create the conduit layout your project requires.

Threaded couplings, connectors and sweeps are used to install rigid metal conduit.

ARMORED CABLE

Armored cable is essentially pre-wired flexible conduit that was popular for use in areas that receive little traffic (like attics) but require protected cable. When running new wiring, most pros today prefer to install conduit and thread it with plain old nonmetallic cable. Conduit and cable are cheaper and regarded as easier to work with.

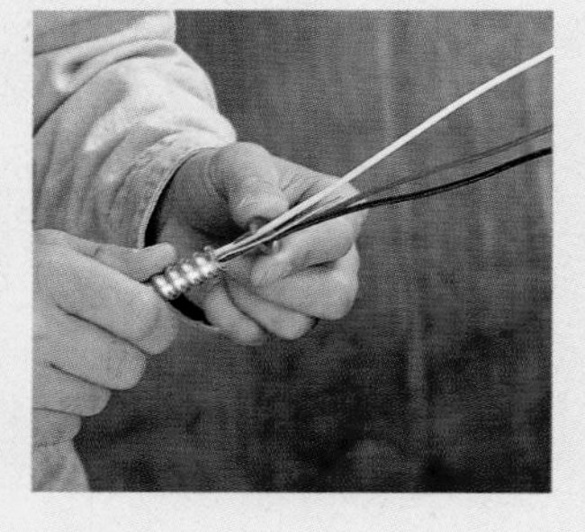

Setscrew fittings are used with EMT and IMC. The removable cover on the 90° elbow makes it easy to pull wires around a corner. An offset fitting connects conduit, anchored flush against a wall, to the knockout on a metal electrical box or to a service panel knockout.

The same metal electrical conduit boxes are used with all conduit types. An L-body fitting is used as a transition between vertical and horizontal lengths of conduit, such as when underground wires must enter a building. The cover can be removed, making pulling wires easier. Plastic bushings cover exposed conduit ends, protecting wires from damage by the rough metal edges. Metal pipe straps anchor conduit against masonry surfaces or wood framing members. Conduit should be supported within 3 ft. of each electrical box and fitting, and at least every 10 ft. in straight runs.

Flexible metal conduit bends easily and can be used for short unsupported distances where rigid conduit is difficult to install. It is frequently used to connect appliances that are hard-wired, such as water heaters. Wires are pulled through flexible metal conduit in the same manner as with other conduit. Armored cable (See previous page) is flexible metal conduit that comes with the wires prerun through the conduit. It is seldom used in new work today.

PVC conduit

Most local codes allow the use of PVC plastic conduit in installations requiring wire protection. Plastic conduit and fittings are lightweight and very easy to install. It is cut and assembled with solvent glue just like PVC plumbing pipe. Check with your local electrical inspector to find out if plastic conduit is okay for your project.

Plastic conduit is generally connected to plastic electrical boxes and fittings that come in similar shapes and sizes to those used with metal conduit. But, as you'll see in one of our featured projects in this book (See pages 154 to 157), PVC conduit can be attached to a metal box by welding a threaded male coupling onto the end of the conduit, then securing the coupling to the metal box with a cable clamp nut.

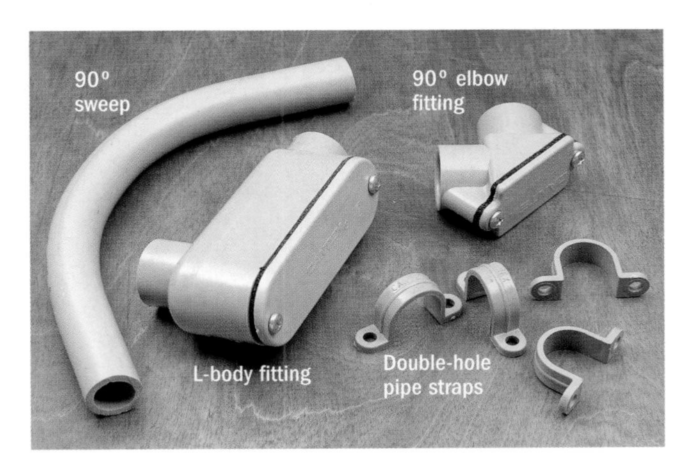

Plastic (PVC) conduit and fittings look very much like their metal counterparts, but are lighter in weight. The material is especially popular in exterior locations because PVC won't rust and the solvent-weld process of connecting creates a watertight joint (See page 152).

TIPS FOR RUNNING CONDUIT

ATTACHING HANGERS TO MASONRY

Anchor conduit to masonry surfaces with self-tapping masonry screws and galvanized metal pipe straps. Conduit must be anchored within 3 ft. of each box or fitting and every 10 ft. in longer runs.

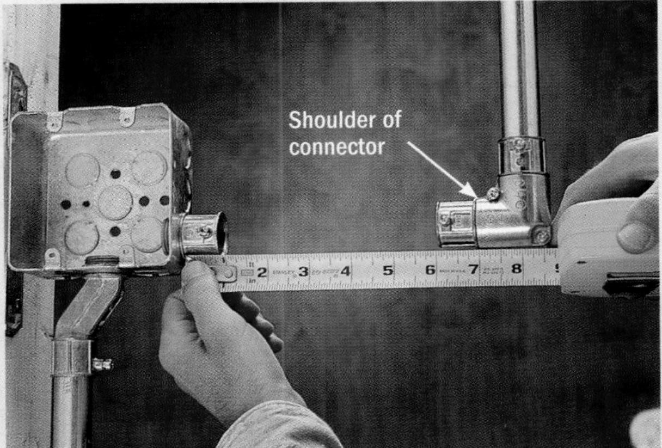

MEASURE FROM SHOULDER TO SHOULDER

Use a tape measure to determine the length of conduit needed between locations. Measure to the shoulders of connectors to determine the distance the conduit will need to span.

ELECTRICAL SYSTEMS

The electrical system serves to distribute electricity from the point where it enters your home to the loads that consume it. The essential components of the system are: the main service panel, which employs circuit breakers or fuses to distribute the raw current into manageable circuits; electrical boxes, where the hook-ups and connections are made; switches to regulate the electrical flow; and receptacles to create points of access to the power. The system is woven together with cables, conduit and fasteners. In this chapter, the essential electrical system components are discussed in detail. By understanding what they are and how they work together, you gain the ability to accomplish almost any home wiring project or task.

The Service Panel

All the electrical service in your house starts at the service panel (also called the load center). It is the heart of the electrical system. It also houses the main cutoff switch and contains protective devices (circuit breakers or fuses) for all the wiring in the house. Every adult in the house needs to know where this panel is and how to throw the main breaker on and off in case of an emergency.

The service panel divvies up the raw power entering your house into organized, controlled circuits. A circuit is a cable that has been installed to power a light, receptacle, appliance or area. Wiring codes are very specific about the number, size and purposes of the individual circuits originating in the service panel. Many home appliances require dedicated circuits of their own. Lights should be on their own circuit so that if an appliance overloads and trips a circuit breaker, the lights will stay on so you can find your way around the house and down to the service panel. Furnaces, garages, stoves and other major kitchen appliances generally command their own circuits. See the chart on page 42.

The main service panel is the heart and the brain of the electrical system. Every adult in your household should be familiar with it, if only to locate the panel and restore power to a circuit breaker that has tripped.

Parts of the service panel

The main breaker. The primary purpose of having a main breaker is to limit the amount of current coming into the panel and house so that excessive current cannot damage the service entrance cable or main panel. Being current sensitive, the main senses the amount of current (amperage) flowing from the meter base into the panel and will throw the main breaker off if the amperage is over the designed limit. The designed limit is normally written on the breaker handle or the panel lid.

NOTE: If an additional cutoff panel is ever installed between the utility meter and the main service panel, the main service panel becomes a subpanel where neutrals must be separated from the grounding system (See page 44).

Circuit breakers. One of the purposes of the service panel is to distribute all the power to the various circuits that feed all the house loads. This distribution is done most often through mechanical/ electrical devices called circuit breakers. They plug into the two hot busses going down the panel center. When the circuit breaker is in the ON position, power flows out of the hot bus and through the breaker, into the wiring, and then to the various loads throughout the house (switches, receptacles and appliances). In the OFF position, the breaker stops the flow of power to those same loads. As the load pulls the power through the breaker, the breaker senses the amount of current and if it is more than the amount allowed on the circuit wiring, 15 or 20 amps for example, the breaker will trip and open the circuit. To reset the breaker once the excessive load has been removed, you must turn the breaker to full OFF first and then back to ON. Otherwise, the breaker will trip back off again.

200-AMP SERVICE PANEL

MAIN BREAKERS

These handles cut off electrical power to the house. They are normally located at the top of the panel. The two incoming hot service entry cables from the meter base connect to these switches. In the ON position the power from the meter base goes through the switches directly to the two hot busses going down the center of the panel.

HOT BUSSES

These are the two copper or aluminum strips, insulated from the metal of the panel, that run down its center. The two busses match up with the two incoming hot cables that feed into the main. Each bus, sometimes called a "leg," supplies power to the circuit breakers contacting it. All breakers tied to the same bus are on the same "phase."

CIRCUIT BREAKERS

Circuit breakers are mechanical/electrical devices that distribute and regulate current flow to individual circuits. Panels contain both single-pole (120-volt) and double-pole (240-volt) breakers. Some panels can be equipped with half-size slim breakers that conserve slot space. GFCI breakers provide reliable ground-fault protection to an entire circuit, eliminating the need for GFCI receptacles on the circuit.

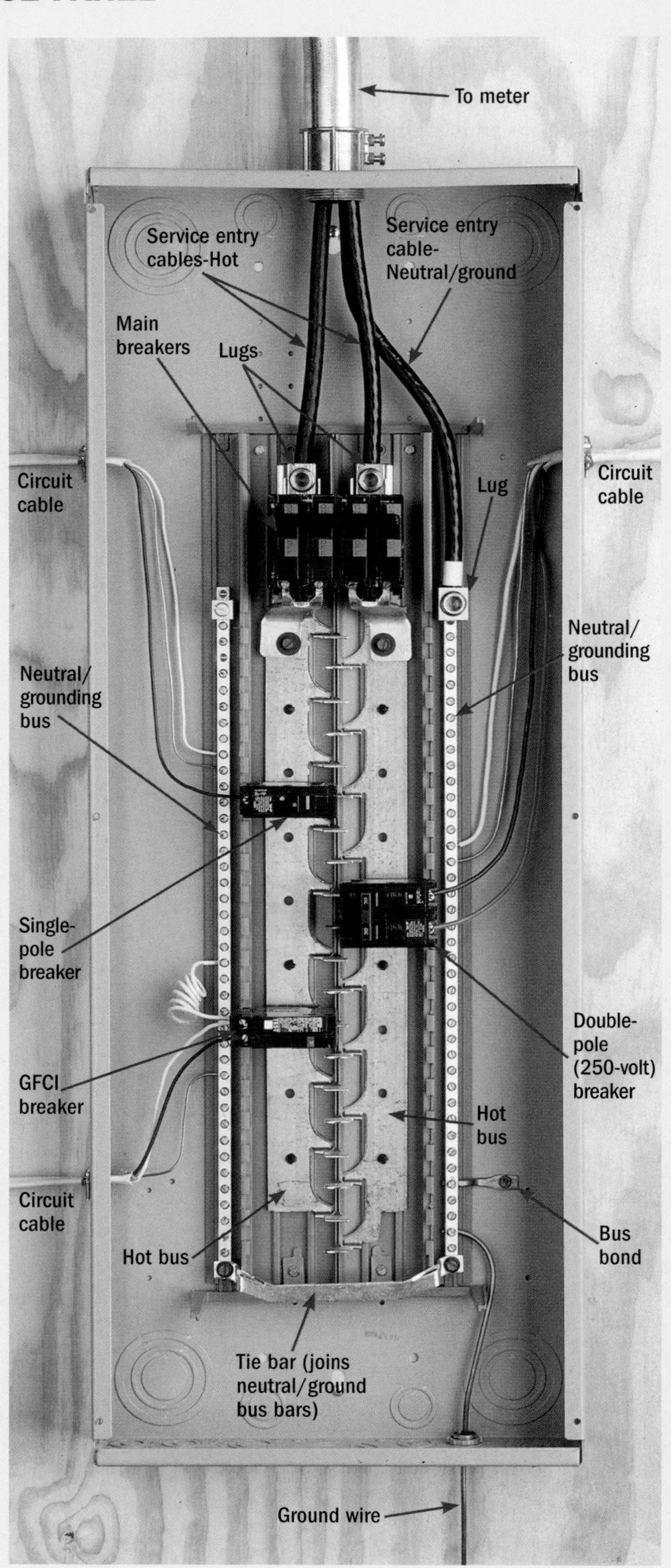

NEUTRAL/ GROUNDING BUSSES

A neutral/grounding bus on a main service panel is a long metal bar with many screw holes where every neutral and grounding wire connects to the panel. All the equipment grounding wires (the bare wires in the NM cable) going to the grounding screws of every receptacle and appliance, as well as all neutral wires (the white ones) connect to a neutral/grounding bus to obtain their 0-volt ground reference.

TIE BAR

The tie bar on a service panel connects the two neutral/ground bus bars. If the tie bar is removed, the panel may be used as a subpanel, which requires separate neutral and ground bars.

BUS BOND

A physical connection from a neutral/ grounding bus to the metal of the panel. This places the panel at ground potential so that if accidentally touched by a hot wire the breaker will kick, cutting off the power. If left unbonded, the panel can become a hot conductor if a hot wire touches it.

GROUND WIRE

Even though the incoming neutral is grounded at the utility pole, a ground wire, usually 4 to 6-gauge bare copper, is installed at the main service panel.

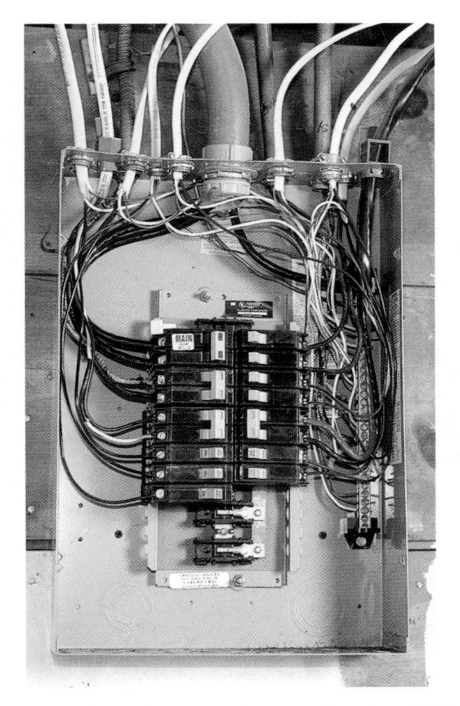

Not all service panels are alike. In addition to the model shown on page 40, here are two common variations that may more closely resemble the panel in your home.

Breakers come in different amperages: 15, 20, 25, 30, etc. The amperage that is used for a circuit is always matched to the maximum allowed current for whichever gauge wire is used in the circuit. For example, 15 amps for 14-gauge wire, 20 amps for 12-gauge wire, and 30 amps for 10-gauge wire. Breakers can be single-pole, double-pole, slim-line or quad styles. A single-pole breaker services one 120-volt circuit, measured from hot wire to ground or neutral. These are the ones with one black wire going to the load and one white wire going to the neutral/grounding bus. The hot wire (normally black) takes the power from the breaker to the load and a neutral (always white) brings it back. The neutral connects to the neutral/grounding bus in a main service panel or to the neutral bus in a subpanel.

A single-pole breaker is the most common breaker in your panel. Double-pole circuit breakers are two single-pole circuits put together with a common trip arm. Double-pole circuits feed 240-volt loads, such as water heaters and baseboard heaters. These circuits also use the black and white wire, each of which goes to the breaker (there is no neutral) but the white wire should have a band of black tape around it to indicate it is not a neutral.

If slot space is at a premium in your service panel, you may be able to substitute slim-line breakers that can run two single-pole circuits from a single slot. These devices, also called two-in-one breakers, do not fit every panel.

Neutral/grounding bus. These are the aluminum bars where the white neutral wires and bare and green ground wires terminate. The returning neutral currents from each circuit collect on this bar, then return to the utility transformer through the grounded neutral of the service entry cable. Remember, all the current starts at the transformer and therefore must return to the transformer. You will not find this bus on a subpanel. Subpanels have a separate neutral bus and grounding bus.

FUSE BOXES

In the old days, the main service panel was usually a 60-amp fuse box. It held two 60-amp, pull-out cartridge fuses for the main service protection, two 40-amp, pull-out cartridge fuses for the stove's wiring protection, and four glass plug fuses for individual circuits.

The old fuse panels were not designed for today's many varied loads. Modern panels can distribute power to as many circuits as the service panel is designed to support (up to 40). This is a tremendous improvement over the early 60-amp fuse box that could support no more than four circuits. This is why the old panels became overloaded and sometimes melted down or caught fire. People would add appliances and increase loads until the fuses blew. To keep from being inconvenienced by a blown fuse, homeowners would replace fuses with higher-amperage 30-amp fuses. Being fused at 30, the wiring that was designed to carry only 15 or 20 amps was allowed to carry 30 amps, which would overheat the wiring and create a fire hazard. Never increase a fuse size just to keep it from blowing. The fuse is blowing to protect the wiring which is being overloaded.

Understanding Circuits

Electricity leaves the panel, goes through the load (switches, receptacles, appliances) and comes back to the panel. The amount of current that leaves the panel must be equal to the amount coming back. Each circuit breaker controls the amount of current flowing through it, via an internal switch. The overcurrent protection protects the wiring, receptacle circuits, light circuits and appliances.

The manner in which current flows through a circuit depends on the type of load placed on the circuit. Here are some examples.

Current path for a light circuit. You're in the bedroom and you turn on your light. Current leaves the hot bus of the main service panel and goes into the circuit breaker. If the current is less than the amount the breaker is designed to open the circuit, the current will flow out of the breaker and into the black wire of the NM cable. It will flow in the cable through the studs, around the windows and doors, and to the light switch itself. From a black wire attached to the switch it continues through the wiring to the light. Once through the light it is now on a white wire—the neutral circuit. The amount of current on the white wire is the same as it was on the black wire—it is a series circuit. On return, it bypasses the switch via a wire cap directly to the white wire of the feeder cable. From there it goes back along the same exact path that it took to get to the switch. Eventually, it winds up back at the neutral bus of the main service panel.

Current path for receptacle circuit. Your computer is plugged into a receptacle and you turn it on. Current leaves the hot bus of the main service panel

HOW MANY CIRCUITS?

Ideally, a home with fully updated wiring should have the following circuits for applicable home features:

- Six circuits for the kitchen: two for the small appliance counter circuits, one for the lights, one for the dishwasher, one for the refrigerator (this is not required, but some people do it anyway), and another for the optional garbage disposal.
- One or two circuits for the garage
- One or two circuits for the laundry
- Two circuits for the water heater
- Two circuits for the electric dryer
- Two circuits for the electric stove
- Two circuits for the electric oven
- Four circuits minimum for interior lights
- Four circuits for a heat pump
- Two circuits for a bathroom heater
- One circuit for bath receptacle
- One circuit for outside receptacles
- Two circuits for a welder
- Two circuits for a water pump
- Two circuits for a sewage pump
- One circuit for a sewage pump alarm
- One circuit for a gas or oil furnace
- Two circuits for each electric baseboard resistance circuit
- One circuit for a small to medium whirlpool, two for a large one

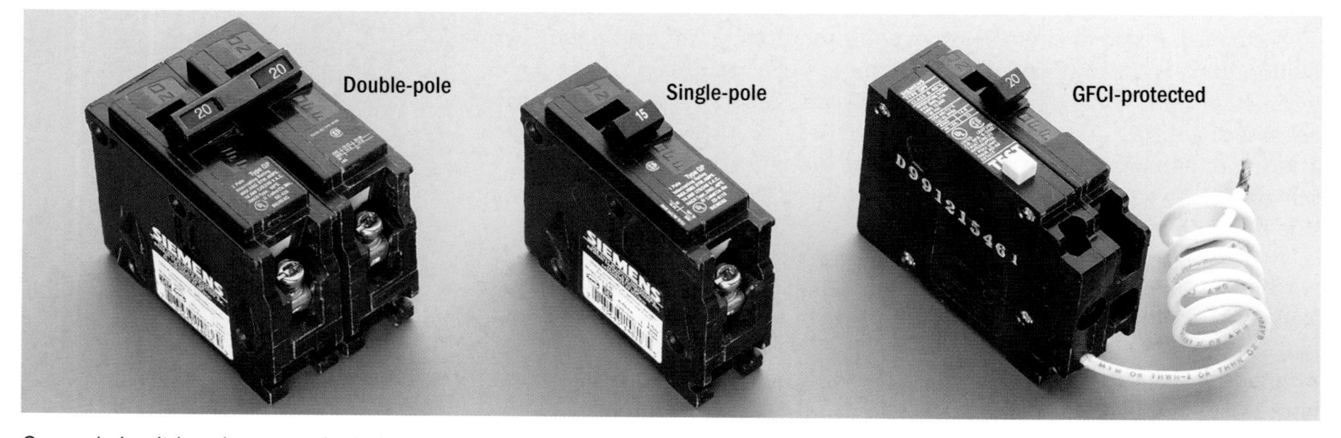

General circuit breaker types include double-pole breakers (left), single-pole breakers (middle) and GFCI-protected breakers (right). Double-pole breakers are used for circuits that carry larger amounts of current and for circuits where two separate hot leads are needed. Single-pole breakers are the most common, with 15- and 20-amps being the most frequent capacities. GFCI breakers protect an entire circuit from ground faults, eliminating the need for GFCI-protected receptacles on the line. In addition to the cost savings gained by using standard receptacles, GFCI breakers are increasing in popularity because they have a longer life expectancy than GFCI receptacles. Use the same brand of breaker to match the service panel brand.

as soon as the receptacle senses the massive current, it opens the circuit before the wire heats up enough to hurt the wiring.

The panel index for a main service panel is located on the inside of the panel door. Take the time to fill it out accurately on a new service panel when adding circuits. On existing service panels, double-check all the index entries to make sure they're correct.

and goes through the breaker just the same as the light switch circuit. Coming out of the breaker in the black wire the current flows within the NM cable and eventually winds up at the brass-colored screw at the receptacle. The current passes through the outlet and into the computer and back to the outlet on the neutral side (the silver-colored screw). It travels all the way back to the main panel in the white wire and winds up on the neutral bus. The amount of current that left the breaker on the black wire is equal to the amount returning to the panel on the white wire.

Current path for a faulted circuit. A clothes washer is plugged into a grounded laundry receptacle. A hot wire inside the washer shorts against the frame. Current speeds out of the service panel, through the breaker and out the black wire, goes all through the house, through the utility receptacle, and into the washer. Instead of going through the washer motor and control circuits, it travels to the frame. Since the frame is grounded, the massive amount of fault current flows into the bare wire of the NM cable. This wire is called the equipment grounding conductor. The current flows from the appliance frame, through the ground wire attached to the receptacle, and back to the grounding bus of the main panel. Since there is no load, there is no load resistance to oppose the current. The current flow is massive and fast. But then,

Planning a new circuit

If you're planning to install a new circuit in your service panel, start by making sure you have space in the panel for a new breaker. Keep in mind that just because a knockout slot cover on the panel cover has not been removed doesn't necessarily mean that there is room for a new breaker behind it. It's not unusual for some of the lower slot covers to be positioned over nothing. You'll need to make sure the slot opening has access to the hot bus bar where the breakers connect. Also, check to make sure at least two screw holes are vacant on the neutral/grounding bus. On some panels these can fill up quickly. If you're planning to install a double-pole breaker, make sure there are two adjoining slots available. In some cases, you may need to rearrange the existing breakers to create access for the double-pole.

If all the slots on the service panel are full, it may still be possible to add circuits if your panel allows you to replace existing single-pole breakers with slim-line breakers. Or, you could install a subpanel (See next page). But before you do either, make sure that a new circuit won't overload the panel. Add up the amperage of the existing circuits—you'll probably find that they already exceed the load capacity of the panel. That's okay, as long as the circuits are balanced on the two hot bus bars. If you have a 100-amp panel, you can actually load it with 200 total amps of circuitry provided that they're split evenly so neither bus is carrying more than 100 amps.

If you find that one bus is carrying more amperage than the other, you should install the new circuit so it draws from the bus with the lighter load.

TIP: Before you go to the trouble of running new cable to the panel to create a new circuit, make sure you can find a new circuit breaker that will fit your panel. If your panel is old or made by a defunct manufacturer, locating a new breaker can sometimes be difficult. If you check with an electrical supply house, however, you can usually track down a compatible breaker (still, you may want to investigate the option of replacing the panel).

Subpanels

A subpanel is a panel downstream from the panel closest to the utility meter—in other words, the second panel after the meter base. For example, if your local area requires a cutoff panel immediately adjacent to the meter base, then the circuit breaker panel (main service panel) in the house is a subpanel. If there is no cutoff panel, then the main service panel is not a subpanel. But if there is a large cable feeding a panel on the other side of the house from the main panel, then that panel on the other side of the house would now be a subpanel.

The reason the code people are so picky about what is and isn't a subpanel is that subpanels are wired differently from a standard main service panel—the neutrals are isolated from the grounds. Assuming you do not have a cutoff panel, the main service panel has its neutrals and grounds connected together on the same bus or busses. It is actually called a grounded neutral because of that.

A subpanel that comes after the main service panel is not required—though normally they are installed to conserve cable if the house is very long. They are also installed as a supplement to the main service panel if all the circuit slots in the main are full (but before doing this, make sure your main service panel receives enough amperage to support the panel and new circuits).

A subpanel requires two insulated hot wires fed from a breaker off the main service panel. It will also need an insulated neutral and a grounding wire. All these wires must connect into the subpanel and connect all the way back to the main service panel. The most common subpanel size is 100 amps.

A subpanel normally doesn't require a main breaker. There are two big lugs at the top of the panel in lieu of the main breaker—this is why they are also called "lugs-only" panels. The main breaker for this panel is considered to be the breaker in the main service panel that feeds the cables going to it.

The most important thing to remember in wiring a subpanel is that the neutral bus must float (not be connected to ground) and the ground must be connected to the metal of the panel. This means that all white neutral wires must connect to the floating bus and all bare ground wires must connect to the grounded bus.

CONNECTIONS FOR A SUBPANEL

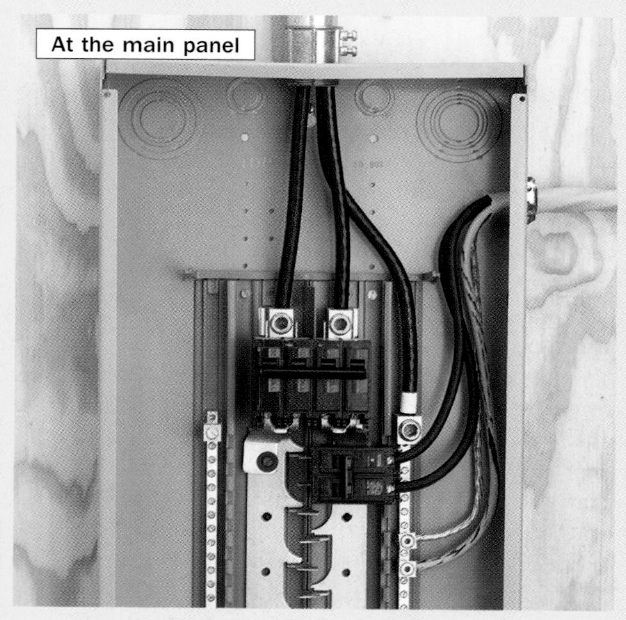

To bring power to the subpanel, a double-pole breaker (100-amp is the most common) is installed in the main service panel. The neutral and ground conductors from the cable (SER 2-gauge aluminum is shown here) are attached to the neutral/grounding bus bar.

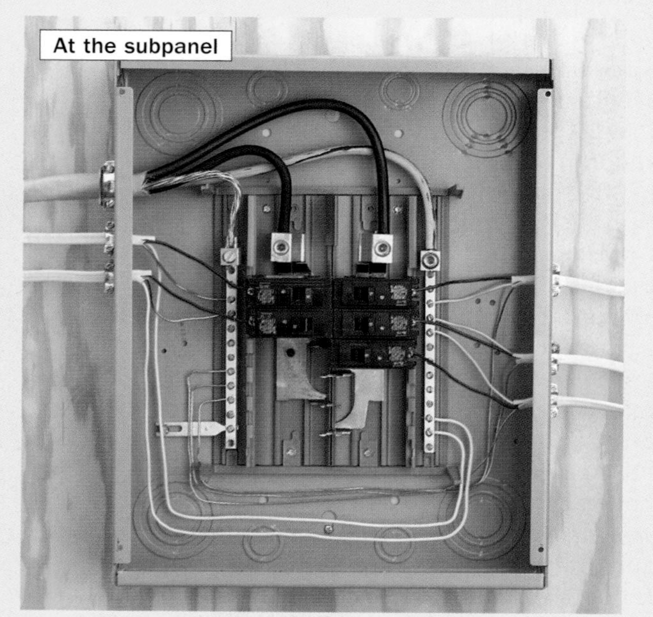

The service entrance cable coming from the main panel is connected to lugs in the subpanel. The two hot leads are connected to the hot lugs. The neutral and ground are connected to separate (unbonded) bus bars. New circuits are installed with neutrals and grounds isolated.

HOW TO ADD A 120-VOLT CIRCUIT AT THE MAIN PANEL

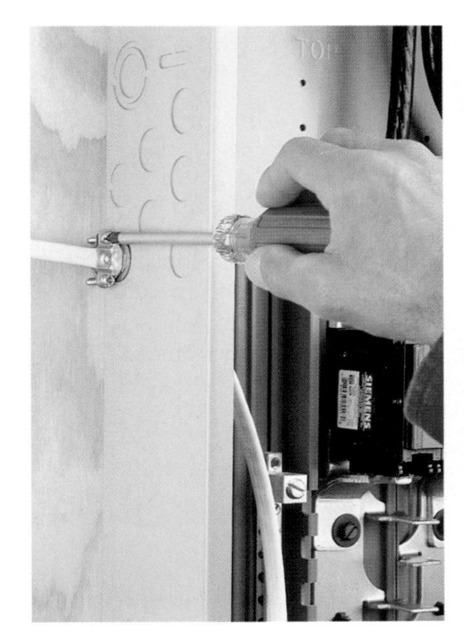

1 Shut power off at the main breaker switch or switches. Remove the panel cover then open a knockout near the new breaker location. Thread the cable for the new circuit through the knockout—you'll need at least 3 ft. of cable in most cases. Strip off the sheathing to within about 1 in. of the knockout and secure the cable to the box with a cable clamp.

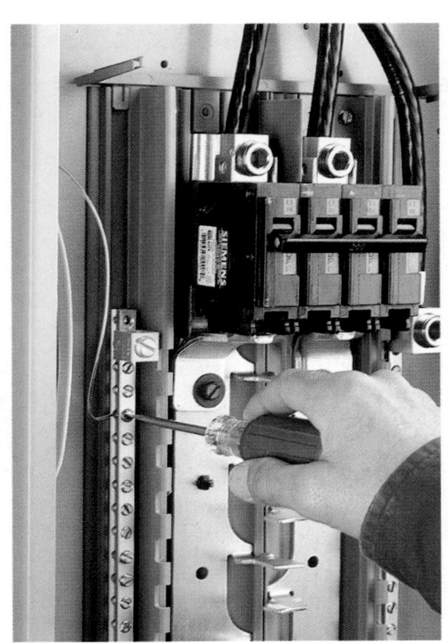

2 Separate the bare copper ground and route it around the inside perimeter of the box panel opening to an open terminal on the neutral/ grounding bus bar. Trim the wire to length. Insert the end into a terminal opening, then tighten the setscrew.

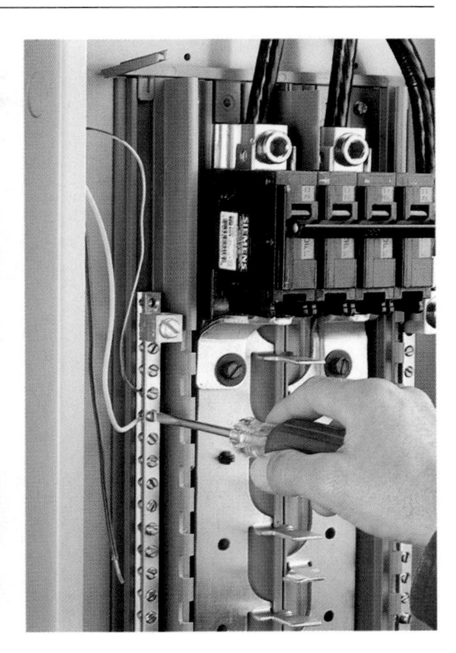

3 Thread the white neutral around the inside of the box, strip off ½ in. of insulation from the end of the white neutral wire and insert it into the opening of a terminal in the neutral/ grounding bus. Tighten the set-screw.

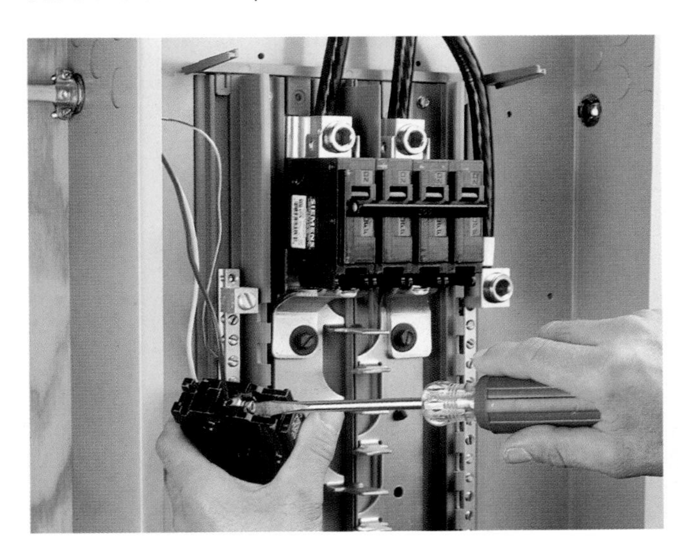

4 Route the black feed wire to the new breaker location, strip off insulation, and insert the tip of the wire into the opening in the breaker. Secure the wire in the breaker by tightening the setscrew. Make sure no bare wire is exposed at the terminal opening.

5 Snap the new breaker into the chosen slot so one end makes clean contact with the hot bus bar and the other end is secured on the panel hook. Because installation methods vary between manufacturers, your breaker might attach in a different manner from the one shown here. Check existing breakers to determine the correct installation method for your panel. Turn power on and test the new circuit. Reattach the panel cover.

VARIATION: HOW TO ADD A 120/240-VOLT OR A 240-VOLT CIRCUIT

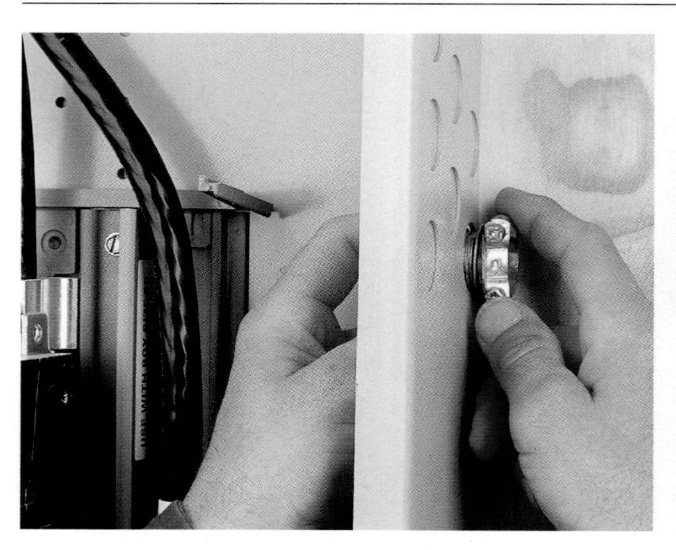

1 A 120/240 circuit supplies both 120-volt and 240-volt current. The breakers for these circuits are double-pole breakers that occupy two slots in the service panel and draw power from both hot bus bars (each bar provides 120 volts of power). 240-volt circuits supply 240-volt service only. With the power shut off at the main breakers, feed the correct gauge wire (for the 30-amp, 120/240-volt circuit shown here, 10/3 w/ground NM cable was used) into the panel through a knockout and secure with a cable clamp sized to match the cable type.

2 For 120/240-volt circuits, connect the bare ground wire and the white neutral wire from the new cable to the neutral/grounding bus, as with a standard 120-volt installation. On straight 240-volt circuits, only the ground conductor is attached to the neutral/grounding bus. The white neutral is used as a hot lead.

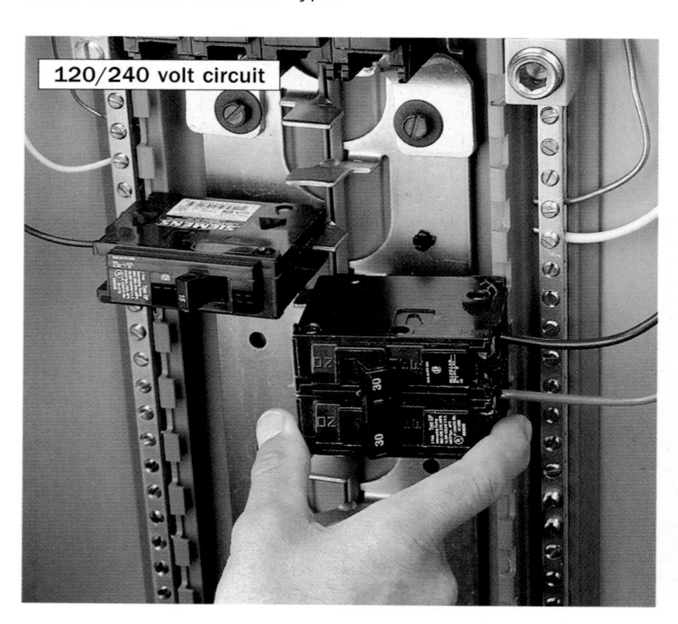

3 Connect the hot leads to the new circuit breaker. For a 120/240 circuit, attach the red and black hot wires to the terminal on the breaker, then snap the breaker over the hot bus bars and into position in the slot. Test the circuit, then replace the panel cover.

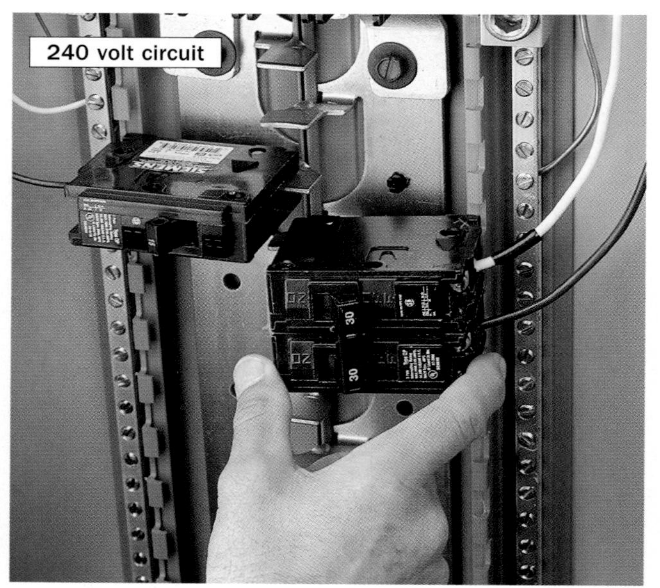

3 (Alternate) Connect the hot leads to the new circuit breaker. For the straight 240-volt, 30-amp circuit shown here, we used 10/2 w/ground NM cable, not 10/3 as was used in the 120/240-volt circuit). For a straight 240-volt circuit, attach the black wire from the new cable to one terminal on the breaker. At the other terminal, attach the white wire, then tag the wire with black electrical tape to indicate that it is hot. Snap the breaker in place, test the circuit, then replace the panel cover.

Boxes

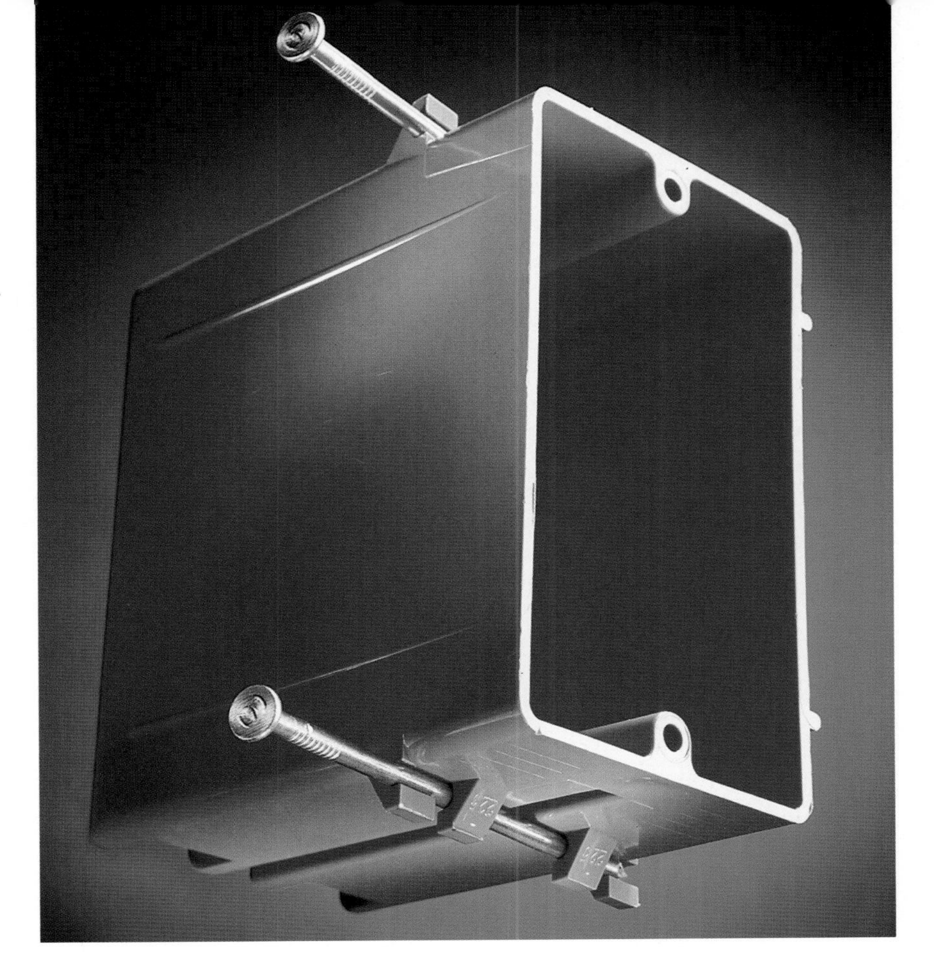

Simply put, without outlet boxes you'd have nowhere to install a switch, a receptacle, or even a light.

The purpose of the outlet box is really twofold. Besides providing the structure to mount the outlet, it provides a place to house all the splice connections it takes to connect the outlet device. And since there are many different types of outlets, there are many different types of outlet boxes.

Whether it's during the rough-in stage of wiring your house or after the finished walls are long up, one of the most frustrating parts of wiring is to find that you don't have the right outlet box for the job. If you've ever made the assumption that a box is a box and any one that's convenient will do, just try answering these questions: Are you going to buy a deep or shallow box? Metallic or nonmetallic? Plastic, fiberglass or *Thermoset*? Captive nail or bracket mount? Square, rectangular or round? Single-gang, double-gang, triple-gang or quad? These are all questions you should consider before you're standing in the store aisle. If you do make a purchasing error, it's tempting to keep the box you bought and try to make it work. But that can be very dangerous—outlet boxes are an integral part of the wiring process and safety demands that care be taken to choose the right one.

Box types. The first thing you need to know when you go hunting for electrical boxes is whether you need a *single*, *double*, *triple*, *quad* or just a *rectangular splice box*. If all you are going to do is to install one switch or receptacle, a single box (technically called a single-gang box) is fine. If two receptacles or switches are needed, you need a double-gang box. Manufacturers also make triple-gang boxes, four-gang (quad) boxes and even larger boxes that are normally used only for switches. If the box is simply going to be used as a master splice box in an attic or crawl space, buy at least a double or triple—you want a lot of room for all the splices.

Box volume. Boxes that are the same type (e.g., all *single-gang* boxes) often have different *volume*: that is, the physical room within the box to hold the outlet and all the splices you will be working with. Overcrowding, or trying to force too many wires, caps and outlets into a box, has been a common problem in the past and continues to be responsible for a lot of electrical problems. In fact, if you look closely at the outlet boxes in most older houses, you'll find that the outlet box is almost always too small to hold all the wires the installer was working with. In most cases, however, you do have to give the old installers credit—they seemed to have finagled the wires into the boxes without too much of a problem. But many times you shake your head in wonder at how they managed it (and cross your fingers that you don't have to take the wires out then put them back in). If you look at many of the boxes in newer homes, you'll find the same problem. Newer homes have even more wires to contend with than do older homes.

The end result of using a box with inadequate volume is broken and shorted wires. But damage isn't limited to just the wiring. Have you ever tried to shove a heaping handful of wires into a small box? It's like trying to shove an elephant into a car. You push the receptacle close to the box and finally get the receptacle's screws to take hold in the box's threads. Then you use its screws to pull the receptacle or switch into the box, in the process cramming the wires and connectors in behind the outlet. Sometimes it works. But sometimes it doesn't and the screws pull out of the box, ripping the threads out as they come. There is a better way: buy a box with enough volume to contain what you are putting into it. There is a complicated formula for finding the amount of cubic inch volume needed per conductor. But rather than work through the math, refer to the chart on page 49. Or just use some basic common sense and buy the deepest box you can find that will fit into the installation area.

Single-gang boxes come in several volumes. However, many building centers and hardware stores (even some electrical supply houses) only stock the most popular boxes, which typically means the cheapest. These are also the ones with the smallest volume. Utility boxes (also called *handy boxes*) fall into the category of "cheap but small." If an installer doesn't know what box to use, it's normally the handy box that gets drafted—obviously that's where their nickname comes from. The end result is the most common code violation in a house. To solve this problem follow the age-old advice of not taking what you are offered—ask for what you want. If the first store doesn't have what you need, go to a store that does. For single-gang boxes, the best and safest box to use for any project has a depth of 3¼ to 3½ in. Volume-wise, this is 20.3 to 22.5

BOX VOLUME

The length and width of boxes is pretty much standard within a size type. Single-gang boxes, like those shown here, generally are 2 in. wide × 3½ in. high. So the volume of a box, which determines how many wires the box is allowed to accommodate, varies according to its depth. The shallowest single-gang boxes (not shown here) are the "handy boxes" which, at 1½ in. deep, have barely 10 cubic inches of volume. By deepening the box to 2¾ in., the volume is increased to 18 cubic inches, which can be loaded with up to eight 12-gauge wires. At 20.3 cubic inches, a 3¼-in.-deep box can handle nine 12-gauge wires. A 22.5-cubic-inch box, which is 3½ in. deep, can hold ten 12-gauge wires.

Each non-ground conductor in sheathed cable counts as one wire. All ground wires in the box count cumulatively as a single wire.

Stackability is one of the best reasons to use metal boxes. One or both sides of the stackable boxes can be removed. By removing the adjoining sides of two single-gang boxes, then fastening the boxes together, you can create an instant double-gang box in a fraction of the time it would take to go out and purchase one.

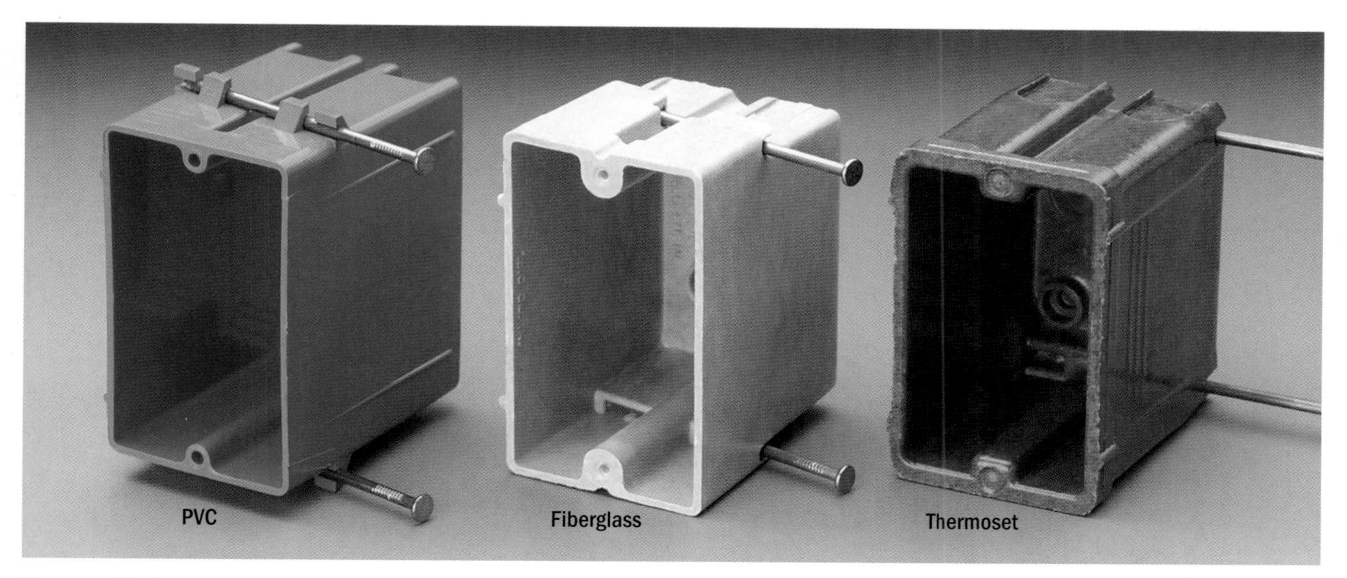

Nonmetallic boxes are generally regarded as safer to use than metal outlet boxes because the wires they contain won't short out if they happen to come in contact with the box. The most common nonmetallic boxes are made of PVC and are most often blue or gray. They're also available made of fiberglass and a more brittle material called Thermoset, which are both more rigid than PVC.

CAUTION: HANDY BOXES CAN BE A HAZARD

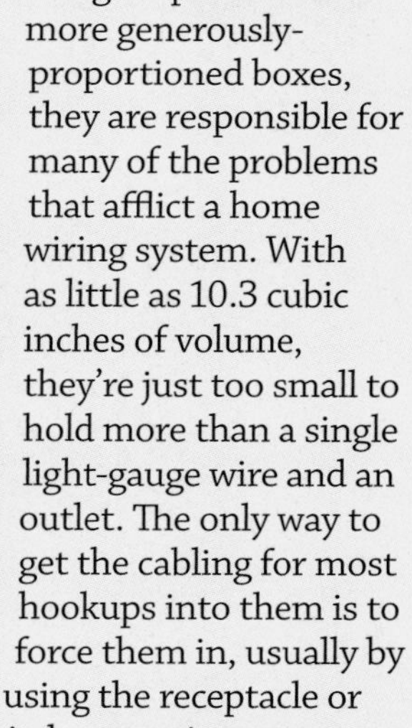

The most inexpensive (and, consequently, popular) outlet box is known in the trade as the "handy box." Although they're readily available, cheap and easier to fit into tight spaces than more generously-proportioned boxes, they are responsible for many of the problems that afflict a home wiring system. With as little as 10.3 cubic inches of volume, they're just too small to hold more than a single light-gauge wire and an outlet. The only way to get the cabling for most hookups into them is to force them in, usually by using the receptacle or switch mounting screws to press the wires back with the outlet as the screws are tightened. This can cause connections to fail, insulation to strip off and wires to short out against the metal box. Avoid the handy box. See the chart to the right for minimum box volume recommendations.

ELECTRICAL BOX WIRE CAPACITIES*

OUTLET BOX		MAX. NO. OF WIRES		
BOX SIZE	**BOX SHAPE**	**#14**	**#12**	**#10**
4 × 1¼	Round/oct.	6	5	5
4 × 1½	Round/oct.	7	6	6
4 × 2⅛	Round/oct.	10	9	8
4 × 1¼	Square	9	8	7
4 × 1½	Square	10	9	8
4 × 2⅛	Square	15	13	12
4 11/16 × 1¼	Square	12	11	10
4 11/16 × 1½	Square	14	13	11
4 11/16 × 2⅛	Square	21	18	16

SWITCH/RECEPTACLE BOX	#14	#12	#10
10.3 cu. in.	3	3	3
16 cu. in.	8	7	6
18 cu. in.	9	8	7
20.0 cu. in.	10	8	8
21.1 cu. in.	10	9	8
22.5 cu. in.	11	10	9

*See "Box Volume" tip, page 48

cubic inches. This volume figure will be stamped inside the nonmetallic box. Metallic boxes do not have the number listed except on charts inside of code books and it will be hard, if not impossible, to find deep metallic boxes. Such deep boxes are necessary when three 12/2 w/g cables, along with a receptacle, are being squeezed into the box (a very common occurrence you need to plan for).

But even with the deepest box, you are limited to the number of cables or wires the box can hold. A good rule of thumb is three 12-gauge cables or four 14-gauge cables. If you are not using the deepest box, then cut the number of cables back by one. If the splicing is kept neat you can probably squeeze more wires in, but technically you may be committing a cable fill code violation.

Box material. Outlet boxes are made from either metal or nonmetallic material, typically PVC (plastic).There are slight variations within each category, mostly related to heat and moisture exposure.

Metal boxes. Once the only box available, metal boxes are becoming supplanted by nonmetallic models because the nonmetallic versions are less expensive, install faster and are nonconductive. But there are still times where it's to your advantage to use a metal box. Use metal boxes in locations where cables and receptacles may be exposed to physical abuse, such as surface mounting in the garage or basement, or where boxes are set in concrete. Metal boxes also are available in more designs and sizes since they have been on the market longer. One useful design element that is unique to metal boxes is their ability to be stacked. Stacking allows you to increase the box volume by attaching them onto each other—simply take two boxes that have removable sides, remove two of the sides that would face each other, and screw the two

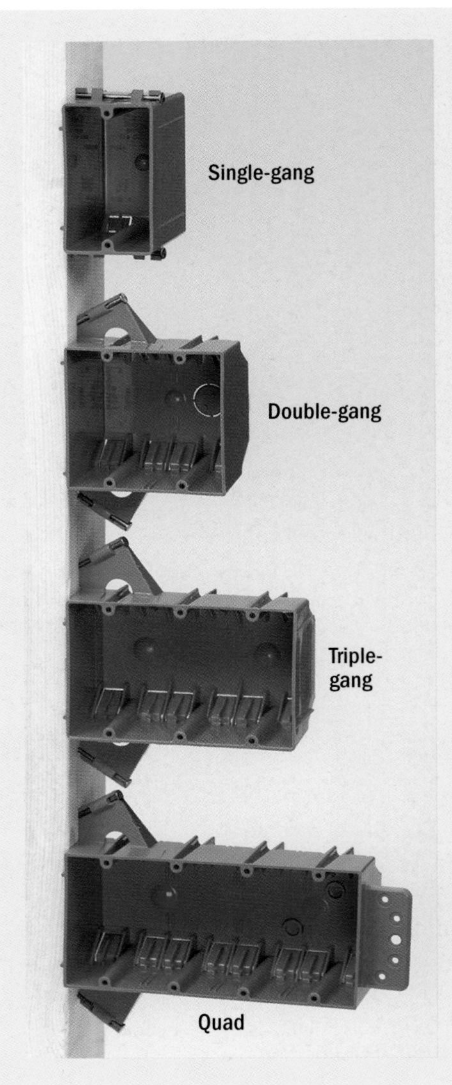

GANGING UP

Switch and receptacle boxes are usually 3½ in. tall with varying depths (See page 48). The width of the box is a factor of how many outlets it's intended to house. A single-gang box is usually 2 in. wide (opening dimension). A double-gang box is about 3¾ in. wide. A triple-gang box is in the 5½-in.-wide range. And a quad box measures around 7½ in. wide. If you need extra room for wires in your box, you can use a box that's one size bigger than needed, then install a single-gang box cover over the unused receptacle or switch opening (See page 54).

The triple-gang box and quad box are plenty roomy, but it isn't always advisable to use them to their full capacity of outlets. There simply will be too many wires coming in and going out. It can get confusing. Instead, use a pair of double-gang boxes or a single and a double (See photo below).

Instead of installing a quad box for wiring four switches, use a pair of double-gang boxes. Doing so reduces the number of wires in each box so they're easier to identify when wiring the switches.

SAFETY TIP: PROTECT METAL BOXES WITH ELECTRICAL TAPE

Line the inside surfaces of metal outlet boxes with electrical tape to help insulate them from contact with live wires or screw terminals. This does not give you license to be careless however, it simply provides some extra protection.

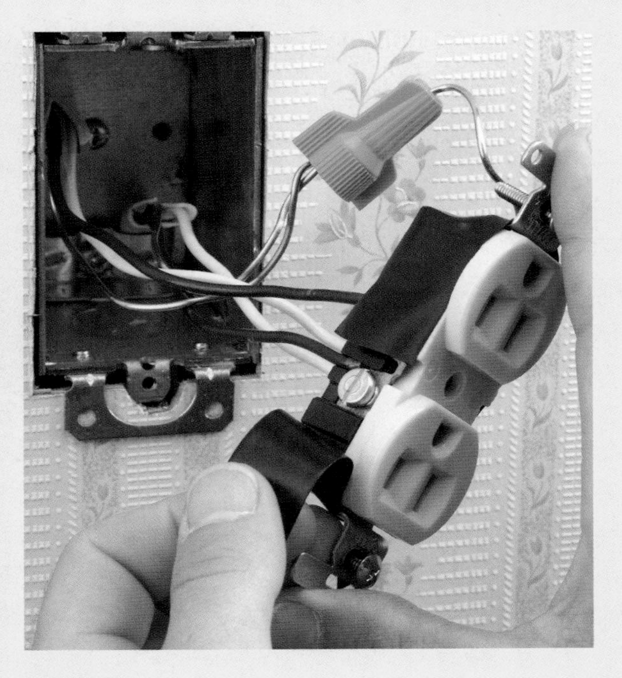

OPTION:

Cover the screw terminals with electrical tape before mounting the receptacle or switch in a metal box.

CHOOSING KNOCKOUTS

Before you wire a receptacle or switch, you must decide where to bring the cable into an outlet box and prepare the cable for attaching it to the receptacle (See pages 34 to 35). The first question you will ask yourself is which knockout hole, of the many that are on the outlet box, do I bring the cable into? Code doesn't stipulate. However, it is worth the time to create your own system. Otherwise, it can become quite confusing telling one cable from another in a box containing multiple cables. For example, one system would be to always bring the hot cable (the cable carrying the power) into the upper left hole of the box. Any other cables, therefore, must be outgoing power cables.

CABLE CLAMPS SECURE CABLES TO BOX

A cable clamp must be used to attach a cable to a metal electrical box. Any type may be used, as long as it is the correct size to fit the knockout opening in the box. Typically, one clamp is used for each cable entering the box. It is important to tighten the clamp so the cable is held securely, but not so tightly that the sheathing or wires are crushed or crimped.

Clamps for single-gang plastic boxes aren't necessary since the cable can be stapled within 8 in. of the box. Plastic boxes larger than 2 × 4 in. and all remodeling boxes, both metal and plastic, must contain internal cable clamps.

boxes together. A single-gang box can be converted to a double-gang or even a triple-gang box.

All metal boxes share the same problem—they're conductive. As the receptacle or switch is inserted into the box the hot screws are only a fraction of an inch away from the metal sides of the box. If the receptacle or switch slides slightly to the side, it could short out. Therefore, always try to keep the receptacle or switch centered in the outlet box as much as possible. Problems can also arise from wires cutting their insulation on the box's sharp edges and shorting out the circuit. To help alleviate this, put some electrical tape against the back of the box. To prevent the receptacle's side screws from shorting onto the metal of the outlet box, wrap some electrical tape around the sides of the outlet, covering the screw terminals. Be careful not to wrap the top and bottom attachment screws.

Nonmetallic boxes. The most commonly used outlet boxes are made of plastic, not metal. Being both nonconductive and inexpensive, these boxes have taken the construction industry by storm. Made from PVC plastic, fiberglass or Thermoset (a brown/black brittle plastic), these boxes are used throughout the house wherever wires are kept within walls. Nonmetallic boxes aren't recommended for exposed areas where they may be subject to abuse, such as when surface-mounted on a wall.

PVC plastic is both economical and flexible, which is why PVC boxes are so popular. But the flexibility means the box can warp very easily—especially if nailed too tightly to the stud or at an angle. The problem gets worse as the boxes get longer—double-gang and triple-gang. Fiberglass and *Thermoset* boxes are much more rigid and don't warp as the plastic boxes do. Despite their rigidity, however, they are brittle—one miss with

(Continued on page 56)

OPTIONS FOR SETTING BOX DEPTH IN NEW CONSTRUCTION

DEPTH RIBS

Some boxes are made with half-round ribs along the front of each side, generally ⅜ in. long, as well as calibration marks at ¼, ⅜, ½ and ⅝ in. from the front edge. Use the ribs and calibration marks to align the box to allow for the thickness of your wallcovering.

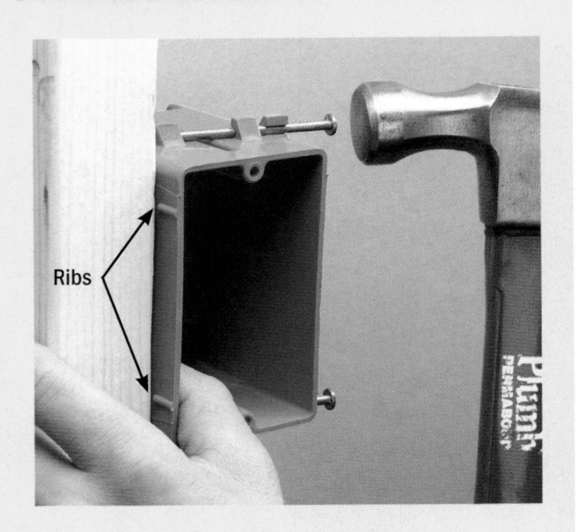

SPACERS

Boxes with no depth-setting device can be positioned correctly using a spacer made from the actual wallcovering material. Simply hold the spacer flat against the framing member and adjust the box until the front edges are flush with the spacer.

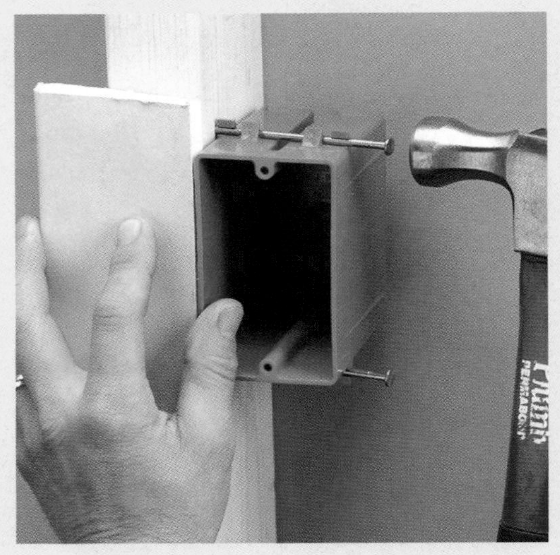

ADJUSTABLE BOXES

Some boxes have a mounting bracket with an adjustment screw attached to the box. By turning the screw, you can move the box backward and forward until it aligns perfectly. The screw is accessible from inside the box, so adjustments can be made even after the wallcovering is installed.

COMMON PROBLEMS TO AVOID WITH NONMETALLIC BOXES

BREAKAGE

Nonmetallic boxes, especially more rigid types like those made from fiberglass or *Thermoset* (above) are brittle and will fracture or splinter from a single misplaced hammer blow.

WARPAGE

Inexpensive PVC boxes are thin and flexible, which can cause them to bow or warp from pressure created by the fasteners. This decreases the volume for wires and causes the mounting holes to be out of alignment with the outlets.

TYPICAL ELECTRICAL BOX HOOKUP

Attach an electrical box to a framing member so the box face will be flush with the finished wall surface. Guidelines for common wall depths are noted on the sides of most boxes. Remove a knockout for each cable that will enter the box (on metal boxes only), using a hammer and screwdriver. Strip cable sheathing so 8-in. lengths of wire extend past the box face and at least ½ in. of sheathed cable extends past the cable clamping device. Anchor cable with cable staples within 8 in. of each box and also every 4 ft. where it runs along framing members.

Do not route cable diagonally between framing members. Cable should cross framing members at right angles. If you need more than one hole in a framing member, drill the holes on top of one another. Keep holes as close to the center of the framing member as possible, with at least 1 in. of wood between the holes. Do not drill holes side by side across the framing member's width.

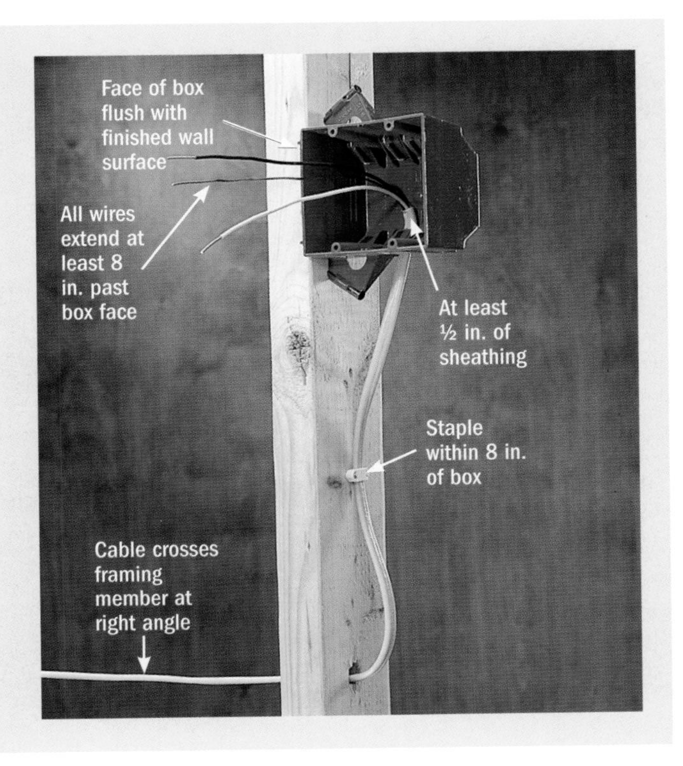

HOW TO INSTALL A BOX IN A SHALLOW WALL CAVITY

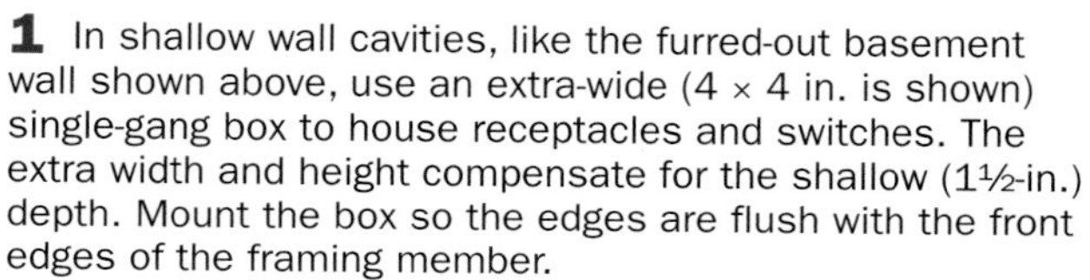

1 In shallow wall cavities, like the furred-out basement wall shown above, use an extra-wide (4 × 4 in. is shown) single-gang box to house receptacles and switches. The extra width and height compensate for the shallow (1½-in.) depth. Mount the box so the edges are flush with the front edges of the framing member.

2 To accommodate the thickness of the wall covering, attach a box cover with a raised profile to the box. The mounting tabs on the receptacle or switch are attached at the screw holes on the cover. With the power OFF, thread the cable through a knockout in the box and secure it with a cable clamp.

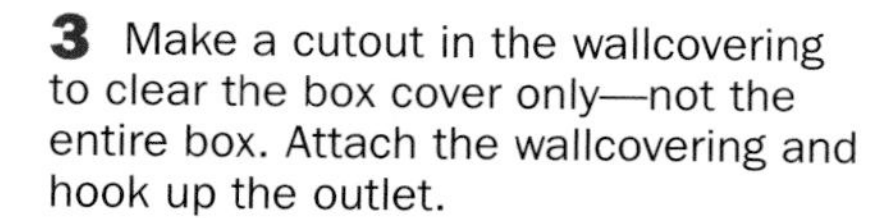

3 Make a cutout in the wallcovering to clear the box cover only—not the entire box. Attach the wallcovering and hook up the outlet.

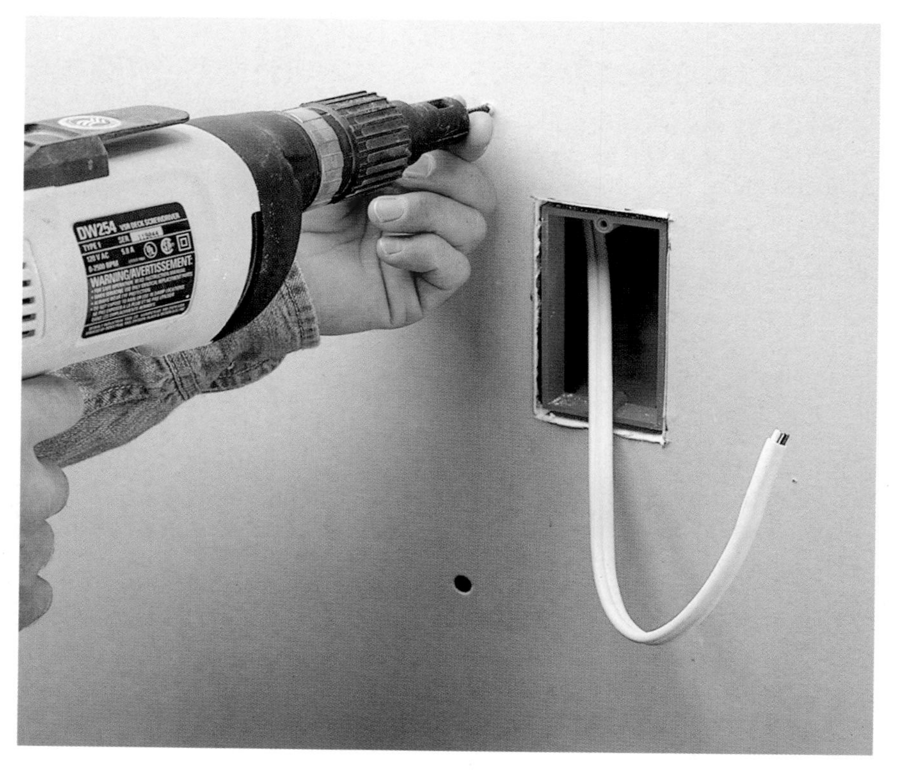

HOW TO INSTALL A CUT-IN BOX

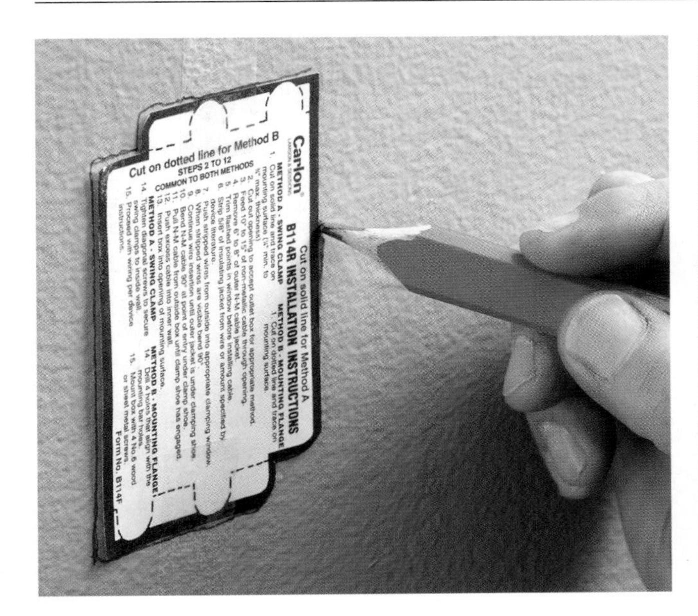

1 Once you have determined where the box is to go (do not locate it over or near a wall framing member), draw an outline of the box onto the finished wall. Use a template, if supplied by the manufacturer, or trace around the box itself. Note that the templates are not square: they contain tabs to allow for the wings.

2 Carefully cut the hole just outside of the line, using a wallboard saw or keyhole saw. This will allow a little room to slip the box into the wall. Either remove the piece of finished wall or let it fall inside the wall. Use a utility knife to trim the cutout as needed to make the box fit.

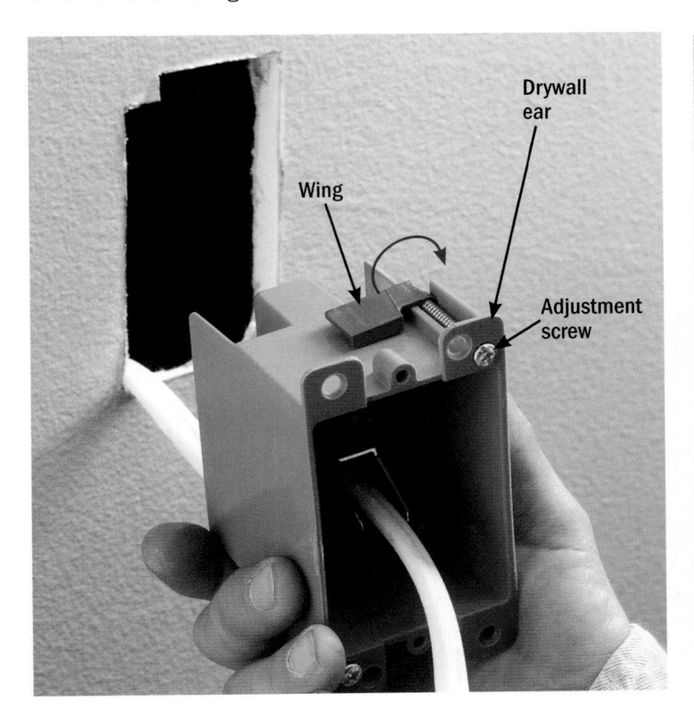

3 With the power off, run the cable through a knockout or hole in the box, using a cable clamp where required. Pull enough cable in so you have around 6 to 8 in. of wire coming out of the hole. Insert the box into the cutout, pushing the cable back into the wall cavity as you go. The drywall ears should be flush against the outer wall surface when the box is fully inserted.

4 Rotate the wings of the cut-in box outward by screwing the adjustment screws on the box in a clockwise direction. Keep turning each screw until the wing is snug up against the back of the finished wall, securing the box. Do not overtighten.

(Continued from page 52)

a hammer as it is being nailed into the wall could ruin the box, and the few pennies you saved by buying the cheaper box will be gone. If you want a box that doesn't warp or break buy metal boxes, which are twice as expensive.

Installing boxes in new construction

Installing receptacle and switch boxes in new construction is very easy. There are no universal specifications regulating receptacle height from the floor, so it's common to install the box one hammer-length up from the bottom wall plate. Receptacles that are dedicated to a specific appliance need to be within 6 ft. of that appliance. Switches need to be no higher than 6 ft. 7 in. from the floor. It's common to mount the switch box around 4 ft. off the floor. Be sure to mount the box so the front edges extend out from the stud a distance equal to the thickness of the finished wall.

When drilling holes in the studs to run the wires, drill the holes around 8 in. higher than the box to allow room to staple the cable to the stud. Drill the stud holes in a straight line across the wall to make pulling the cable easier. Once you've pulled the cable through the holes, bend the cable and insert it into the box allowing 6 to 8 in. of slack within the box. Go around doors and windows by running the cable into the attic, through the crawlspace or within the shim space of the door or window. If the cable is run within 1¼ in. of the edge of the stud, a steel protector plate (a minimum of ¹⁄₁₆ in. thick) must cover the area to protect the cable from nails and screws. See page 112 for more information on running cable.

Today, the most common box-mounting method in new construction is to use nonmetallic boxes with pre-attached nails—called *integral nail boxes*. The problem with the integral nail box is that you must nail the box onto the stud at exactly the right spot, allowing for a perfect flush fit with the finished wall (some boxes come with spacers molded into the box edge as an aid in getting the distance just right). One trick for getting the box installed so it's perfectly mounted (flush to the finished wall) every time is to make a spacer. That is, a piece of finished wall that you hold onto the stud edge. If you mount the box to be flush with the spacer, it will be flush with the finished wall.

If a plastic box is accidentally mounted so it projects out too far, you can sometimes trim the edges so they'll be flush with the wall surface. But if you attempt to trim the box edges, remember that you are also cutting the plastic holders that retain the screws that hold the outlet in the box. When you get done cutting the box there may be no place to screw the receptacle into, which renders the box useless. For a few pennies more you can buy boxes with a bracket that, when nailed onto the stud front, will automatically place the box at the right depth. The easiest boxes to adjust for depth are adjustable after mounting. They have a bracket that snaps around the front of the stud, along with a screw-activated depth adjuster that moves the box in and out of the wall for a perfect fit.

There will be times when not enough depth is available in the wall cavity for a box of adequate volume, as when a carpenter furs out a basement wall. A carpenter will normally nail the stud flat against the wall (or use 2 × 2s instead of 2 × 4s for framing members), leaving only 1½ in. of depth for an electrical box. You can knock holes in the block wall everywhere you want a receptacle, but this is messy and time-consuming. It's easier to expand the box outward to get the volume you need, and this means using a special wider

CUT-IN BOX TYPES

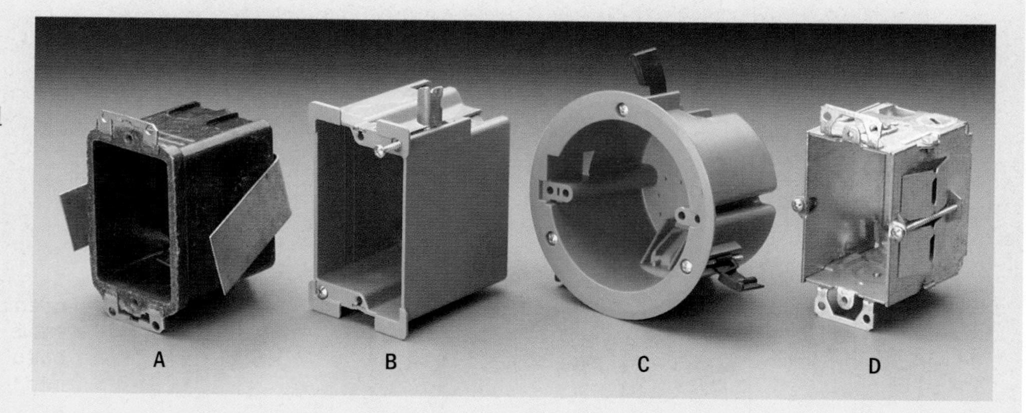

Most boxes designed for retrofit, called cut-in boxes, employ a system of toggles or wings that are drawn in tightly against the interior of the wall to hold the box in place. They are designed to be "free-floating" in that they mount anywhere on the wall surface; many will not work properly if installed next to a wall framing member where the operation of the wings will be impeded. The types shown above include: (A) Thermoset box with metal tension straps; (B) PVC box with metal flip-out wings; (C) PVC fixture box with plastic flip-out wings; and (D) metal box with screw-tightened compression tabs.

box. The boxes you need to solve the furring out problem are plastic or fiberglass 4-in. square boxes. Although they're only 1½ in. deep, they contain a full 20 cubic inches of volume. The extra width and height compensate for the shallowness and allow plenty of splicing room. The receptacle or switch is attached to a raised area on a special cover that attaches to the box front with screws. The boxes can be attached directly onto a flat wall from the back or fastened to the stud like a standard box. After the cover is on, the finished depth of the box is around 1½ to 1⅝ in. When the finished wall goes up, be sure that the wall is cut around the raised area of the receptacle, not the box itself. Do not use the commonly available metal handy boxes for walls that have been furred out.

Installing cut-in boxes

Also called old-work boxes or remodeling boxes, these are employed in situations where the finished wall or ceiling is already in place and you would rather not remove it to expose wall studs. The cut-in boxes all have some type of gripping mechanism that can grab onto the wall-covering material to secure the box. Available in both plastic and metal, the most common cut-in boxes have drywall ears that fit against the front of the wall with some type of anchor that presses up against the back of the wall—thus the wall becomes the middle of the sandwich.

Be careful when locating the holes in the finished walls for cut-in boxes. At least some cut-in boxes cannot work properly if placed next to an existing stud wall.

All cut-in boxes have one thing in common: the need to have their access hole cut almost perfectly in dimension (the same size as the cut-in box that is going into the hole). Since you are dealing with finished walls and the coverplate is only marginally larger than the box, you'll have very little margin

HOW TO RETROFIT A STANDARD BOX

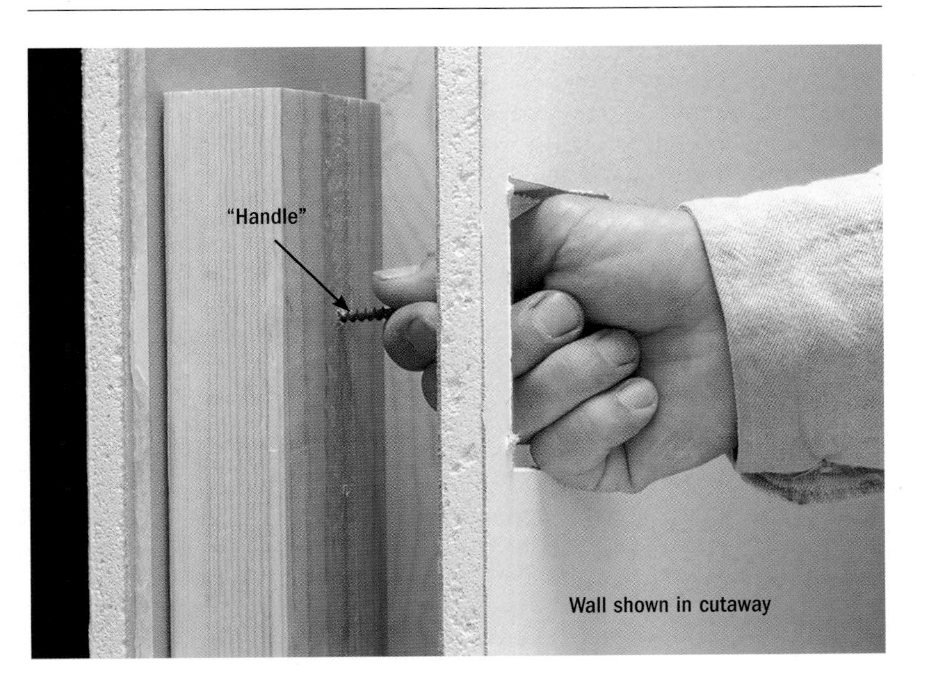

1 It is possible to install a standard (not a cut-in) box in an existing finished wall if you have access to the wall surface on the opposite side of the wall opening. Make the cutout for the box in the wall. Measure the depth of the wall cavity, then measure the depth of the box you plan to install. Don't forget to allow for the thickness of the wallcovering—the box should be installed so the front edges are flush with the outer wall surface. Subtract the box depth from the cavity depth, then find or cut a piece of scrap wood with that thickness. The scrap will fill the gap between the box and the opposite wall. Drive a temporary screw partway into the scrap to serve as a "handle" for the scrap. Insert the scrap into the wall cutout to make sure it fits through the hole (trim it if necessary). Attach the scrap to the wall with adhesive (we used silicone caulk), directly behind the cutout opening.

2 After the adhesive has set up, remove the temporary handle (the partially-driven screw) from the wood scrap. Drill a pair of guide holes in the back of the box you'll install (some boxes have predrilled screw holes for ground screws that you can use, but make sure there is at least one hole available for the ground). Also remove the knockout, if any, from the box to create an opening or openings for the cable you'll be running in and out of the box. Insert the box into the cutout so the drywall tabs are tight against the wall surface and attach the box to the wood scrap with screws.

for error when making the cut. Some manufacturers even provide a template with the box to help you lay out the cutout just right. If the hole gets too big, the toggles or wings that are supposed to catch onto the interior surface of the wall will slip out through the hole.

Experience has shown that it is best to have several cut-in box designs on hand when dealing with finished walls. In other words, several different cut-in boxes with different physical sizes.

TIP: *If volume allows, use the smaller box template as the initial cut size. If you mess up the cut and make it too big, use the bigger box to fit the bigger hole and pretend you designed it that way. If the hole is too big for even the largest cut-in box (this happens if the drywall cracks or breaks as you cut the opening), use whatever box will cover the break. You may have to use a standard box and improvise to get it to stay in the cavity.*

Here are a couple of additional fixes in the event you make the cutout too large:

- Use a double-gang box to provide the extra width so you can cut out the damaged finished wall. To get the double-gang box to stay in the wall, glue a board to the back of the inside wall of the opposite room within the same wall cavity. Make the board thickness the exact depth needed so the outlet box will be flush with the finished wall in the room you are working in.
- Glue a thin cedar shim (the kind used to shim doors and windows) against the inside of the finished wall across the part of the hole that is too big (clear silicone caulk is an excellent choice of adhesive). After the adhesive has dried, cut a piece of finished wall the exact size of the over-cut and glue it onto the shim. This will require some additional finished wall work (i.e., spackling and taping the wallboard around the hole).

HOW TO PATCH AN OVERSIZE CUTOUT

1 It's not uncommon for a cutout hole to be too large for the box you want to install (layout errors occur, you may be replacing a larger box with a smaller one, the wallboard may have broken when you made the cutout, and so forth). To patch the hole, first insert the box into the hole and measure the portion of the opening you need to patch.

2 Cut a piece of scrap (we used a cedar wood shim) an inch or so wider and longer than the patch area. Drive a temporary screw partway into the scrap to function as a handle, then attach the patch to the inside surface of the wall with adhesive (we used silicone caulk). The amount of wood exposed should back the patch area.

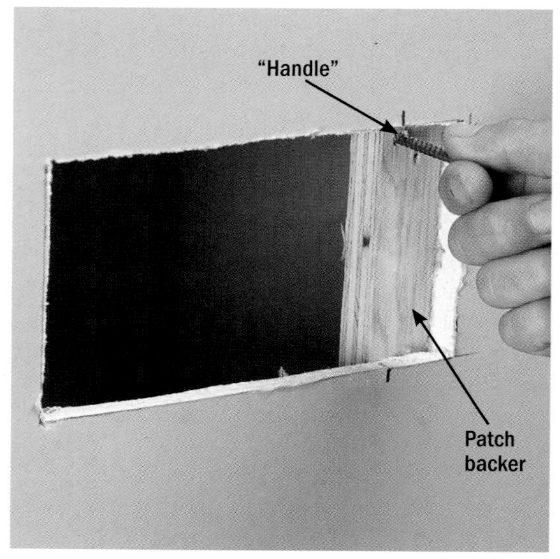

3 After the adhesive has set, remove the "handle," then cut a piece of wallboard to fill the repair area. Bond the patch to the scrap-wood backer with adhesive or wallboard joint compound. Apply wallboard tape and joint compound over the patch and smooth out the compound so the surface is even with the surrounding wall.

Fixture Boxes

A common light fixture can be wired to almost any type of ceiling box—and there are many to choose from. Unlike regular electrical boxes, fixture boxes are usually round or octagonal. The standard size is 4 in. in diameter, but the depth varies as with regular boxes. It's always a good idea to use the largest (in this case, the deepest) box that the ceiling joist cavity will accommodate.

Before choosing the box to install for your light fixture or ceiling fan, assess the access to the joist area. If the space above the joists is unfinished, as with an attic, you can use a box that mounts directly to the

Boxes used to mount ceiling fixtures can be attached directly to the ceiling joists in situations where you have access to the ceiling joists from above. But if there's no access from above, you'll need to use a ceiling box with an attached metal brace that spans between joists. You'll also need to use a brace if you want to position the box so the fixture is located between joists. The top and bottom boxes in the photo to the left can be adjusted along the braces to get the box exactly where you want it. The tabs at the ends of the braces attach to the joists with screws or nails, so they're best suited for installations with access from above. The middle box fits on a brace that's inserted into the ceiling cutout then telescopes so the ends are held in place with pressure against the joists—making it well suited for retrofit situations.

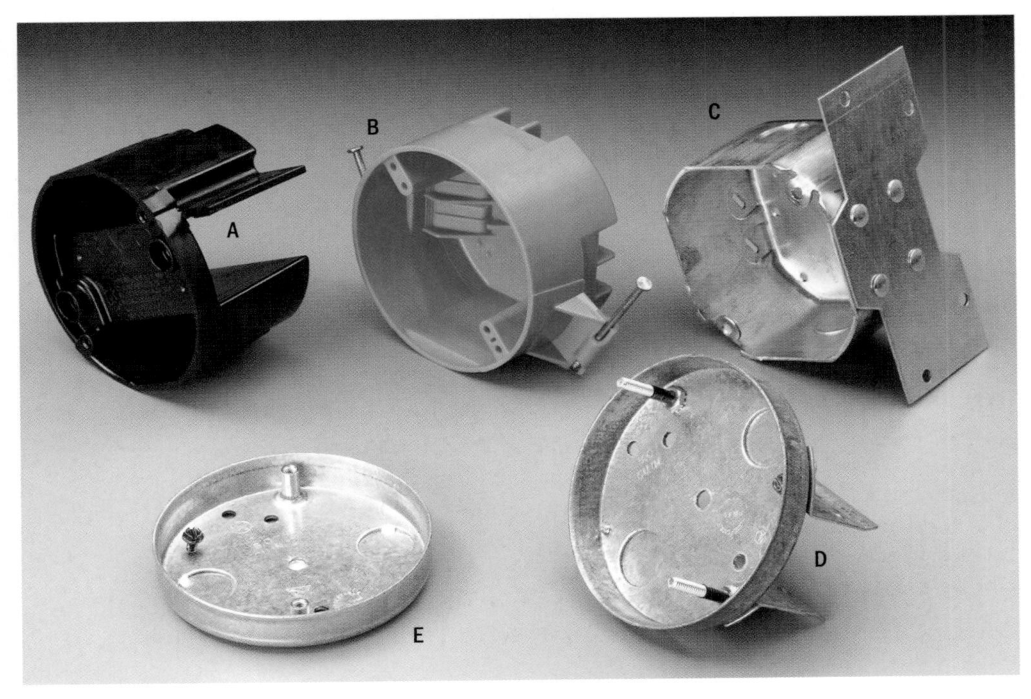

Direct-mount fixture boxes are attached to joists or wood crosspieces between joists, using the same basic installation methods as with a regular wall outlet box. These fixture boxes also can be installed in walls for wall-mounted lights. The boxes shown here include: (A) a heavy-duty fan box with slot for mounting on a 2 × 4 crosspiece; (B) a nonmetallic nail-in box; (C) an octagonal metal box with nailing strap; (D) a "pancake" box with flanges for attaching to a 2× crosspiece; (E) a "pancake" box for direct mount to joist.

Ceiling fans and fixtures that are very heavy (in excess of 50 pounds) require heavier-duty ceiling boxes that are directly supported by a joist or crosspiece. These boxes are labeled "Approved for use with ceiling fans."

Nail-in boxes are cheap and easy to install. They can be attached to ceiling joists, wall studs or to crosspieces attached between joists or studs.

ceiling joists—these boxes are cheaper and easier to install. But if you have no access from above (and don't want to cut out a big chunk of the ceiling) you'll need to use a cut-in box designed for retrofit work.

If the fixture weighs over 50 pounds then it needs to be independently supported, usually with a brace attached to a ceiling joist. Or, you can use a box that's approved for heavier weight loads (See photo, above left). If you're using a metal box, you must have a way to ground it. Attach a bare wire pigtail that comes off the ground splice in the outlet box to the grounding screw on the box.

"Pancake" fixture boxes are very shallow, low-profile boxes intended to be mounted flush to a ceiling joist or directly onto a finished ceiling. The boxes are shallow enough to be covered with a domed escutcheon plate.

You do not just wire and mount a light fixture as you might assume. When you buy a light fixture it will come with a mounting strap—it is to this strap that the light attaches, not to the outlet box. The mounting strap is a piece of metal that spans across the outlet box and attaches to its two screw holes. Pull all the wires in the outlet box off to the side and screw the strap to the box (two screws are provided in the light kit).

"CUT-IN" FIXTURE BOXES

Fixture boxes designed for retrofit work install using the same basic toggle or swiveling wing mechanisms that are used to mount cut-in wall boxes: you simply insert the box into the cutout, then tighten the screws that control the swiveling wings so the wings press tightly against the top surface of the ceiling. Because they are not supported by braces or joists, they are only suitable for very light ceiling fixtures.

HOW TO INSTALL A RETROFIT BRACE FOR HEAVY-DUTY BOX SUPPORT

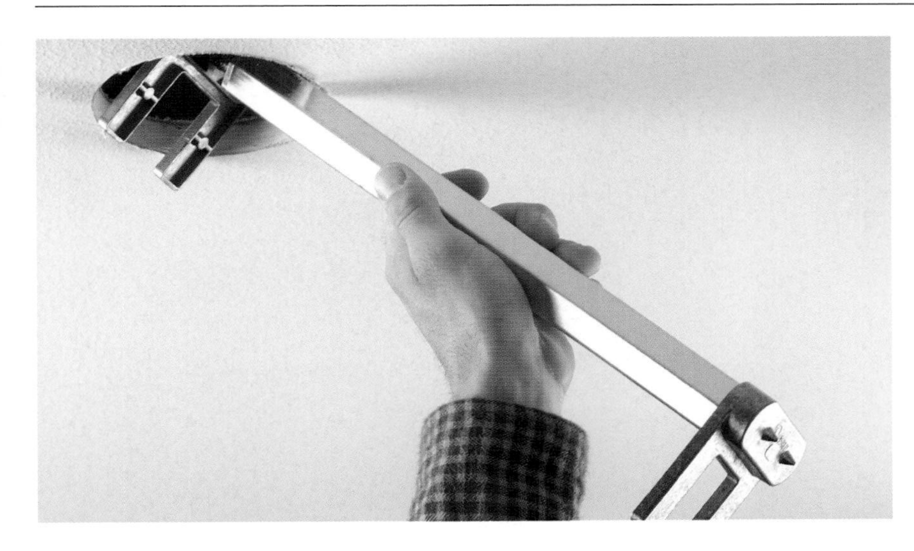

1 A standard swiveling-wing type cut-in box is not rated to support heavy fixtures or ceiling fans. If you're installing one of these items and don't have access to the ceiling joists, install a heavy, telescoping box support brace, like the one shown here, between joists. First, make the cutout in the ceiling, between ceiling joists, for the box (if you're installing a ceiling fan, make sure the box is fan-approved—See previous page). Insert the brace into the cutout hole.

Shown cut-away for clarity

2 Position the brace directly over the center of the cutout with the ends square to the ceiling joists. Hand-tighten the telescoping function by rotating the bar. When the bar is held in place, check to make sure it is level and centered over the hole, then tighten it with an adjustable wrench until it's good and snug. Then, fit the upper and lower saddle piece onto the bar over the center of the cutout hole. Thread the long bolts provided with the brace kit through the top saddle, then through the bottom saddle plate so the bolt ends point downward.

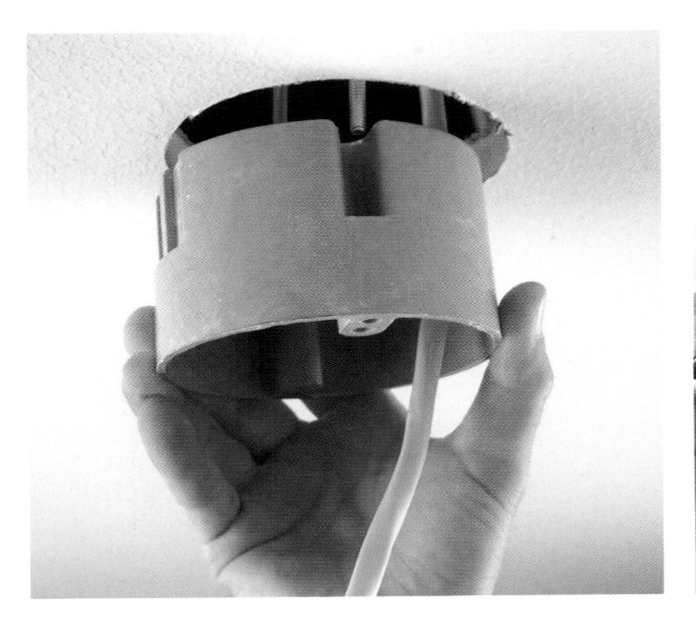

3 Insert the fan-rated box into the cutout opening and, with the power off, thread the power cable into the box. The long bolts fit into the guide holes at the sides of the ceiling box.

4 After the bolts are through the guide holes, thread nuts onto the ends of the bolts and tighten them until the edge of the box is flush with the ceiling surface. For an example of a ceiling fan installation, see pages 130 to 135.

CEILING BRACE TYPES FOR NEW CONSTRUCTION OR ABOVE-ACCESS MOUNTING

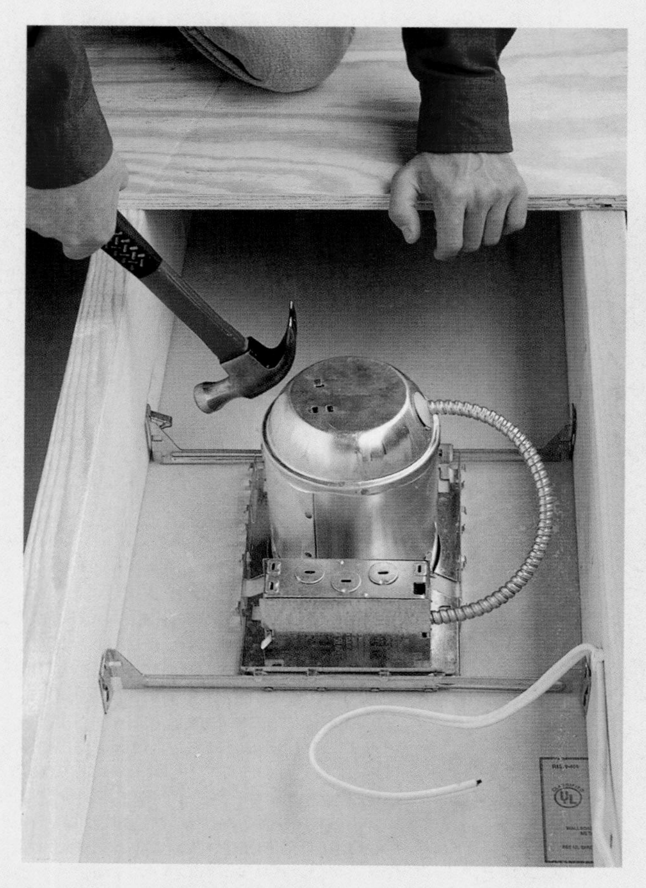

Some recessed canister lights come with mounting kits that include a pair of metal braces. If the light has an integral junction box, a separate ceiling box is not required. Simply make the cutout in the ceiling between joists, then position the fixture so it is aligned over the cutout by sliding it along the braces. Attach the ends of the braces to the joists with nails or screws.

A ceiling fixture box with an attached metal brace is also meant to be installed from above. Fit the box into the ceiling cutout, making sure the edges are flush with the finished surface of the ceiling. Attach the tabs at the ends of the brace with screws (they're less likely to disturb the position of the box than nails and a hammer).

HOW TO INSTALL A WOOD CROSSPIECE FOR CEILING BOX SUPPORT

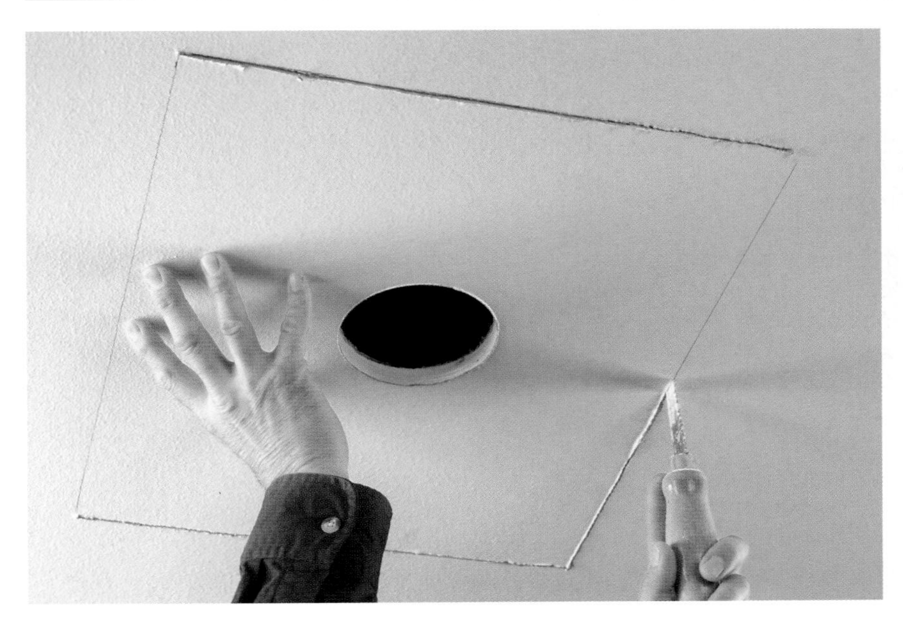

1 Any ceiling fixture box can be supported by a wood crosspiece installed between ceiling joists. If working from below, this project will require that you remove enough ceiling material to have easy access to the joists on both sides of the installation area. First, make the cutout for the ceiling box. Then, cut the ceiling material along each joist with a wallboard saw or keyhole saw (make sure there are no wires in the area first!). Connect the ends of the cut and carefully remove the section of ceiling (you'll be installing it as a "patch" later).

2 Use the ceiling box you'll be installing as a template for positioning the crosspiece. Hold the box so the edges are flush with the finished surface of the ceiling covering. On each ceiling joist, draw a reference line along the closed end of the box.

3 Cut a 2 × 4 crosspiece to fit snugly between the ceiling joists. Position the crosspiece so the bottom face aligns with reference lines you drew to mark the top of the ceiling box. Attach the crosspiece to the joists by driving screws toenail style through the crosspiece and into the joists. Make sure the crosspiece stays flush with the lines. Also install scraps of plywood at the ends of the opening to provide a surface for reattaching the ceiling section. Lay the scraps across the ends of the opening so they overlap the ceiling material, then attach them by driving screws up through the ceiling and into the scraps.

4 Reinstall the section of ceiling you removed by screwing it to the crosspiece and to the plywood scraps at the ends of the opening. Make sure the hole is underneath the crosspiece and that the power cable is accessible. Then, attach the ceiling box to the crosspiece, threading the power cable into the box (with the power off). Patch the edges of the repair area with wallboard tape and joint compound. Make sure to cover any exposed screwheads with joint compound as well.

Exterior Boxes

Boxes that are installed outside of the house need to be sheltered from the rain and snow. Special exterior-rated boxes are available, usually made of either cast metal or plastic. You can also use a regular plastic or metal box for an exterior outlet as long as the box is installed inside the wall and covered with a weather-tight box cover.

Whether you use a flush-mounted exterior-rated box or an in-the-wall ordinary box depends largely on what kind of siding you have. If your house is sided with beveled lap siding, what happens if the lapped siding hits at the point where the box is located? It will be physically impossible to put the cover on. Making a cutout in the siding so the weather-tight cover can fit flat against the exterior sheathing isn't a good solution either, since the thick beveled edges of the siding can impede the operation of the box cover. In short, if your exterior wall has beveled siding, install an exterior, weather-tight box that mounts to the wall, cutting away the siding so the box rests against the wall sheathing. On a flat, reasonably smooth wall you can install the box in the wall cutout, so the edges are flush with the exterior wall surface, then attach a weather-tight cover. Among other benefits, this keeps the projection of the cover from the house to a minimum. Whichever method you use, be sure to caulk the joints where the box contacts the siding.

When installing an exterior-rated outlet box onto the house siding, the cable should go directly through the sided exterior and into the back of the box. Attach the box to the wall with at least two screws, and be sure to fill the cable hole that was cut through the siding with silicone caulk so no water can leak behind the box and get into the wall or box. Do not forget to ground the box if it is metal—use a separate screw from the one that holds the box to the siding.

You'll need to decide whether you want a standard receptacle configuration or a GFCI receptacle configuration. GFCI receptacles are a lot less expensive than GFCI breakers, but sometimes have very short lifetimes when exposed to the weather (if you opt for the standard receptacle, you'll need to install a GFCI-protected breaker in your service panel—See page 42). One last decision: do you want a single-gang duplex outlet or a double-gang outlet?

A weather-tight, exterior-rated electrical box can be flush-mounted to smooth exterior house wall or rim joist. A good time to use this type of box is when you're running conduit from the box to power a light, receptacle or outbuilding, as is being done above.

A standard receptacle/switch box or fixture box can be installed inside a wall as long as the siding allows the box cover or light fixture to fit cleanly against the wall surface. In the photo above, the box is midway between bevels, rather than cut through a bevel edge, so the in-the-wall installation can be accomplished.

HOW TO FLUSH-MOUNT AN EXTERIOR-RATED BOX WITH COVER

1 Turn the power feeding the circuit that will provide service to the box location to the OFF breaker position at the service panel.

TIP: Unless you need to run a new circuit from the service panel, the easiest way to tie into an existing circuit is by locating the exterior box on the opposite side of the wall from an interior receptacle. With power off, remove the inside receptacle from the box, check to make sure no wires are running behind the receptacle, then bend back or remove one of the knockouts. Use this hole to guide the drill bit to the sheathing. Drill at an angle so the exterior box will be offset, and not directly behind the interior box. From outside, run cable through the hole and into the exterior box. Clamp the new cable. Splice the conductors from the new cable to the feed cable for the receptacle, pigtailing to the receptacle. See pages 34 to 35.

2 With power off, run cable through the wall and thread it into an exterior-rated box, using appropriate cable clamps to secure it. Make sure you have enough cable (at least 6 to 8 in.) projecting into the box to make your connections.

3 Seal around the cable exit point on the wall with silicone caulk. When the caulk has set up, loosen the cable clamps and press the box tightly against the wall, feeding most of the excess cable into the box (running the majority of the excess back into the house will break the caulk seal). Retighten the clamp.

HOW TO FLUSH-MOUNT AN EXTERIOR-RATED BOX WITH COVER (CONTINUED)

4 Attach the box to the wall siding with mounting tabs and exterior screws (on masonry siding, use self-tapping masonry screws). Seal the joint with a bead of clear silicone caulk.

5 Hook up the outlet and mount it in the box (See pages 83 to 110 for receptacles or pages 67 to 82 for switches). Attach the box cover and foam gasket to the box.

BOX COVER OPTIONS

Whether the box is inside the wall or surface-mounted on the siding, it should have a watertight cover. There are two types of these. The first is the common spring-lid cover (left photo). This one works just fine until you open it—then it is not watertight. This means you cannot have Christmas tree lights plugged into it or a low-voltage transformer for your sidewalk lights. If the lid is open, rain and snow can get in. What is required for these usages is a cover or lid that is weathertight-while-in-use, called a safety outlet enclosure (right photo). Safety outlet enclosures come in many different varieties, including shallow and deep. A deep lid will be required if a low-voltage transformer is to be used for the outside lights. If the transformer is so large that it can't fit into the box lid, then plan for the transformer to be plugged into a garage outlet.

Switches

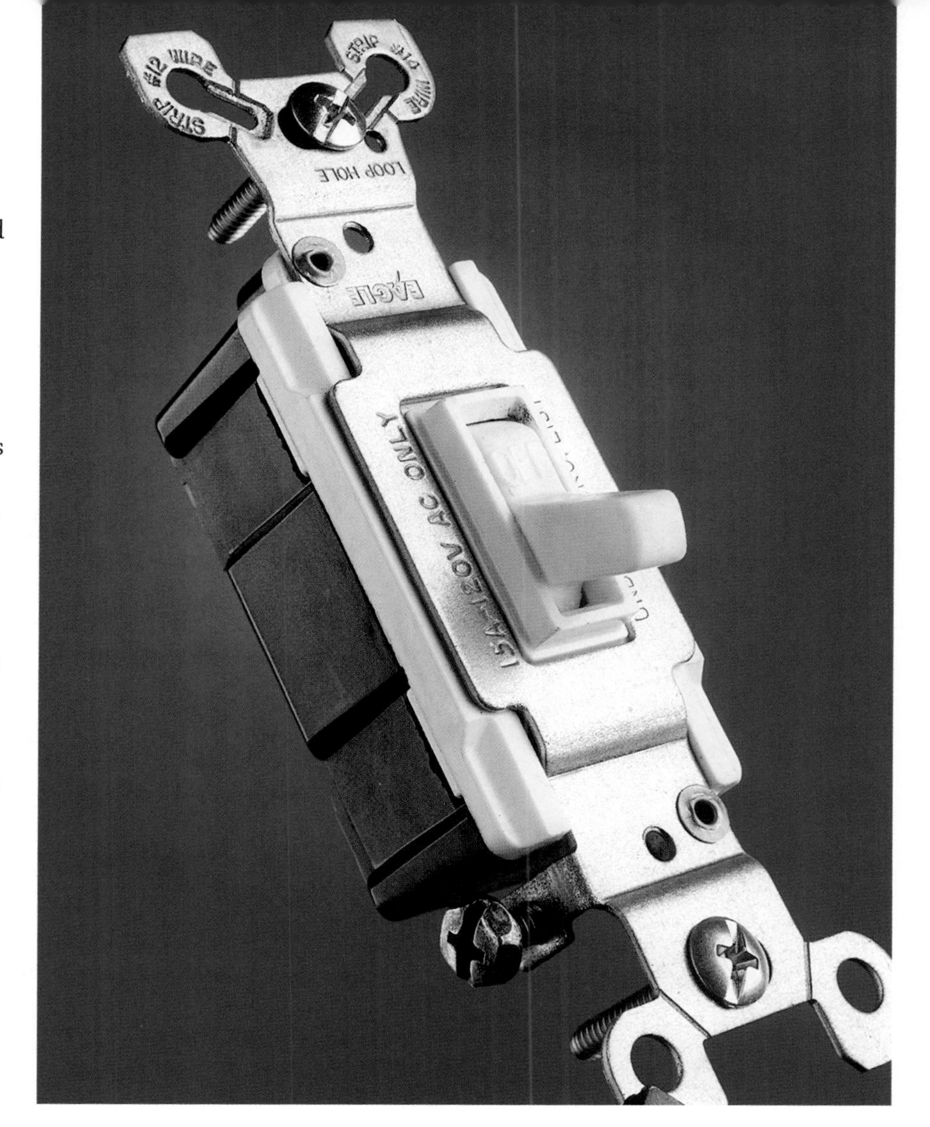

The purpose of a typical household switch is to connect power to a load, normally a light, when you throw it to the up position. Like receptacles, switches come in different amperages. The most common switch used throughout the house is rated 15 amps at 120 volts and can be used for motor loads up to ½ HP at 120 volts. In theory, the switch can pull its full rated current except for motor loads—for that, it is limited to 80% of its capacity. Experience has shown that the typical residential 15-amp switch should be limited to currents well under its rated amount. If the current is of any significant magnitude (10 amps or more as an arbitrary figure), you might consider an upgrade to a SPEC grade or equivalent switch and perhaps even to a 20-amp switch.

The biggest problem with the low-cost, residential switches is not amperage—it's breakage. The cheap, brittle plastic breaks easily. Many break as they are taken right out of the box—others the minute a wire is tightened down on a screw. This is just one more reason to upgrade to a better type of switch.

Never use the push-in terminations provided in most low-grade switches. They have the same problem with the wires pulling out as the push-in receptacles.

Like receptacles, switches come in various grades. Most people are familiar with the low-cost version—the thin, residential grade that breaks under the lightest pressure. Better grades are available and are in the bins adjacent to the cheap grades at the larger distributors. These will have bodies twice as thick as the residential grade.

High-quality switches offer many advantages over their low-cost cousins. For example, better conductivity and less heat buildup within the switch body. Extra large silver cadmium contacts (where the electrical connections are made internally) reduce the wear; a neoprene rocker keeps the switch working for years; and a nylon handle eliminates breaking. All are typical of a high-quality switch.

Most better switches are a one-piece design that uses no rivets, as compared to the bottom-end line. Some are color-coded—blue for 15-amp, red for 20-amp, and green for 30-amp, for example. (The 30-amp switch is what you would use at the water heater as a cutoff switch.)

High-quality switches, like receptacles, have an automatic grounding feature that grounds the outlet if screwed into a grounded metal box (See photo, page 86).

Switches, in general, share many quality indicators with receptacles. For more discussion on the quality issue, see pages 85 to 86 in the Receptacles chapter.

Types of switches

Single-pole switches. Also called a *snap switch*, a single-pole switch has only two screw terminals plus a grounding terminal. They are very simple to wire since it makes no difference which wire goes to which terminal. One wire brings in power and another takes it away to the load once the switch has been thrown on. When the switch lever is raised, the wires are connected electrically within the switch.

A single-pole switch is the most commonly used of all the switches—controlling most of the power to the lights. The most common mistake made when wiring a

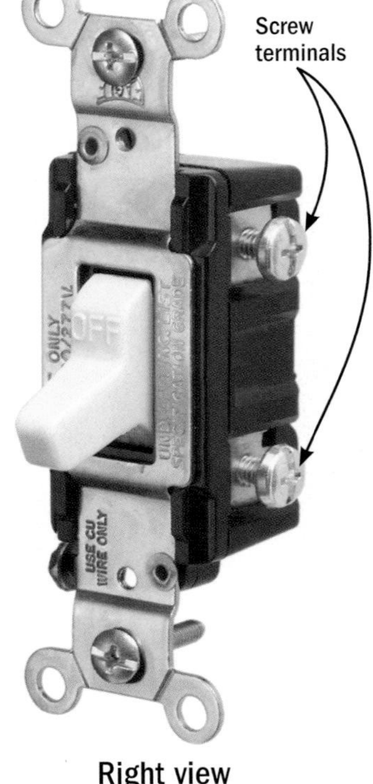

A single-pole switch is far and away the most common type of switch in use today. Employed mostly to control lights, they are very simple in construction and easy to wire. The switch shown above is of particularly high quality, with a heavy, durable plastic case and thick metal parts.

An economy switch is made of much lighter materials than a higher grade switch, and the assembly is held together with lower quality rivets. You'll also feel a noticeable difference in the amount of "snap" when the switch is flipped. In just about every case, you'll be better off spending a little more money on a longer-lasting, more reliable switch like the one shown at the top of the page.

single-pole switch is installing the switch upside down—the "ON" will be upside down.

There are two wiring situations for a single-pole light switch, depending on whether the power is brought first to the switch or to the load being controlled by the switch. It is always better to bring the power into the switch box rather than the light fixture because the light-switch box is an easier location to work and troubleshoot.

Another wiring situation comes into being if you want to tap off the incoming power for a switched receptacle (See pages 89 to 91).

Double-pole switch. A double-pole switch is normally used to shut off a 240-volt appliance. It is simply two single-pole switches with one handle. It will have four screws and ON/OFF indication. Normally, you connect one cable (white and black wires) to the top two screws and the outgoing cable to the bottom two screws. When the switch handle is in the down or OFF position, the switch is an open circuit to the wires—the load is disconnected from any power. When the switch is throw up like a light switch, the switch closes and 240 volts is applied to the load.

3-way switch. A 3-way switch is used in light-switching applications when the load is to be controlled from two different locations. Most common locations are at the top and bottom of the stairs, both ends of long hallways, and at two different entrances to the same room. A 3-way switch has no ON/OFF indication, since the positions change relative to the other switches in the series.

4-way switch. A 4-way switch is similar to a 3-way switch—the main difference being that it has four screw terminals, not three. This allows you to control a light from switches in more than two locations.

Specialty switches. There are many different types of specialty switch designs on the market. Lighted switches are very nice to have in childrens' rooms—they provide a useful night-light and show the kids where to turn the lights on in case of an emergency. For temporary loads, like bathroom heaters, timer switches are available. *Programmer switches* are made to turn the lights and radio on at preset times so it looks like the house is inhabited when the owner may be on vacation. *Dimmer switches* vary the amount of power flowing through the switch and to the light by interrupting the current flow at extremely fast rates of speed, causing the light to brighten or darken depending on the switch position. Fan control switches work like dimmers, but are used to control the speed at which the blades of a ceiling fan rotate.

Wiring Switches

Single pole (*See illustrations, pages 72 to 74*). A basic, single-pole switch is simple to wire. If the power is coming to the switch first from the source, you simply attach the incoming black wire to one screw terminal and the outgoing black wire to the other screw terminal. Splice the white neutrals together, bypassing the switch. Also splice the bare grounds together, but run a pigtail to the grounding screw on the single-pole switch. If the power arrives first at the load (usually a light), attach the white neutral from the feeder wire to the neutral terminal on the load. Run NM/2 cable from the load to the switch. Splice the incoming black wire to either the black hot wire from the NM/2 or to the white wire (but be sure to tag the white wire black with electrical tape). Attach the wire spliced to the black feeder to one switch terminal. Attach the other wire in the NM/2 to the other switch terminal at one end and to the hot terminal on the light at the other end. Attach the NM/2 ground wire to the grounding screw on the switch. At the light, splice the incoming and outgoing ground wires to a pigtail and attach the pigtail to the grounding terminal on the fixture.

Double-pole (*See illustration, page 80*). Since double-pole switches are used on 240-volt circuits, there is no white neutral; only two hot wires and a ground wire. Attach the hot wires from the feeder cable to the lower terminals on opposite sides of the switch. Attach the outbound hot wires to the upper terminals on opposite sides of the switch. Run the outbound hot wires to the appliance being switched (a water heater or pump, for example). Pigtail the grounds and attach them to the grounding screw on the switch.

3-way switching system (*See illustrations, pages 77 to 78*). To wire a 3-way switching system (two switches that control a single outlet, usually a light), you'll need 3-conductor cable (two insulated hot conductors—red and black, along with a neutral and ground wire), a power (LINE) cable (usually NM/2 with ground), and a LOAD cable (also NM/2). The 3-conductor cable provides the conductors for the back and forth switching, the LINE cable brings the power from the source, and the LOAD cable takes the power to the light.

There are practically as many ways to interconnect the cables in a 3-way switch system as there are people who can wire them. Whichever system you use, always follow a repeatable order for running the cables when you install a 3-way switch system. Remember, eventually you are going to have to troubleshoot a 3-way switch system that doesn't work properly. Therefore, it would be advisable to always have the cabling the same in each 3-way circuit you wire and to always keep it simple.

A double-pole switch has a pair of screws on each side so it can accept two hot leads to supply a 240-volt circuit.

The simplest (and the easiest to troubleshoot) method of installing 3-way switch cable is called the "EZcable" system:

1. Mount the two boxes for the 3-way switches and the light outlet box. If there is more than one light, use one light outlet box as your main box and feed the rest of the lights off that one.
2. Run 3-way switch cable from one 3-way switch box to the other 3-way switch box.
3. Bring power cable into one of the switch boxes—never the light outlet box. The latter will work if wired properly, but is more complicated.
4. Bring the cable from the light outlet box into either 3-way switch box. Now all you have to do is wire them. Once the cabling has been run, wiring a 3-way switch is not hard if you understand how a 3-way switch operates. It has three screws: one input (the darkened screw called a common

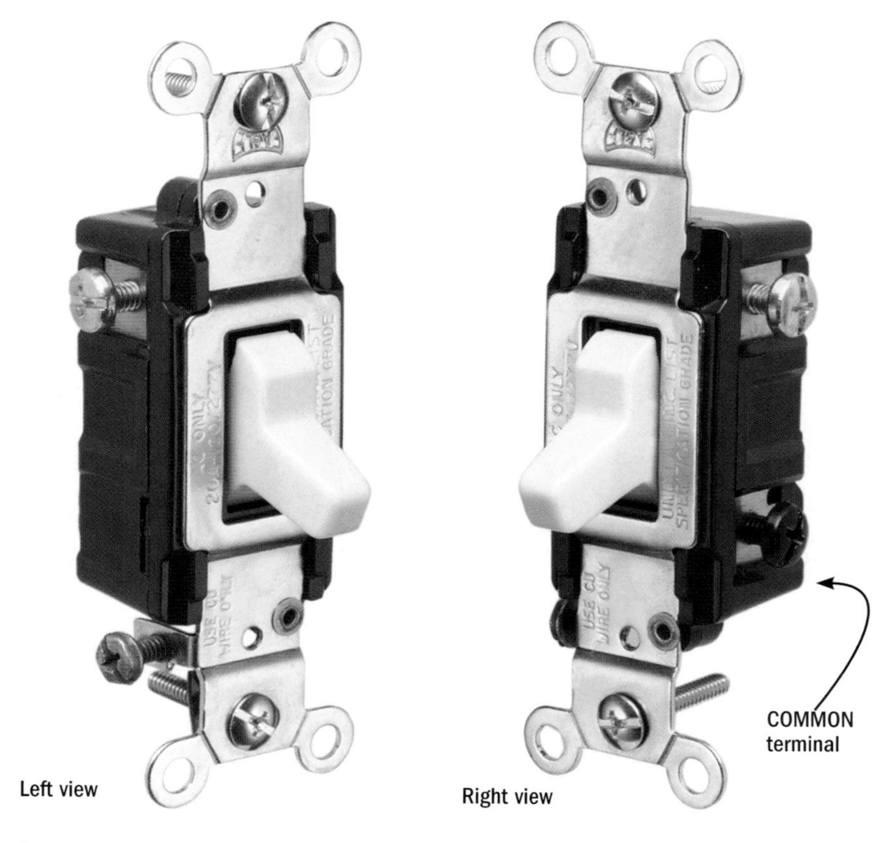

3-way switches are used in a wiring system that controls a single light so it can be turned on and off from two different locations—for example, at both the top and bottom of a staircase.

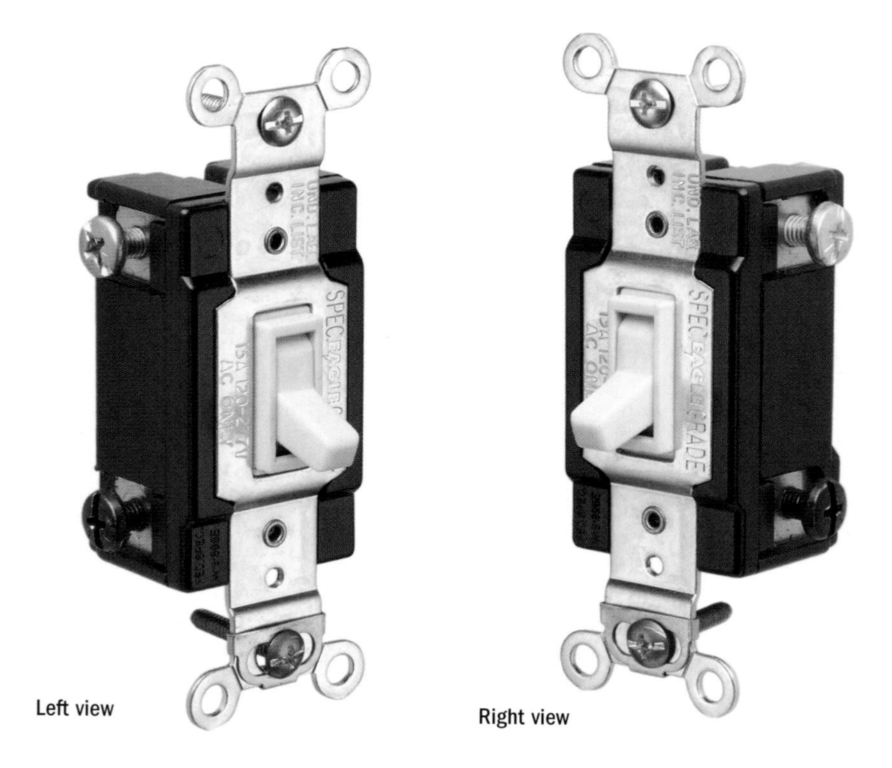

4-way switches are used in a wiring system that controls a single light so it can be turned on and off from more than two locations.

or tongue) and two alternating outputs. The common (COM) terminal can only connect to one output screw at a time. The incoming power is attached to the common pole and is transferred to one or the other two screws depending on which way the switch is thrown. This type of switch has no ON/OFF indicated on its front.

5 Find the power cable that you brought into the first box. It will have two insulated wires (black and white) and a ground wire. All ground wires within each box are connected together and then connected to the outlet itself.

If the power cable is brought into one box and the load cable brought into the box on the opposite end, wire the system as shown in the illustration on page 77. If both the power cable and load feed into the same box, wire the system as shown in the illustration on page 78.

4-way switching system (*See illustration, page 79*). If the light needs to be switched at more than two locations, this is called multipoint switching and you will need one or more 4-way switches—any number can be installed. Four-way switches are only used between two 3-way switches—never at the ends. Therefore, the switches at each end, regardless of the number of 4-ways installed, must always be 3-way switches.

Beware. The 4-way switch can be easily mistaken for a double-pole switch since they both look physically very similar, with two hot screw terminals on each side. Identify a 4-way switch by checking to make sure the switch has no ON and OFF markings.

Installing cabling for multipoint switching is quite easy. Simply run 3-conductor cable between all the switches. Start at one of the end outlet boxes (one of the 3-way switches) and connect all the switch

Specialty switches are becoming more commonplace as wiring technology advances, now using computer circuitry and sophisticated photo-sensitive cells for practical applications. A few of the more popular specialty switches available today include: a programmable timer switch that can turn lights and appliances on and off at scheduled times when you're away from home; dimmer switches in an amazing variety of shapes and styles (the classic rotary dimmer and slide dimmer are shown above); motion-activated switches; fashionable rocker switches; and a "pilot light switch" with a neon indicator that glows when the switch is turned on.

boxes together with 3-conductor cable until you reach the end—the other 3-way switch. The end boxes will have one 3-conductor cable, while all the switch boxes in between will have two—one incoming and one outgoing. From there the system cabling is identical to wiring a 3-way switch system. Run the power cable into one end box and the load into the other.

Once the cables are run you can start the wiring. Wire the two end boxes the same as in a 3-way switch system. Once that is done, you can start inserting and wiring the 4-way switches. A typical 4-way switch switches the upper screw to the lower screw (same side) and then as the lever is thrown, it switches the upper screw in a diagonal to the lower screw on the opposite side. This is why it is said that a 4-way switch switches in an "X" pattern. However, every 4-way switch may not switch with the same switching arrangement, so each switch should be checked with a continuity checker or with a pictorial that comes with the 4-way switch.

Each outlet box with a 4-way switch will have two 3-conductor cables, each with three insulated conductors. Of these three insulated conductors, two will be travelers—the two wires that are wired to the two traveler screws on the 3-way switch. These are the two wires that will be switched by the 4-way switch.

WIRING DIAGRAM: SINGLE-POLE SWITCH #1

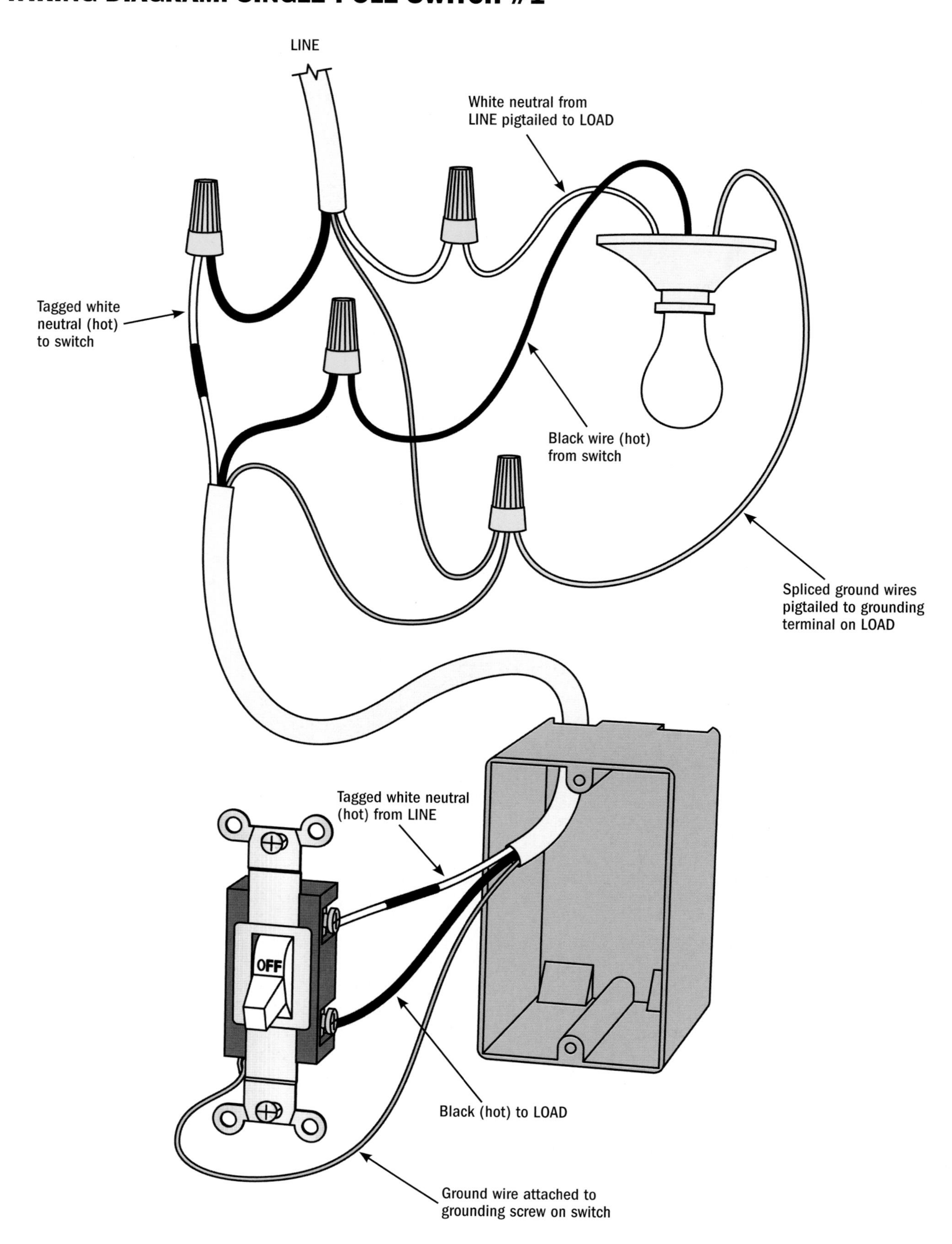

WIRING DIAGRAM: SINGLE-POLE SWITCH #2

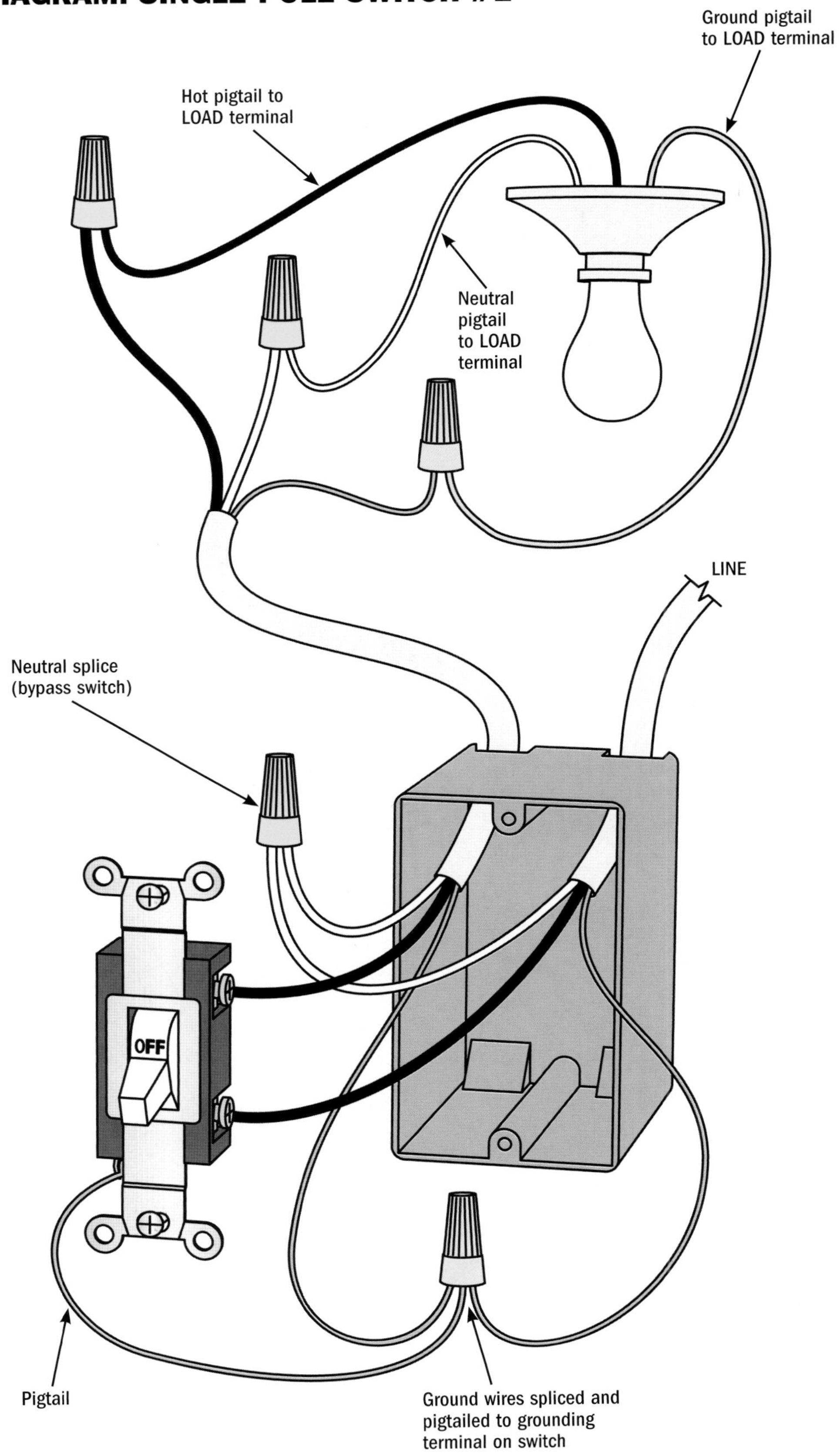

WIRING DIAGRAM: SINGLE-POLE SWITCH WITH JUMP TO RECEPTACLE

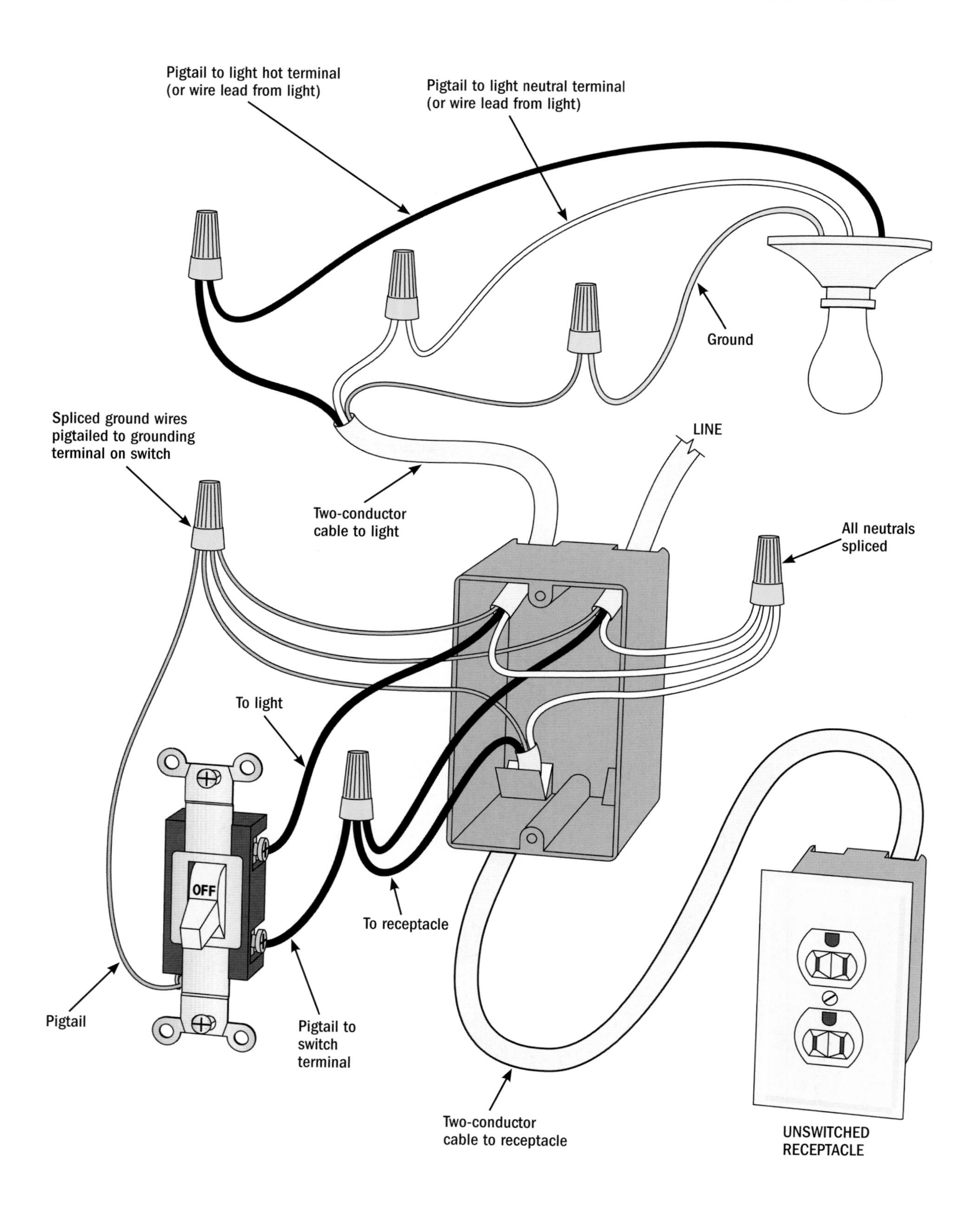

HOW TO REMOVE & REPLACE A SWITCH

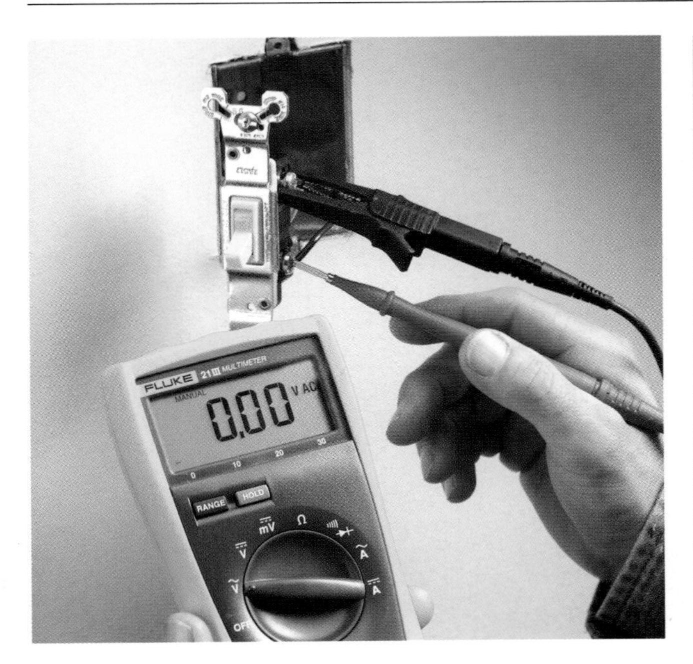

1 Remove power from the circuit by shutting off the circuit breaker or removing the fuse. Test the switch to make sure power is off by touching the probes of a multimeter to both screw terminals on the switch. The multimeter should read "zero."

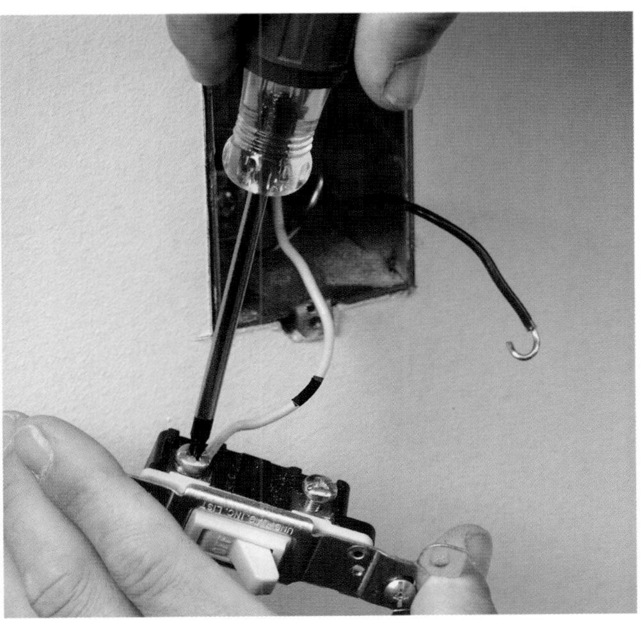

2 Remove the old switch by disconnecting the wires from the screw terminals.

3 If the exposed ends of the wires are nicked, kinked or in less-than-perfect condition, cut the wires at the point where the insulation is stripped. Strip ¾ in. of insulation for each wire. Twist a loop into the end of each wire, using a long-nosed pliers.

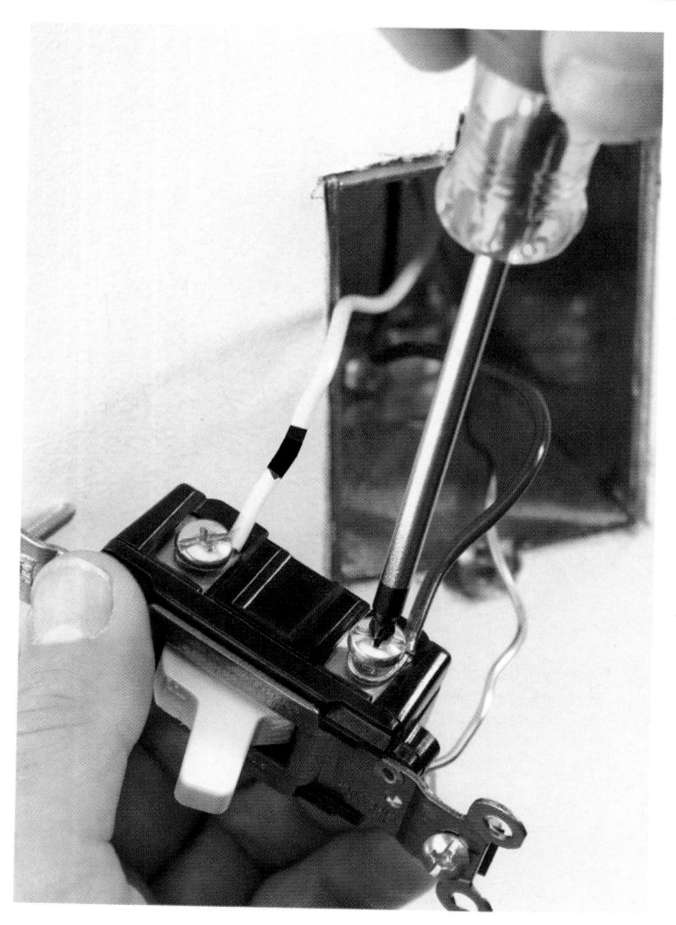

4 Attach the wire loops to the screw terminals on the switch. It doesn't matter which wire goes to which terminal. Attach the bare ground wire to the grounding terminal on the switch. Make sure the switch is right-side up; the ON and OFF markings should read correctly, from left to right.

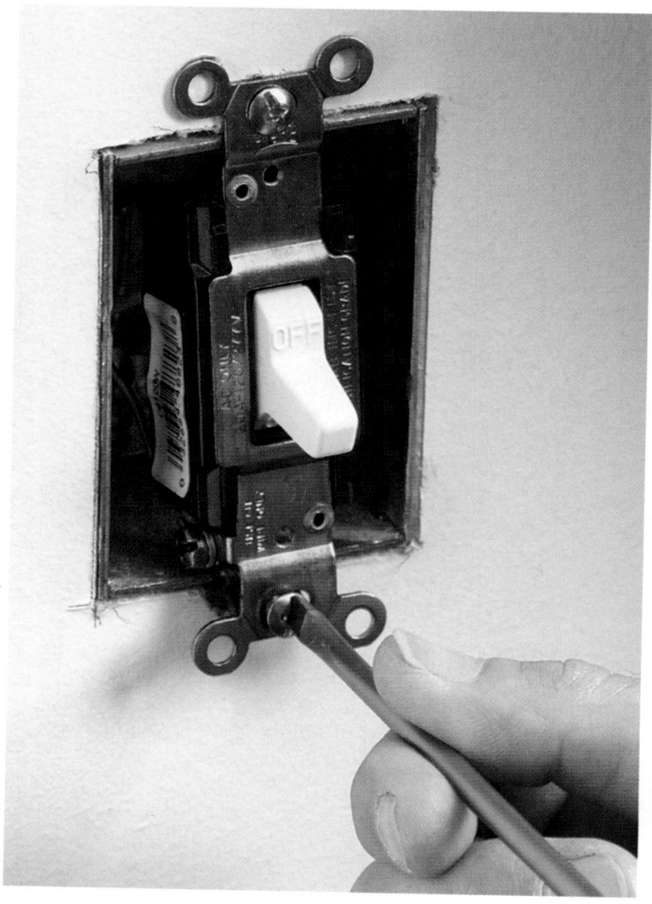

5 Fold the wires back into the box, starting with the ground. Attach the new switch to the box with mounting screws. Attach the coverplate then turn the power on and test the switch.

Troubleshooting Switches

The first troubleshooting procedure for a suspected faulty switch is to note how it feels or sounds as it is switched. Many times a faulty switch just doesn't feel or sound the way it used to. If this is the case, replace the switch (remove the power first).

Never overlook that the problem could be as simple as a bad bulb. You can shake it and listen for a broken filament, but it's always best to make a continuity check (See page 28). Or screw the bulb into a known good lamp. Look inside the faulty light's screw-in base to observe the center contact. It could be excessively bent over and not able to make contact with the bulb's center terminal. Use a pencil eraser to clean the terminal and then, with a small screwdriver, bend it up slightly (⅛ in.). Make sure the power is off.

A common problem with the excessively cheap fixtures is the screw-in base itself (the threaded portion). Instead of brass or copper, they are plastic with a tiny strip of copper or aluminum as a conductor that just barely touches one of the turns of the threads. These are notorious for not making a good connection, resulting in a light that doesn't work or is intermittent.

The not so obvious, however, is what troubleshooting is all about. To determine if a

WIRING DIAGRAM: 3-WAY SWITCH SYSTEM #1

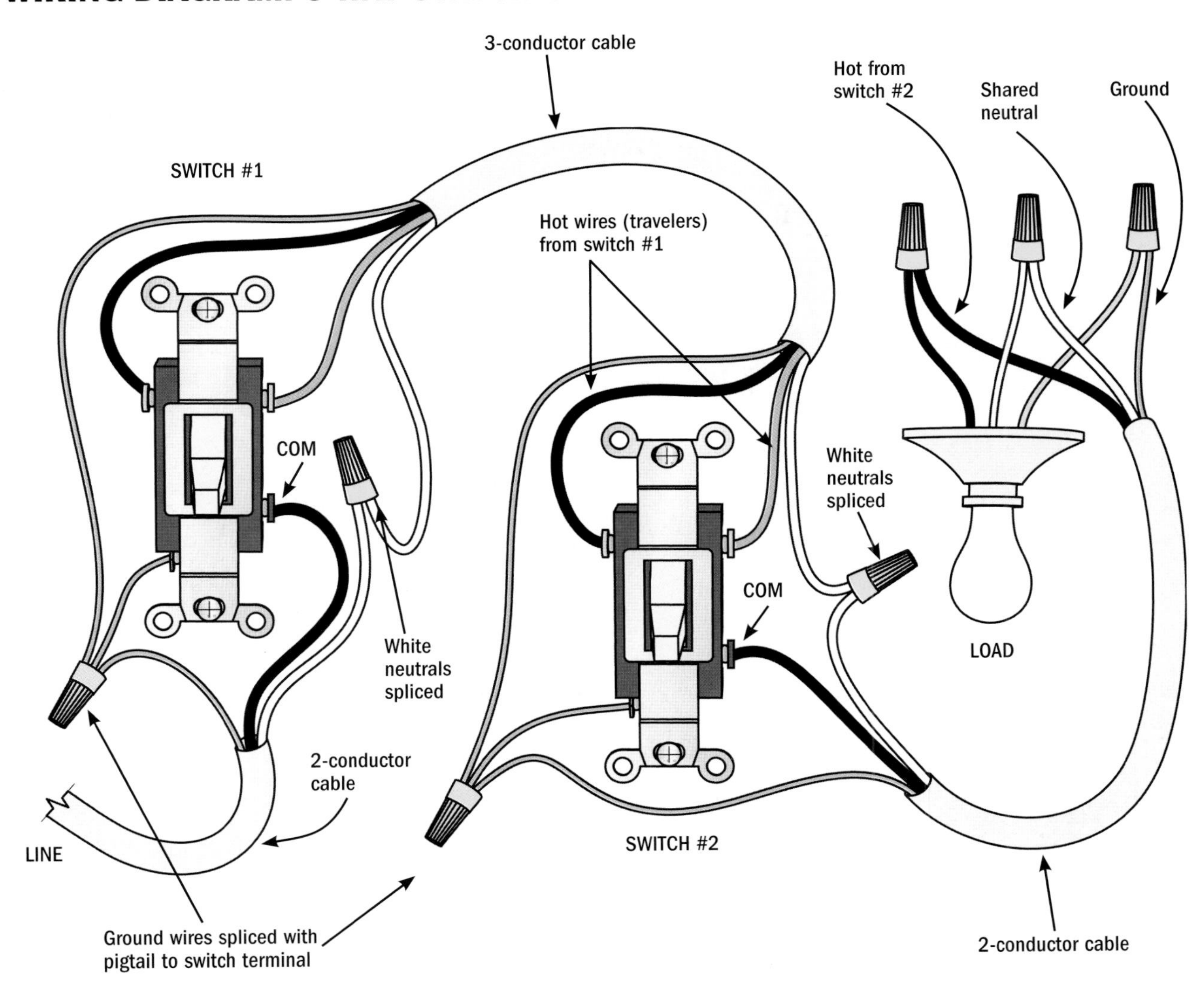

common single-pole switch is working properly, simply measure the resistance across its two terminals (remove the power to the circuit first) or do a continuity check. This can be done with the switch still in the outlet box. With the cover plate removed, place one probe on each switch screw, being sure not to short out the probes on the sides of a metal box. A standard single-pole switch should have continuity (short) across its two terminals when the switch is on and then be an open circuit when the switch is off.

Three-way switches should be checked with a continuity checker (again with the power off) from the COM terminal to each of the two traveler screws. One side should always read continuity and the other should not. It doesn't make any difference which side reads what, as long as the readings are the opposite of one another. When changing the switch out, be very careful when reconnecting the wire on the COM terminal. Some manufacturers change the location of the COM terminal, which means you sometimes cannot change the switch out screw-for-screw. The COM terminal normally has its screw marked by black paint and will have the letters "COM" or COMMON written by it. That particular wire is the only wire that you have to make sure gets properly connected. The other two are traveler wires, and it makes no difference how they are connected.

WIRING DIAGRAM: 3-WAY SWITCH SYSTEM #2

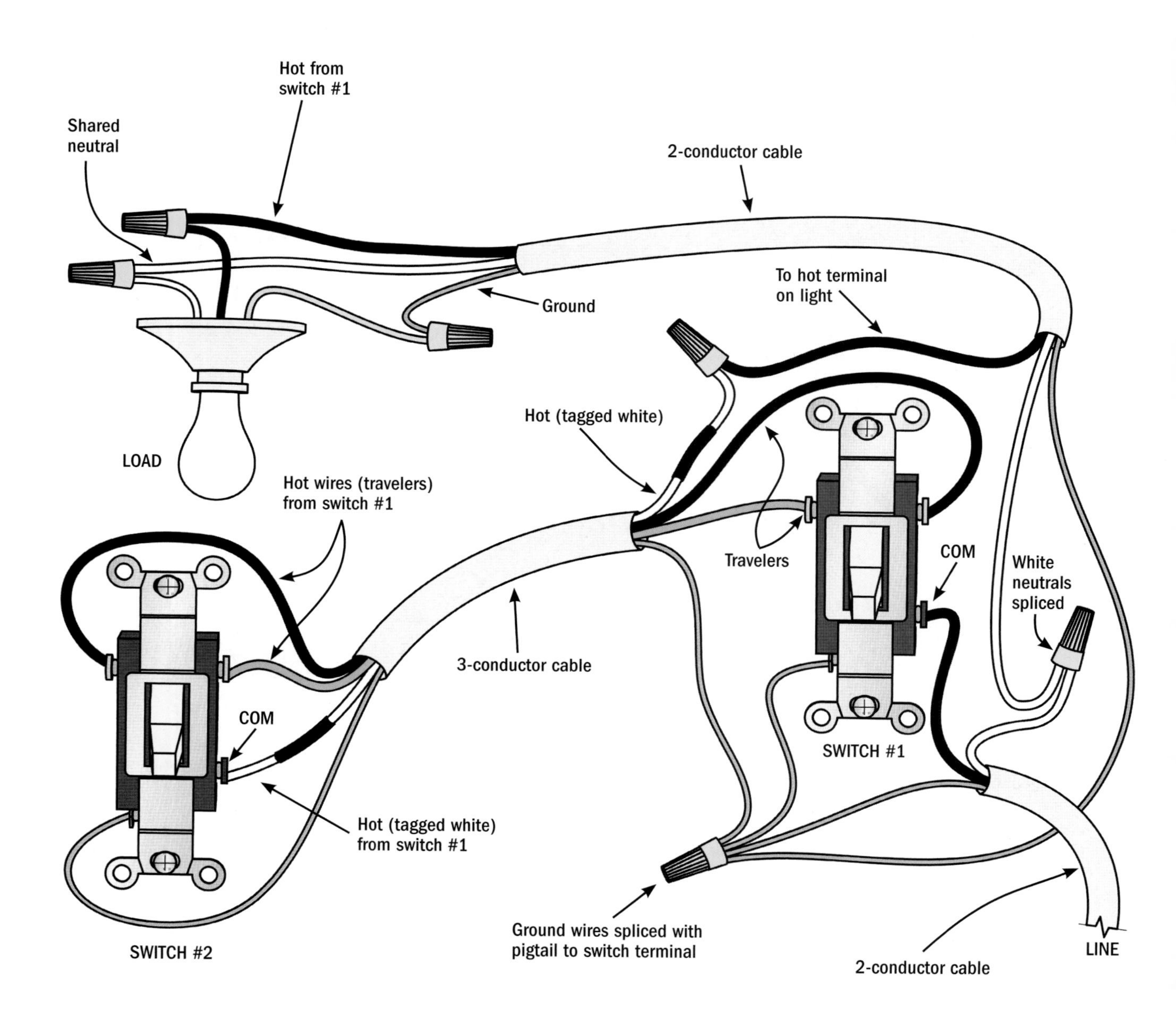

WIRING DIAGRAM: 4-WAY SWITCH SYSTEM

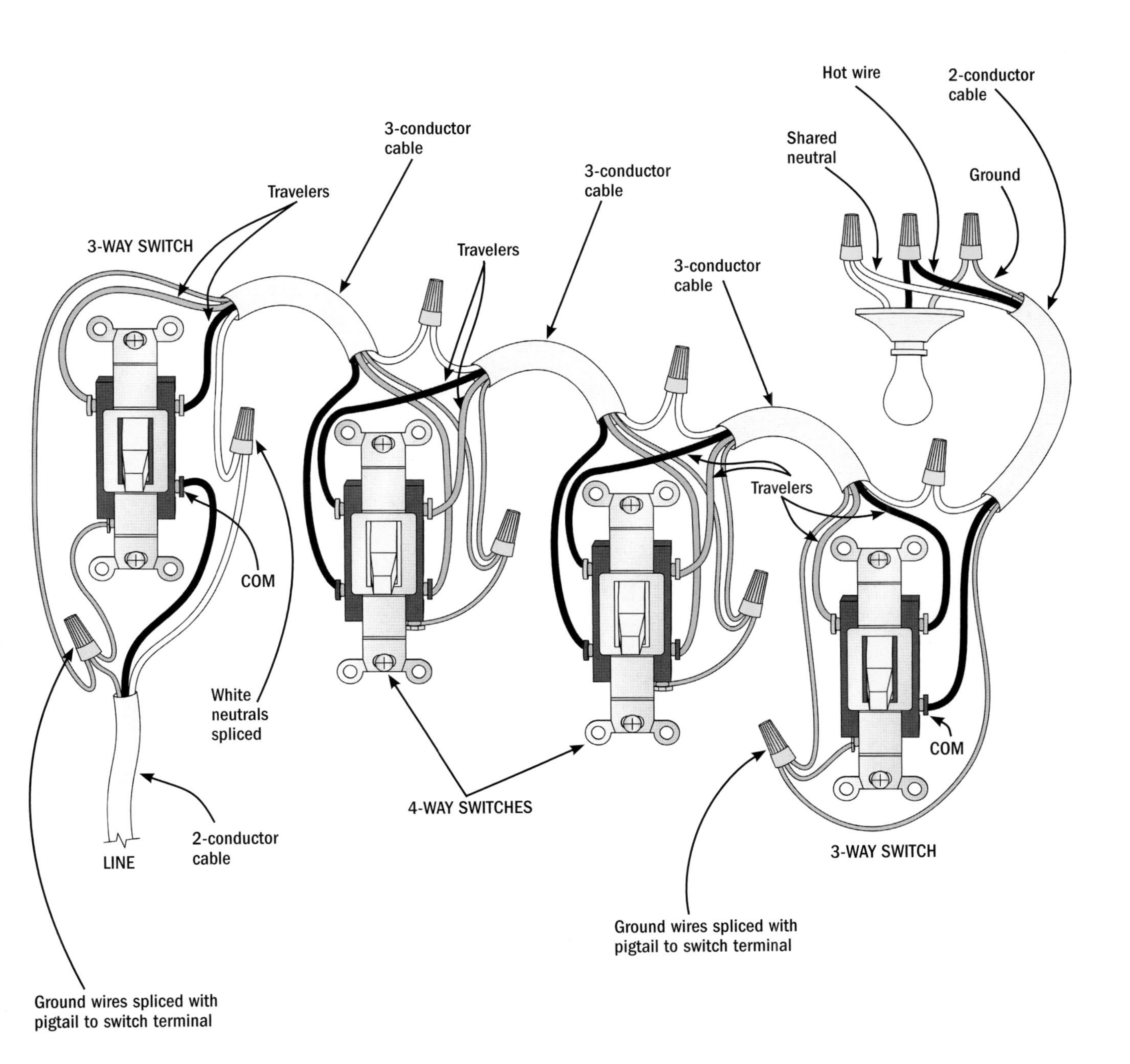

Dimmer Switches

A dimmer switch allows you to control the mood of the room. The added benefit is that it also allows you to save money. Dimmer switches have a habit of being noisy, so always shop for one that has some type of RF (radio frequency) filter. Dimmers can be plain with a round knob or fancy with touch control and a series of LEDs (light emitting diodes). Wattage is around 600 watts, so bear this in mind when shopping for a light system.

The front part of a dimmer is all metal—this is called a heat sink. It normally does not need to be grounded. Do not be alarmed if you feel heat coming from the heat sink. By the definition, it is supposed to "sink" or pull the heat out of the dimmer and dissipate it into the air. For high wattages, look for dimmers with large metal pieces mounted on their front—these do the same, but can dissipate a lot more heat.

Replacing a single-pole light switch with a dimmer switch is quite easy. As always, make sure there is no power on the circuit, wire and switch you are working with. A dimmer switch normally has two wires, but some have a ground wire in addition. One will be the wire to the feeder—the other, the wire to the load. Follow the manufacturer's instructions as to which wire goes where.

Dimmers require a lot of physical space. In new installations, be sure to install a box with plenty of splicing room. In retrofit installations, make sure there is physical room for the dimmer, and make the wiring neat to occupy less room.

A typical rotary-style dimmer switch can be used for a one-to-one replacement of a standard switch controlling an incandescent light (but not fluorescent).

WIRING DIAGRAM: DOUBLE-POLE SWITCH

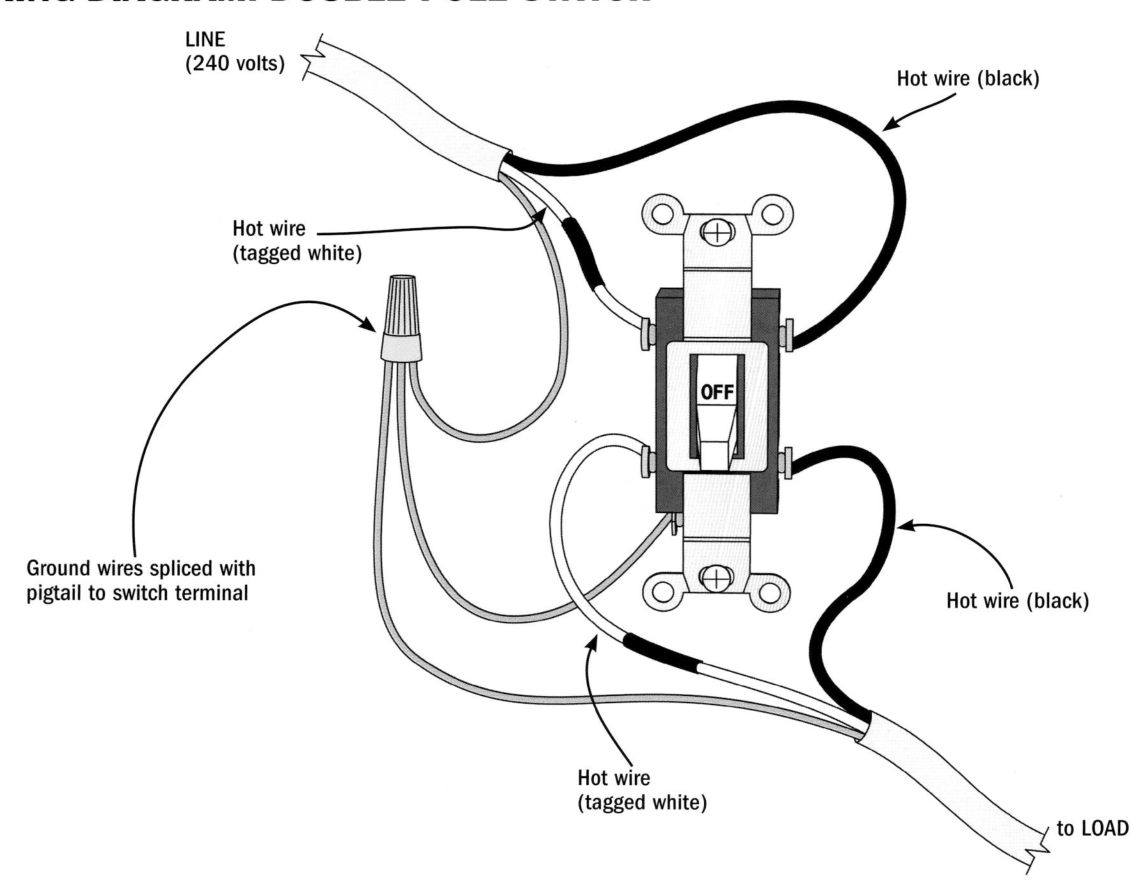

HOW TO INSTALL A DIMMER SWITCH

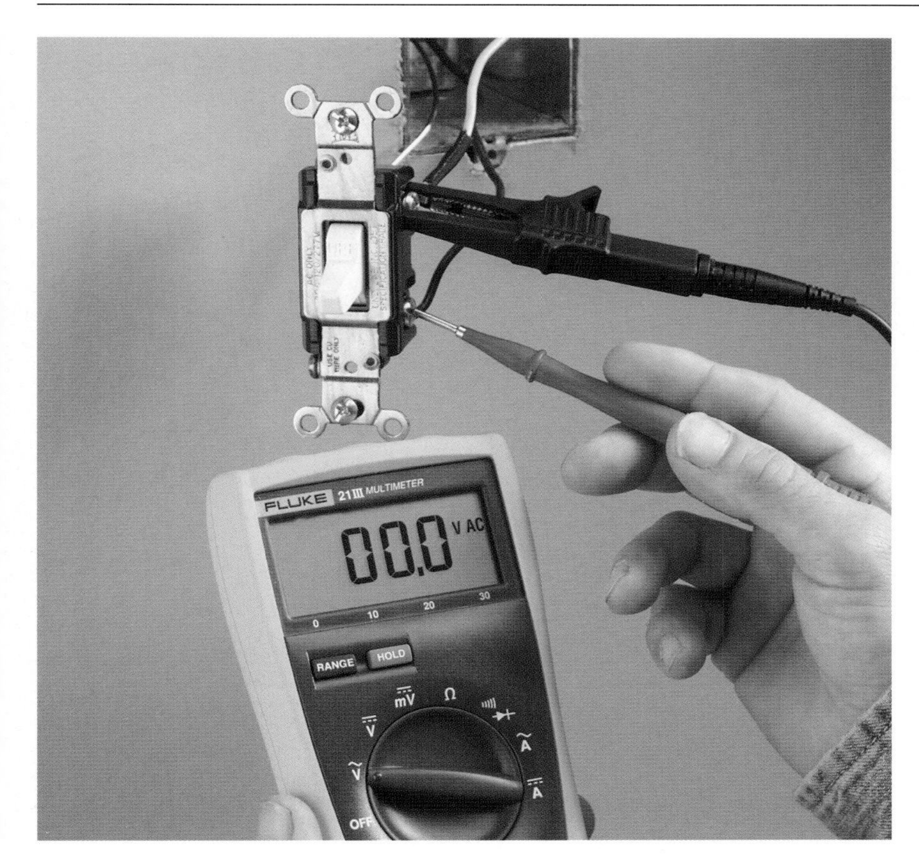

1 Remove the electricity from the circuit you are working on by turning the circuit breaker to OFF or unscrewing the fuse. Verify loss of power with a plug-in checker or multimeter at the switch. Touch a prong to each screw terminal on the switch.

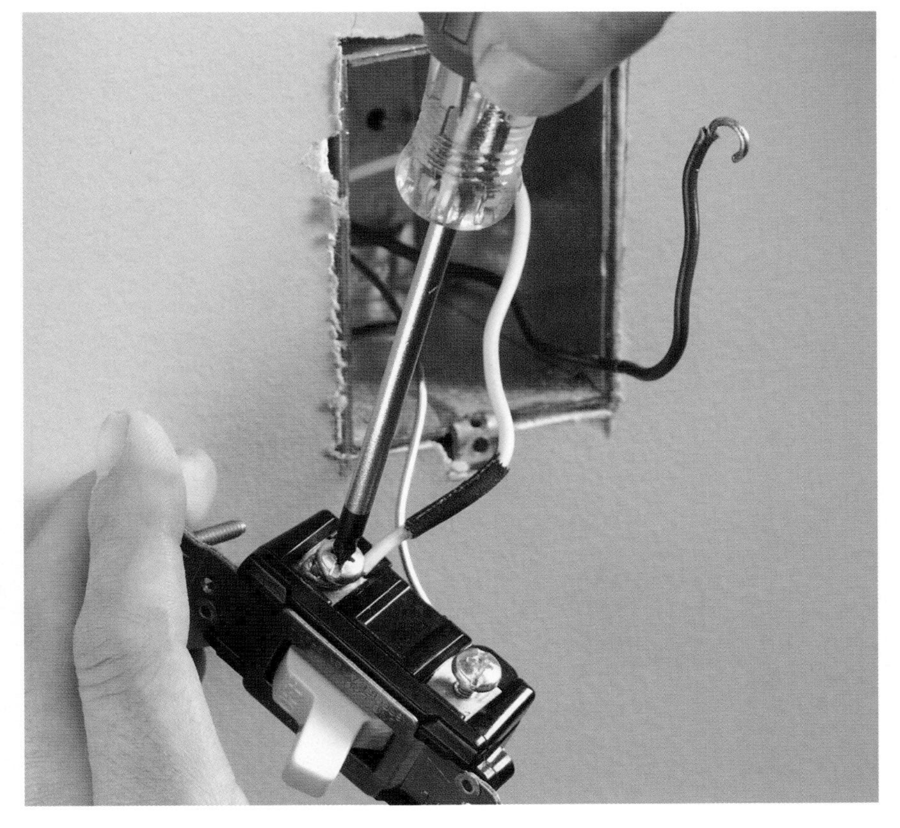

2 Disconnect the wires and ground, and remove the old switch. If your new dimmer switch doesn't have a ground wire, bend the ground wire from the cable back into the box. Use pliers to straighten the bare ends of the two wires you disconnected from the screw terminals.

HOW TO INSTALL A DIMMER SWITCH (CONTINUED)

3 Connect the dimmer wires (you will need two small wire caps—sometimes these come with the dimmer). The common dimmer will have two black prestripped wires that look identical. Twist one of the dimmer wires onto one of the switch wires you removed from the switch. Screw the cap onto the twisted wires. Connect the second dimmer wire to the second switch wire the same way. The cap is installed properly when it is snug, and no part of the bare wire splice is showing beneath the cap. Make sure the switch is right-side up; the ON and OFF markings should read correctly.

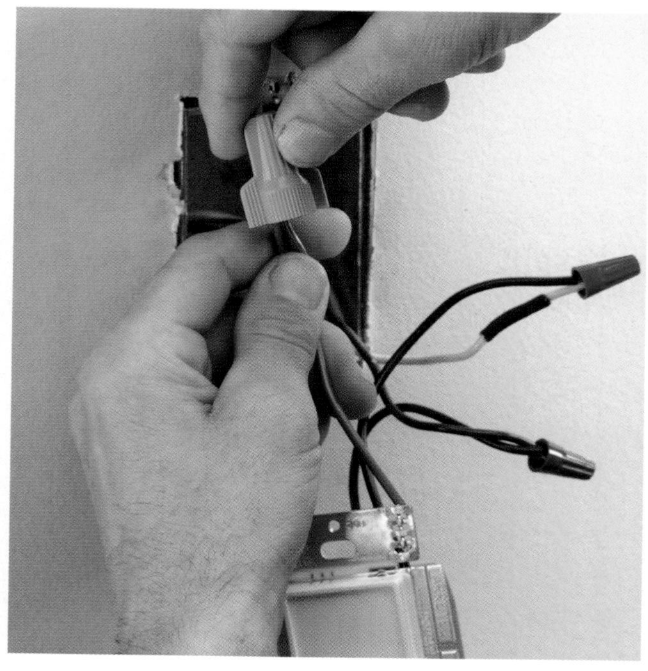

4 Connect the ground wire from the power cable to the grounding wire on the dimmer switch (if present), using a wire cap. Push the wires neatly back into the box with your fingers. First, prebend the wires with your fingers the direction you want them to fold into the box. If you did it right, the wires should accordion neatly back into the box in a Z pattern.

5 Push the dimmer back into the box and screw it in via the top and bottom attachment screws that are threaded through its metal heat sink. As you tighten the screws, note that you can turn the dimmer left and right to a slight degree. This allows you to plumb the dimmer.

6 Reattach the cover plate. The old switch plate will fit over the dimmer using the same screws on a rotary dimmer, but fancier types, like the slide dimmer shown here, will require a new coverplate that's typically provided with the switch. Reapply power and test the new switch.

Receptacles

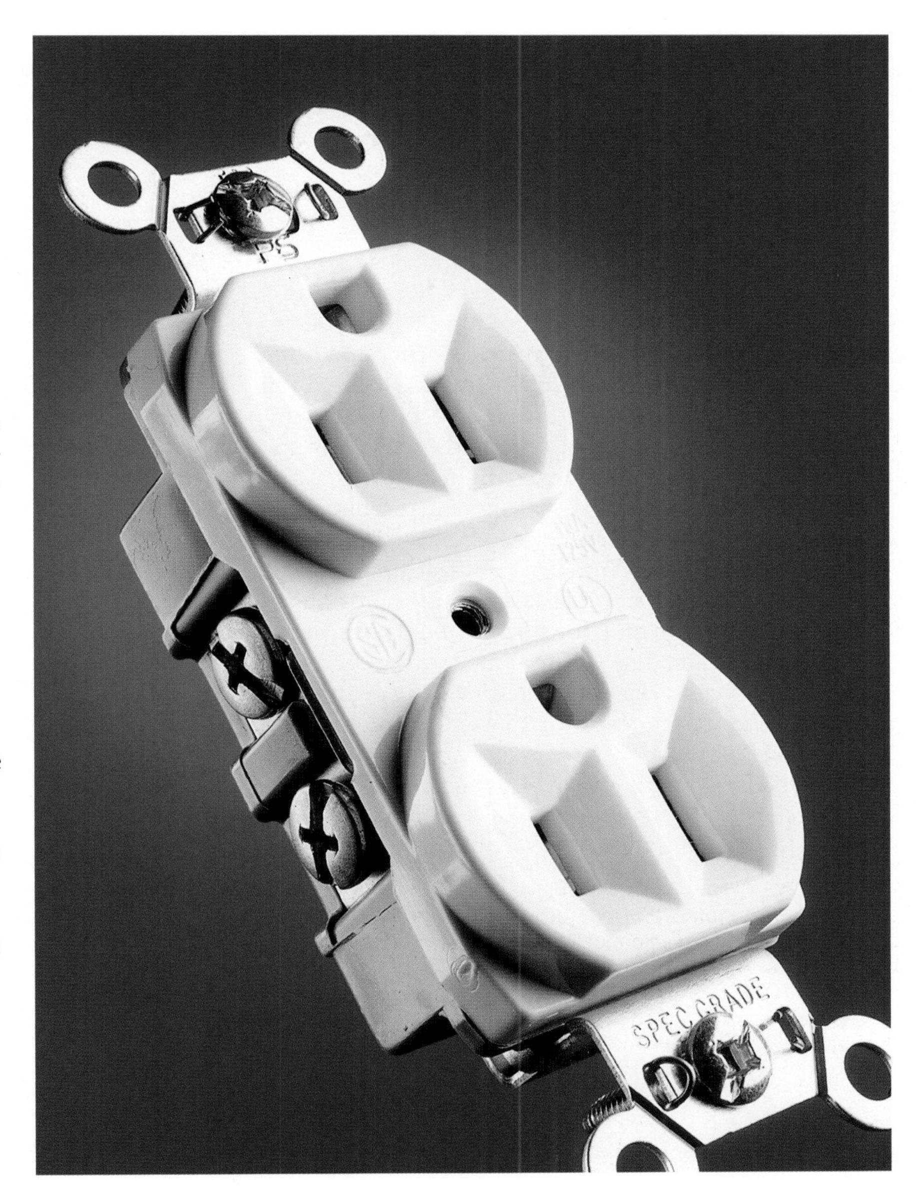

Receptacles, commonly called outlets, provide the means to access and use electricity. **NOTE:** In the trade, the term *outlet* refers to any device, including switches, that directly distributes electricity for consumption.

Before wiring a receptacle you need to know the basics of a receptacle—how it works and what each screw terminal does. As always, before working with anything electrical, remove the power to minimize the risk of injury.

The purpose of a receptacle is to provide access to electrical power. The actual voltage is applied to metal fingers within the receptacle. The front of the receptacle, called the face plate, has openings or slots that allow the prongs of a plug to be inserted. When a plug is inserted into the slots, the prongs push the metal fingers apart to make contact and access the voltage. It is done this way so no one can accidentally touch a hot terminal from the front of the receptacle.

The front of a typical, modern receptacle has a narrow slot, wide slot and ground. The narrow slot allows access to metal fingers that are internally wired to the side-mounted brass-colored screws adjacent to it. They, in turn, are attached to the black hot wire that comes into the outlet box—the one that receives power directly from the main service panel. The wide slot on the receptacle front provides access to the metal fingers that connect to the silver-colored screws on its adjacent side opposite the brass screws. These screws secure the white neutral wire and provide the return path to the main service panel for the electricity provided by the black wire. The grounding slot on the receptacle front connects to the green grounding screw on the receptacle back. The bare wire, called the equipment grounding conductor, connects here and returns any appliance fault current (hot wire shorting against a frame) to the main service panel so the breaker can trip to OFF.

A standard receptacle has two screws on each side which can connect to two conductors on each side. Since you cannot put two wires under one screw, you are limited to two hot conductors and two neutral conductors. If you have more than two wires of each color coming into the outlet box, you must splice all wires together and then run a short wire, called a pigtail, to one of the screws. Be sure to put the wire cap covering the splice on securely. Push-in wire connections are available on some types of receptacles. Do not use them—they are for lazy installers only and sometimes fail after installation.

A receptacle can be either *duplex* (two outlets to plug into) or single (one outlet to plug into). A single receptacle has only one place to plug something in. Normally you will want a duplex receptacle—the more slots to plug into, the better. But there are a few times when you will need a single receptacle. For example, if you want to put a freezer or refrigerator in an unfinished basement or garage where receptacles are supposed to be protected by GFCIs. Rather than connect them to an outlet that might false trip and remove power to the appliance, you are allowed to feed them directly without GFCI protection. But they must be fed via a single outlet so no one will be tempted to plug a portable appliance into the receptacle and possibly be electrocuted when using it.

A duplex receptacle has tabs on both sides that allow the voltage to go to both halves of the duplex when there is but one wire on the side. When broken, the tab will isolate one screw from the other and thus isolate the plug-ins on the duplex. This allows you, for example, to control one plug slot in a receptacle with a switch while the other is unswitched—as when you want to have a table lamp turned on by a switch at the door. There are tabs on both sides of the receptacle—one for the brass screws and one for the silver screws. The one for the silver screws (the neutral side) is rarely, if ever, broken because the neutral is normally common to both top and bottom parts of the duplex.

Receptacles can be rated for almost any amount of current. The receptacles for 120-125 volt appliances around the house are rated for 15 or 20 amps. A 15-amp rated receptacle (by far the more common of the two) can be wired with either 14-gauge or 12-gauge

A GHOST STORY?

I did one service call where the owners thought the house was haunted. The problem didn't make sense. Heat was coming off receptacles that were not in use—you could feel the heat with your hand held six inches away. Where something was plugged into the receptacle, but not in use, the heat was deforming the plug. The problem turned out to be simply that lower quality receptacles were used, and they were installed using push-in connections. In this case, there was a window air conditioner upstream and its current was running through all the receptacles on that particular circuit. None of the push-in connections were making a good internal contact with the wire so all the receptacles became overheated. Upon contacting the contractor (this was a new house) he said that this problem had occurred before and he had just switched receptacle brands trying to eliminate the problem. He paid to replace every receptacle and switch in the house.

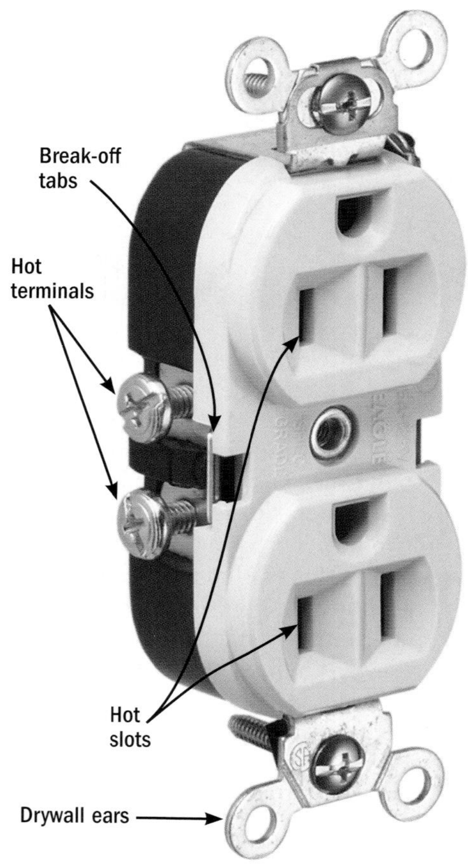

Viewed from left

A standard 120-volt receptacle has polarized slots (one—the neutral connection—is larger than the other—the hot connection). Modern receptacles also have a round plug-in hole for the grounding prong and a green grounding terminal connected to the body of the receptacle. The brass screw terminals (left photo) designate which terminal the hot (usually black) wire is connected to. The silver screw terminals are intended to accept the white neutral. Following this scheme will ensure that the polarity of your outlet is correct.
NOTE: In this photo and throughout this book, the receptacles are shown with the grounding hole up, even though it's more common to see a receptacle with the ground beneath the slots. This is deliberate. See page 88 for an explanation.

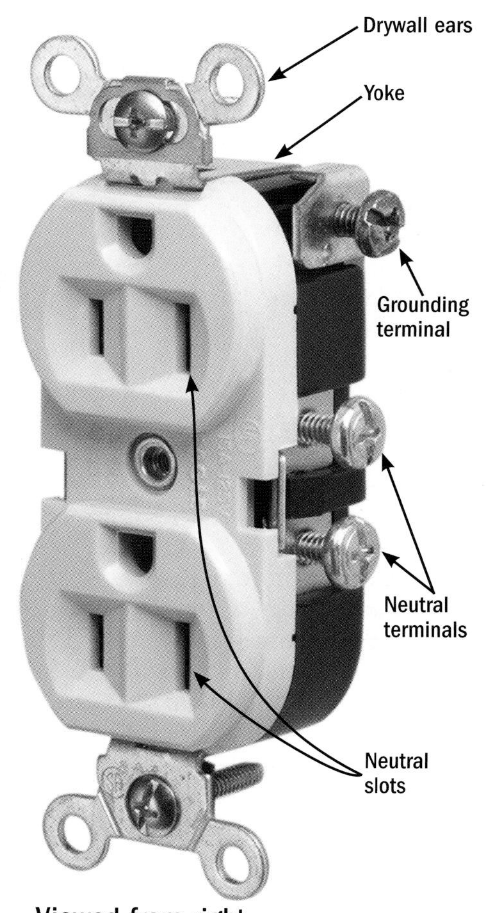

Viewed from right

wire. It is assumed that because there are so many outlets on a circuit and they're not all in use at the same time, it is unlikely that any one of them will pull an excessive amount of current. A 20-amp receptacle must be wired with 12-gauge wire to handle the higher amperage. The 20-amp outlets are easy to distinguish from 15-amp models—one slot, the wide one that connects to the neutral conductor, will have a horizontal slot perpendicular to the vertical slot.

The reason there are two different types of 120-volt receptacles is that they must match the two different types of plugs produced by appliance manufacturers (light-load appliance plugs and heavy-load appliance plugs). Most people are familiar with the standard light-duty plug with the two vertical prongs. This type of plug can be used in both 15- and 20-amp receptacles. The logic is that a light or medium load can be handled by a circuit designed for a light or medium load, as well as by a circuit designed to accept heavier loads. But a heavy-duty appliance, such as a window air conditioner, may come with a 20-amp plug that includes the horizontal prong. It must be limited to circuits designed for heavy loads—12-gauge circuits that can handle the heavy current draw without voltage loss on the wires.

SAFETY TIP

Never attempt to use a receptacle if the side screw has stripped out the receptacle's internal threads. This happens all the time on the low-cost receptacles. Sometimes, as you try to get the wire tight, the threads strip out on the receptacle—the screw will turn and turn and never tighten. You have to throw the receptacle away. Any attempt to use the receptacle will result in a loose connection that can start a fire.

QUALITY COUNTS

One of the first discoveries a new installer makes is that cheap receptacles can break apart with just the slightest amount of stress. Others that survive installation may break apart as they are used. But it doesn't have to be that way. If you compare the myriad of receptacles you'll find at any building center, you'll note that there are several key indicators of receptacle quality. You can also look at the price. Low-cost units sell for less than a dollar—the good ones, two dollars or more.

The best indicators of the general quality of a receptacle (or of a switch, too, for that matter) are the thickness of the metal and the type of plastic used. Better receptacles are built with more metal and a more durable plastic for a longer life. Thicker metal means the outlet can dissipate heat better and make stronger, much tighter electrical connections. Even the material the outlet itself is made of is better on higher-quality items. Nylon or other high-abuse plastics are used in higher-quality outlets, which means they won't easily break apart.

Another good barometer can be provided by the assembly method used. For a receptacle, look for something called a *wrap-around yoke*. This is a large piece of metal that holds everything within the receptacle together by wrapping around the top, bottom and back. High-quality receptacles also have an automatic grounding feature that automatically grounds the outlet when it is screwed into a grounded metal box. They also allow for four wires to come off each side, rather than two, which will save you the time and effort of pigtailing two wires together in the box and running the pigtail to a single terminal.

Receptacles that should be avoided are those designed with the wire holes in the back to allow fast and easy wire attachment. The option of pushing wires into the receptacle's back instead of using screws is not recommended since the wires have been known to pull out, leaving you with an open circuit or—even worse—an intermittent circuit that can cause a fire.

Designer receptacles, also called decorator models, are becoming more popular. Internally, these are the same as standard switches—they're just fancier outside. Shop for these the same as you would the standard series—shop for quality. The good thing here is that most designer series are of the higher quality. There is one big disadvantage to the designer series—they are expensive. However, don't fall into the trap of paying a high price for a cheap switch just because it has a little extra styling and color.

The biggest reason designer switches and receptacles have become popular is that they come in a wide array of colors. Along with the standard ivory and brown, you can get almost any color, including today's popular white. Most have a flat face, as opposed to the truncated faces surrounding standard receptacle slots. The truncated face has a purpose—it aids in inserting a cord plug. If smooth-faced receptacles undergo frequent plugging-in and unplugging, expect them to become scratched as the plug's metal prongs scrape back and forth searching for the slots.

(Continued on page 86)

QUALITY COUNTS (CONTINUED)

Higher-quality receptacles have thicker metal and plastic components, including a metal yoke that binds the receptacle together and automatically grounds it when it is installed in a grounded metal box. The thicker metal and higher-impact plastic increases durability and allows the receptacle to operate more smoothly and with a firmer grip on the plug prongs.

Economy receptacles can cost half as much, or less, than their higher-grade counterparts. And for some projects they may work out fine. But in general, it's worth investing a bit more to avoid the need to replace the device soon, or even to avoid having it break during installation. Lightweight plastic all around is a good indicator (along with price). You can easily tell the difference between the receptacle on the far left and the cheaper one shown here by weighing both in your hands.

Avoid receptacles with push-in wire connectors. The connection created when the stripped wire is inserted into the push-in hole in the back of the receptacle is not nearly as strong and secure as that formed when the wire is anchored to a screw terminal.

Ever wonder why plugs fall out of receptacles? The low-cost outlet doesn't have enough metal in its slots to hold the prongs in tightly. Solution: buy better quality receptacles. Expect to pay around $2 or more for a good receptacle.

Wiring a Receptacle

How you should wire receptacles depends on how you want the receptacles installed in the circuit—in series or in parallel. The series wiring method (See Illustration, page 90) is the most common; you see it all the time. This is where both incoming and outgoing cables physically wire onto the receptacle screws. This system wires fast and easy, but has a major drawback. If one wire becomes loose and pulls off the receptacle or if the receptacle just fails, power is lost to all the downstream receptacles. It's the identical problem afflicting old Christmas tree lights. You have to spend a lot of time trying to identify which receptacle the wire has pulled out of when you lose power on the circuit.

The parallel method is where all splicing is done in the back of the outlet box and two short pigtail wires jump from the splice to the receptacle terminals. This method (See Illustration, page 89) takes longer to wire but has the advantage of making each receptacle independent. Note that all current going to and coming from the upstream receptacles will go through the splice and not through the receptacle. You can even take the receptacle out of the box and it will have no effect on the circuit.

Grounding. In a nonmetallic box, the way you handle the grounding depends on the number of incoming cables. If the receptacle is at the end of the run so only one cable comes into the box, simply fasten the bare ground wire to the grounding screw terminal on the receptacle. If multiple cables are entering the box, splice all the bare ground wires together with a wire connector and run a pigtail from the splice to the grounding terminal on the receptacle. In a metal box, an incoming ground wire should be attached to both the receptacle and the metal box (an exception being receptacles with a solid metal yoke and an automatic grounding feature, which only require that the incoming ground attach to the receptacle grounding screw—See page 86, top left). Splice all incoming bare ground wires together, along with a pair of bare-ground pigtail wires. Attach one pigtail to the grounding screw on the receptacle and the other to the metal box. You can buy grounding pigtails with preattached grounding screws that you simply screw into a screw opening on the box (you're not allowed to use the same screw that connects the box to the wall stud).

How to wire receptacles

The following are the most common methods for wiring receptacles. It is assumed that all boxes are nonmetallic and do not require a ground wire.

One cable, one receptacle. This is the simplest of wiring situations. Series or parallel distinctions don't apply. If you have but a single cable, all wires

Two-slot receptacles should be used only if your home wiring is not grounded to the service panel—do not install a receptacle with a grounding prong hole if the circuit is not grounded. The better and much safer solution, however, is to rewire your house so all circuits are grounded back to the panel.

A 20-amp receptacle has a horizontal leg in the neutral slot to accept a plug from an appliance requiring a 20-amp circuit. The 20-amp plugs will not fit into a 15-amp circuit.

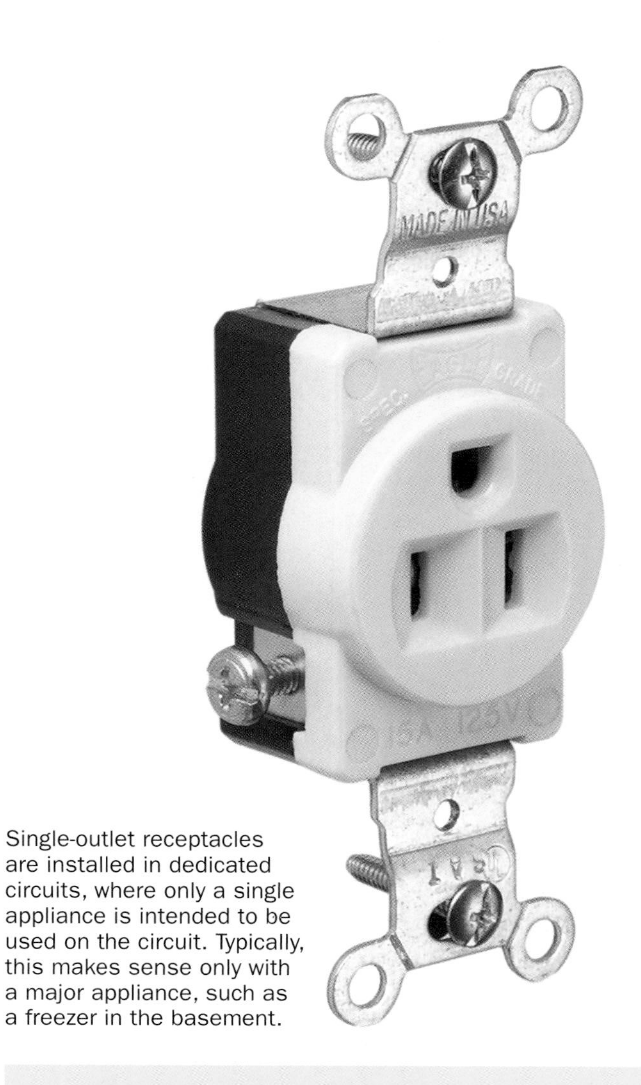

Single-outlet receptacles are installed in dedicated circuits, where only a single appliance is intended to be used on the circuit. Typically, this makes sense only with a major appliance, such as a freezer in the basement.

attach to the receptacle. The black wire is looped under the bronze-colored screw, the white wire is attached to the silver-colored screw, and the bare wire is grounded. This type of hookup is seen mostly at the end of run, where there are no more loads downstream on the circuit. The final receptacle in a series is wired this way (See the last receptacle on the right in the Diagrams above and on pages 89 and 90).

Both incoming and outgoing cables. This is the second most common receptacle hookup situation. Here we have one incoming cable bringing in the electrical power and one outgoing cable taking the power to another receptacle or downstream, or perhaps feeding a switch outlet box. Once the sheathing is stripped away, there will be two black wires, two

SAFETY TIP

Never invert an immediate-turn plug. Some plugs, such as those for clothes washers and refrigerators, are molded into an immediate turn. Some have the ground pin in the up position and some have the ground pin in the down position. Never install the plug in such a way that its own weight will pull it out of the wall. As the cord's weight pulls its prongs out of the receptacle, it presents a hazard to anyone coming in contact with it, creating the potential for a short to ground or to neutral.

GROUND HOLES UP OR GROUND HOLES DOWN?

There is an age-old debate among professional electricians: Should the grounding prong holes in the receptacle be oriented above or below the slots? The answer is that there is no absolutely right or wrong orientation. You can do whichever you prefer. However, experience has shown that a problem can occur with the receptacle installed the most common way (ground down). With the ground down, the neutral and hot wires are open to a direct short if something falls onto the blades or prongs. With the ground up, anything falling down onto the plug blades will be deflected by the ground prong. The most common thing that falls is a metal coverplate. When this happens, the plug, the receptacle and the coverplate are ruined. **NOTE:** If the receptacle will be used for an appliance with an immediate-turn plug, install the receptacle with the ground hole down (See Safety Tip, above).

white wires, and two ground wires that must terminate in the outlet box. There are two ways to manage this situation: wiring in parallel and wiring in series.

In parallel (*See Diagram, below*). Splice all the black wires together in the back of the box, along with a 6-in. black pigtail. The pigtail connects to a bronze receptacle screw. Do the same with the white wires, connecting the pigtail to a silver terminal. The power comes into the box, and at the pigtail connection it continues ahead to the next receptacle. If there is more than one outgoing cable, then you must use the parallel system of hookup.

In series (*See Diagram, next page*). Connect the black wires to the bronze screw side of the receptacle, one wire under each screw terminal. Connect the white wires to the silver-screw terminals. The ground wires should be pigtailed together and connected to the ground-screw terminal on the receptacle. Power comes in, connects to the receptacle, jumps across to the outgoing wires and leaves.

Wiring a switched (split) receptacle. A switched (split) receptacle can be wired two different ways. Either way produces the same result. The object is most often to eliminate the overhead light by providing switched lighting of a table lamp. But to avoid having to add another receptacle to provide the required non-switched power in the room, the installer wires the receptacle so one of the plug-ins receives a constant power supply. To do this, the installer breaks the hot tab (the tab on the brass-screw side) off the receptacle. When unbroken, the hot tab bonds the hot contact points on the plug-ins together. Now the top half of the receptacle is power-independent of the bottom half. The neutral tab stays intact. Once the tab is broken off, the receptacle can be wired in one of two ways.

WIRING DIAGRAM: RECEPTACLES IN PARALLEL

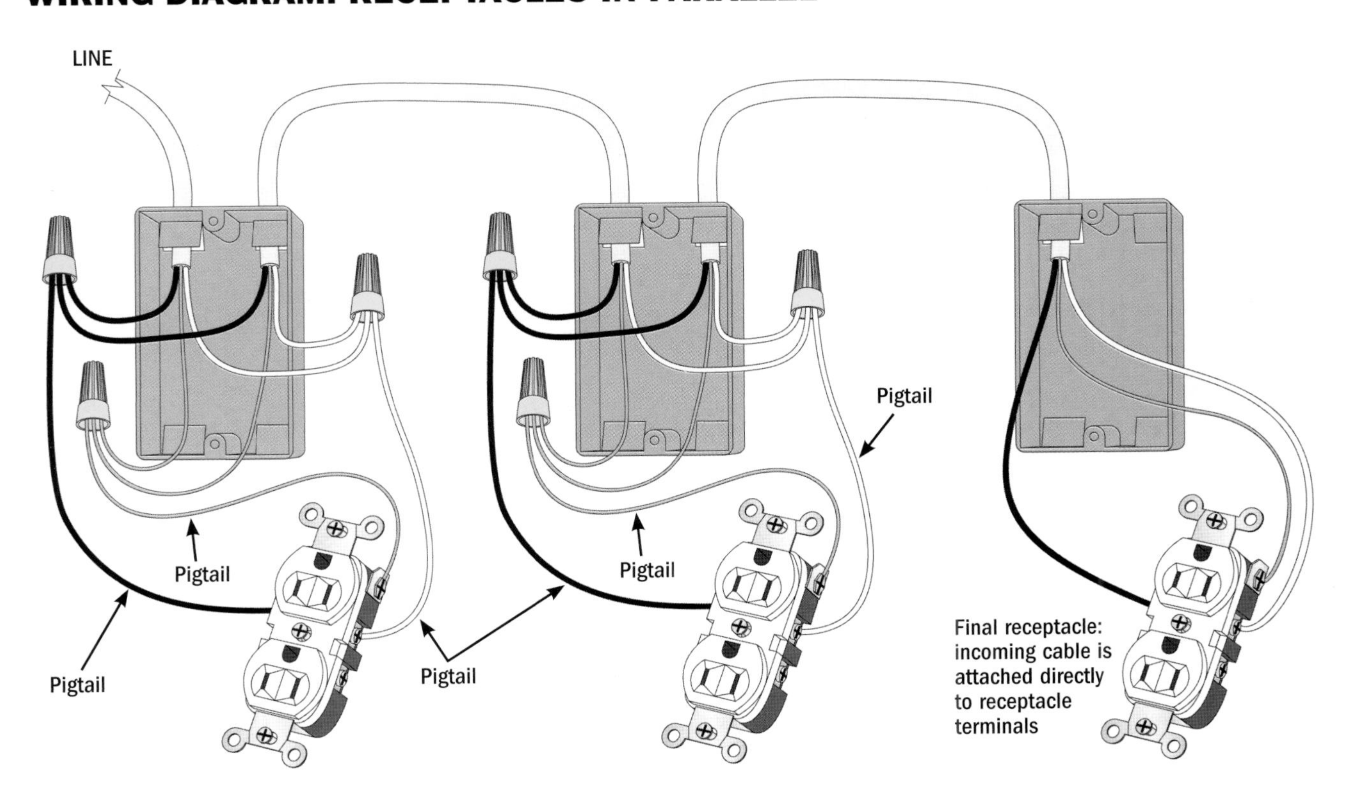

Using this method of wiring offers a big advantage when installing multiple outlets on one circuit. Because the hot wires that feed each receptacle are pigtailed from the LINE, a broken or disconnected receptacle will not have any effect on other receptacles downstream (as it will if wiring in series—next page). This method takes a little longer owing to all the pigtailing, but you'll recover the extra time, and more, if one of the receptacles fails, since you won't need to test all the receptacles to find out which one is bad. To wire in parallel, simply run the power into the first receptacle box. Cut pigtails for all wires (white, black and ground). Run cable out to feed the next receptacle in the circuit. Splice the incoming and outgoing blacks with the black pigtail, then attach the black pigtail to the brass or bronze-colored screw terminal in the receptacle. Splice the whites and attach the pigtail to the silver terminal. Splice the bare grounds and attach the pigtail to the grounding screw on the receptacle. Wire each receptacle downstream the same way until you reach the final one, where you simply attach the wires from the incoming cable directly to the appropriate screw terminals.

Switched receptacle wiring method No. 1 (See Diagram, page 91). This method uses 3-way wire or cable with red and black hot conductors, a white neutral and a bare ground. This cable runs from a switch located near the entry area of the room to the outlet box containing the receptacle. The red wire will be the switched hot, the black the unswitched hot, while the white and bare wires provide shared neutral and ground. The switch box needs only one other cable—the incoming power feed.

Switched receptacle wiring method No. 2: This method requires no special wiring such as an expensive 3-way switch cable. To wire via this method, bring the standard NM/2 w/ground feed cable into the receptacle box first, instead of the switch box. Run another cable from the switch box to the receptacle box. Attach the neutral and ground feeder wires to the receptacle as with a standard hookup, pigtailing them to the proper terminals on the receptacle. But instead of wiring the black hot wire to the receptacle, splice it together with the black wire from the cable to the switch and with a pigtail in the back of the receptacle box. Attach the pigtail to one plug-in of the duplex receptacle (one of the bronze screws). Half of the receptacle is now permanently hot. To control the other plug-in on the receptacle with the switch, first tag the white wire to the switch with black electrical tape to indicate that it is hot, not neutral. At the wall switch, tape the white wire black for the same reason. Attach the tagged white hot wire from the switch to the brass terminal on the switched plug-in. At the switch, attach the tagged white wire to one of the screw terminals. Attach the black wire going to the switch to the other switch terminal.

WIRING DIAGRAM: RECEPTACLES IN SERIES

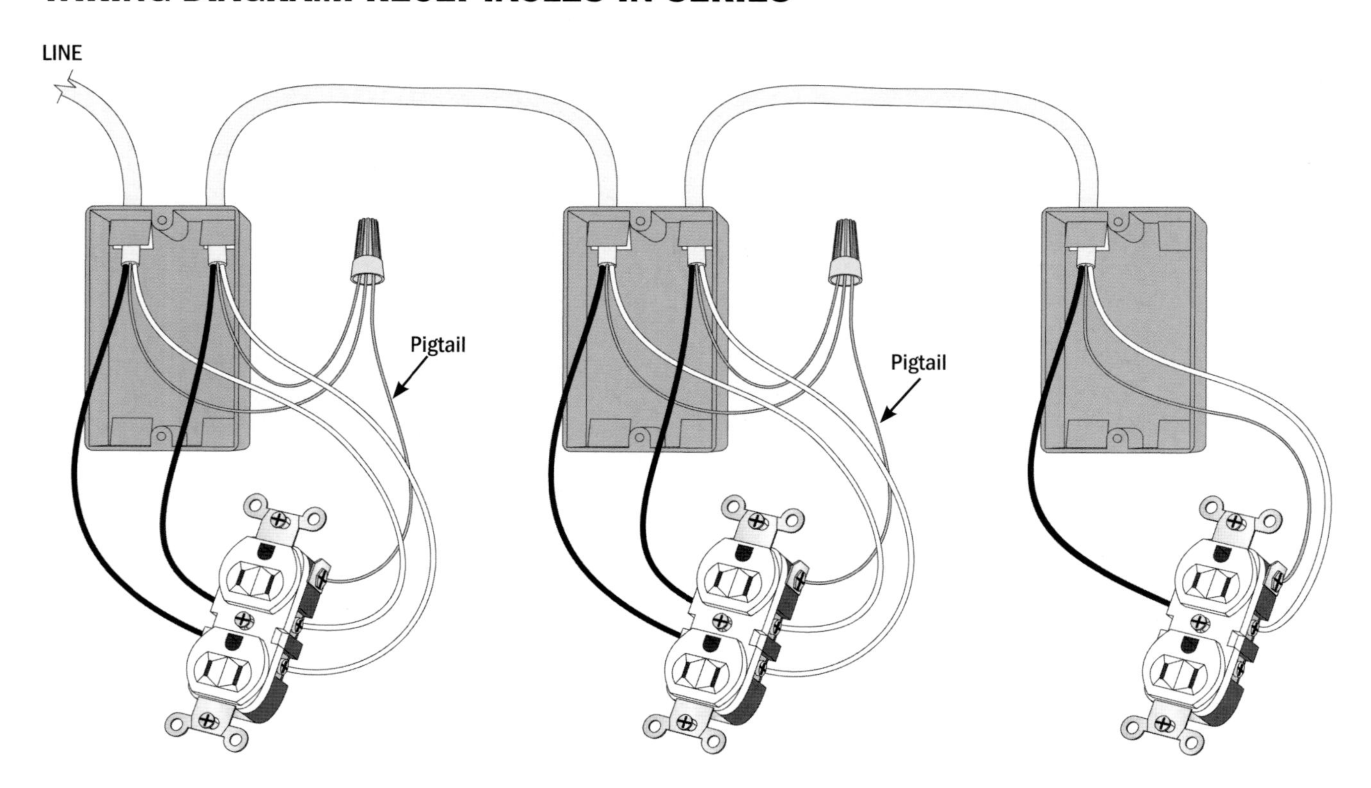

Also referred to as a "daisy chain," this is the quick-and-easy way to install multiple receptacles on the same circuit. You simply bring power into and out of each receptacle in turn: no pigtailing involved, except on the ground wire. But because each receptacle becomes an integral part of the current flow, any problems that arise with any single receptacle will interrupt the circuit and all receptacles following it will not receive power. But if you're using good-quality receptacles and you do careful work, you should be able to use the receptacle circuit for years without any problems at all.

To wire receptacles in series, simply bring the power from the LINE into the first receptacle outlet box. Strip off the insulation and attach the incoming wires directly to the screw terminals on the receptacle: black to one of the bronze or brass screws; white to one of the silver screws. Attach the black and white wires from the outgoing cable to the remaining brass and silver screw terminals (respectively). Then, splice the bare grounds together, with a pigtail, and run the pigtail to the grounding screw. On the last receptacle, attach the bare ground directly to the grounding screw.

WIRING DIAGRAM: SWITCHED RECEPTACLE

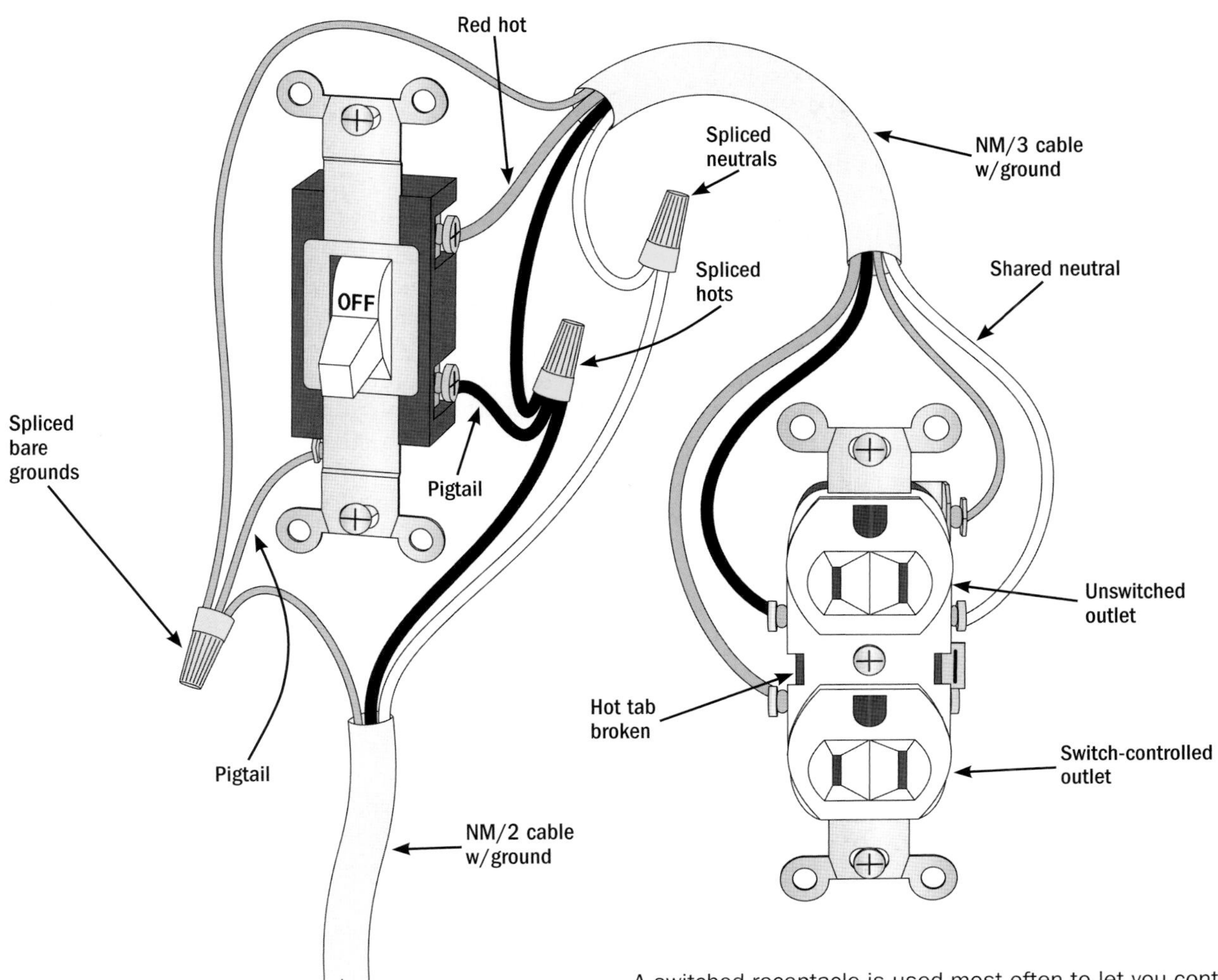

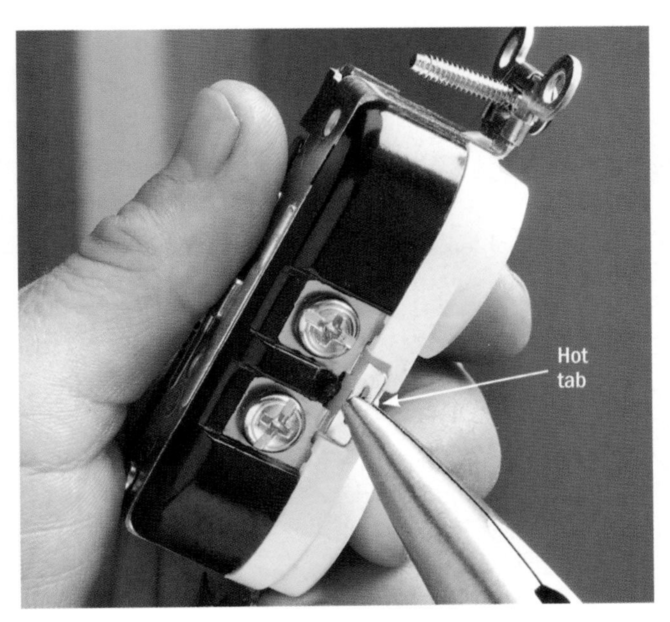

A switched receptacle is used most often to let you control a lamp that provides primary room lighting. One of the outlets on a duplex receptacle is controlled by a wall switch. The other outlet on the duplex is wired for constant current flow. To accomplish this, the metal hot tab that bonds the hot contacts on each outlet must be broken (See photo, left). Breaking the tab with a pliers or screwdriver isolates the two outlets so they can be wired independently. The easiest way to wire the switched receptacle is to bring power to the switch, then run NM/3 cable from the switch to the receptacle. Connect the red hot wire from the brass-screw terminal on the switch-controlled outlet to a terminal on the switch. Splice the black wire from the power source to the black from the NM/3 wire and run a pigtail from the splice to the brass-screw terminal on the unswitched outlet. Splice the white neutral from the power source directly to the white neutral from the NM/3, bypassing the switch. Connect the white neutral from the NM/3 to a silver terminal on the receptacle (don't break the tab on the silver terminals—both outlets share the neutral). Splice the grounds from each cable together and pigtail them to the grounding screw on the switch. Connect the ground from the NM/3 to the grounding screw on the terminal.

You can also wire a switched receptacle using NM/2 cable running from the receptacle to the switch with a neutral tagged hot (See description, page 90).

BUYER'S GUIDE

If you are looking for the ultimate receptacle, look to the Hubbell 5262. This is probably the most copied receptacle in existence. It was so good when it came out in 1950 that other manufacturers allegedly copied the number just to cash in on some of the business. This receptacle has heavy-duty everything. If you have life-support equipment in your house, this is the receptacle you want it plugged into. Get it at the large electrical supply houses.

Pushing wires back into the box

Once the receptacle is wired, one of the most common mistakes occurs: incorrectly pushing the wires back into the box. They're often kinked, gouged, broken and skinned. Wires should not just be stuffed back into the box. They need to "accordion" back into the box. Excess wire also should be removed. You want just enough wire to allow easy access to the receptacle, but not so much as to overcrowd the box. You wired with a plan in mind and you should push the wires back into the box with a plan in mind. Along with making sure you push the wires in using the correct technique, pay attention to the order in which you push them back.

First into the box are the ground wires. Circle and push the ground wires so they fit flat against the back of the box, completely out of the way. It doesn't matter whether you circle them in a clockwise or counterclockwise direction.

Next into the box are the white neutrals. These go parallel to and up against the ground wires, back against the flat of the box back. Do not position the wire connector holding the grounds together on top of the wire connector holding the neutrals together, this takes up too much space. Arrange the neutrals so the wire connector is flat against the back of the box, just as the ground wire connector is.

Finally, push in the hot wires. Installing them last keeps them away from the back of the box where they could short out and also allows easier access if voltage measurements need to be taken.

Polarization

Polarized cords can be plugged into a polarized receptacle with only one orientation, so the neutral and hot can never be reversed. This is done by designing receptacles with one narrow (hot) and one wide (neutral) slot. Correspondingly, newer appliance cords have a narrow (hot) and wide (neutral) prong. As long as you pay attention and connect the hot conductor from the feeder cable to the bronze or brass-colored receptacle screw terminal, and connect the neutral to the silver terminal, polarization will automatically be correct. However, problems can arise in older houses that do not have polarized receptacles: that is, both slots are the same shape and size. In such cases, you may have some difficulty determining which is the hot and which is the neutral wire when replacing the receptacle with a polarized receptacle—especially since the sheathing or braiding on old wires doesn't always indicate which wire is which. The question of which is which can be solved easily if the old wiring is in metal flexible conduit, however. Since the conduit is grounded back at the main service panel you now have a reference. Take a voltage reading from each screw to the metal box (which is connected to the flexible conduit). The screw that reads zero volts is the neutral. The screw that reads 120 volts is the hot or black wire. If there is no conduit to use as reference then you must find a ground or neutral reference somewhere else. If none is available, you may have to take a wire all the way back to the main panel frame or neutral/grounding bus to use as a reference.

Troubleshooting Receptacles

Nothing lasts forever, and that is especially apparent in the electrical arena. The most common problems involve lights and receptacles that become intermittent or just stop working. Some troubleshooting only requires a little common sense to solve the problem; other problems will require some special tools such as a multimeter—a meter that measures voltage and can give you resistance and continuity checks (See pages 26 to 28).

Receptacles are easy to troubleshoot. A simple plug-in tester (See page 29) will indicate whether the receptacle is miswired or not, but always have a multimeter ready to check for low voltage. The most common problems result from reversing the hot and neutral wires and unconnected or incorrectly connected ground wires. Both problems are indicated on the tester's lights and are easily fixed by reversing the wires or connecting the ground wire. Like cheap switches, cheap receptacles are easy to break. Never use a broken receptacle or one that has its screw terminals stripped out.

The most common outlet complaint is "The receptacles just stopped working." First, check the fuse or circuit breaker. If a circuit breaker is half-way off (the handle is half-way between ON and OFF) the breaker is kicked. If the breaker is kicked or the fuse blown (it happened for a reason) something is drawing too much current or a wire shorted out. If that's the problem find out what, if anything, was plugged into the circuit when the receptacles stopped working. The appliance could be bad. If the circuit was just overloaded, most likely it will be a plug-in portable heater or hair dryer/curler.

If the breaker is still on, and it is still good, the most common problem is that someone used the push-in terminals on the back of the receptacles during the initial installation and they are now just starting to pull out. What you have to find is the receptacle that is getting power but can't transfer the power upstream because those wires have pulled out. A lot of it is just luck. First, turn off the power to the entire circuit. Try to imagine how the original wiring was run and make your best guess as to which receptacle should be checked first. All suspect receptacles will have to be pulled from the box and the wires checked to verify they are still making good contact with the receptacle and have not pulled loose. You'll find as you pull the receptacle out of the wall, even if this is not the bad receptacle with the wire pulled out, the wires will start popping right out of the receptacle back. All the wires will have to be looped and inserted under the screws before the receptacle is put back into the wall. The troubleshooting continues until you finally find a receptacle with the wire pulled out. If none are found, the problem is elsewhere and an electrician should be brought in.

240-volt Receptacles

Hooking up a 240-volt receptacle is a different process than hooking up a 120-volt outlet. The main point of departure is that a 240-volt unit is not wired with a white neutral. Instead, the white wire is tagged black and connected to the hot bus bar on the circuit panel (via a circuit breaker). The black hot is connected to the other terminal on the breaker, which contacts the opposing hot bus bar. Thus, 120 volts of power is brought into the receptacle through each wire, for a total of 240 volts. And because the power is split between both phases of power at the panel, they balance out and no neutral is required.

To connect a 20-amp, 240-volt receptacle, use 12-gauge NM/2 w/ground wire. With the power off, run the 240-volt circuit from the main panel (See page 46). At the outlet box and at the panel, tag the white wire hot with black electrical tape. Hook the tagged white up to one terminal on the receptacle, and attach the black hot wire to the other terminal. Connect the bare ground to the grounding terminal on the receptacle.

Because 240-volt circuits generally are used to power appliances that draw significant amperage, they are seldom wired in series, but are installed as dedicated circuits instead.

20-amp, 240-volt receptacle

15-amp, 240-volt receptacle

30-amp, 120/240-volt receptacle

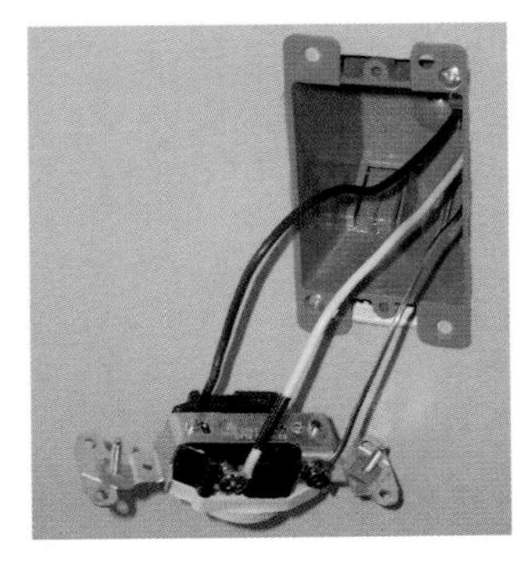
240-volt receptacles are wired with two hot leads and no white neutral. The tagged white lead brings 120-volt power from one leg of the service panel, and the black wire brings 120-volt power from the other leg, totalling 240 volts.

Replacing a Receptacle

Receptacles break, burn up, and lose their ability to hold a plug in their slots. Cheap receptacles especially have a habit of breaking. Some have screws that strip out the minute they're installed, others just break or don't have enough gripping strength due to old age. Other times you'll be changing a receptacle just because you may want to have a certain color to go with the finished wall or want a designer series. The bottom line is someday you will probably need to change a receptacle. And unless you want to pull in an electrician and pay him/her for an hour or two of work to do a five-minute job, it's nice to know to how to do it yourself. As always make sure there is no power on the circuit, receptacle, or wire you are working with.

HOW TO REPLACE A RECEPTACLE

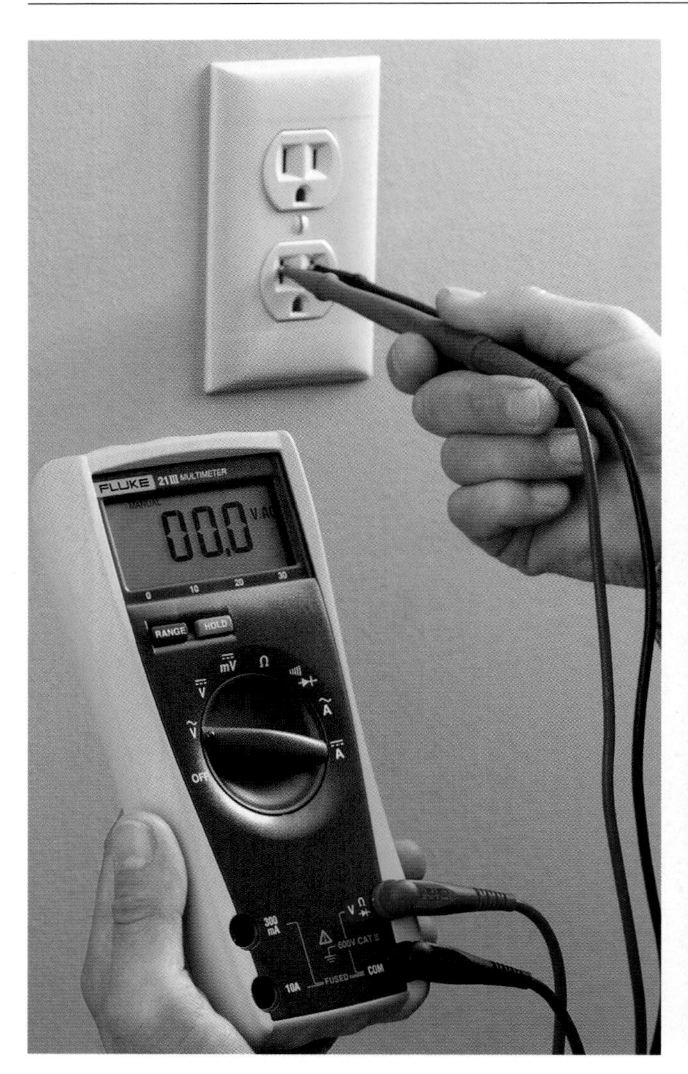

1 Remove the electricity from the circuit you are working on by turning off the breaker or pulling out the fuse. Verify loss of power with a plug-in checker or multimeter at the receptacle.

2 Remove the receptacle's coverplate by unscrewing the tiny center screw. Remove the receptacle's top and bottom attachment screws and pull the receptacle slightly out of the outlet box. To do this, grab the receptacle by its T-shaped drywall ears and pull straight forward. You will have to pull it forward enough to be able to remove the wires from the screws on its sides.

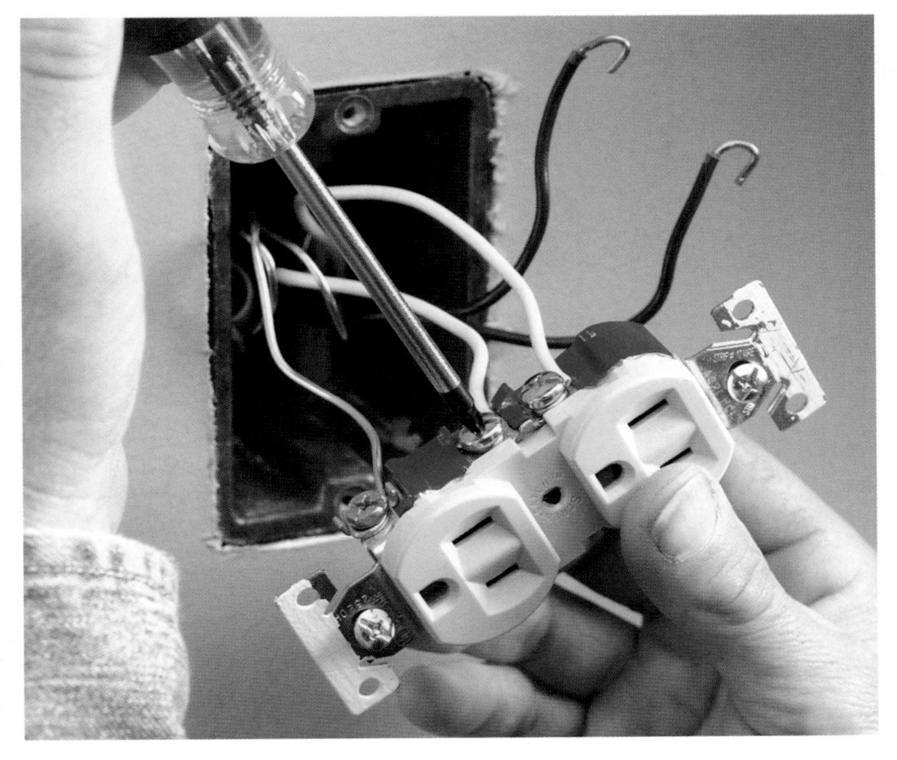

3 Remove the wires from the receptacle's brass-colored screws and pull them aside (for this you will need a flat-bladed screwdriver and long-nosed pliers). These will normally be the black wires. Insert the screwdriver into the screw and turn counterclockwise. It isn't necessary to remove the screws. Also disconnect the white wires from the silver screw terminals.

Note on tightening screws. The amount of pressure you use to tighten a receptacle screw is only learned by experience. Too little and you have a loose connection. Too much and you strip it out. The higher the quality of the receptacle, the more pressure you can use. Once you've stripped out one or two receptacles you will learn how much pressure they can take. Never reuse a stripped-out receptacle—throw it away.

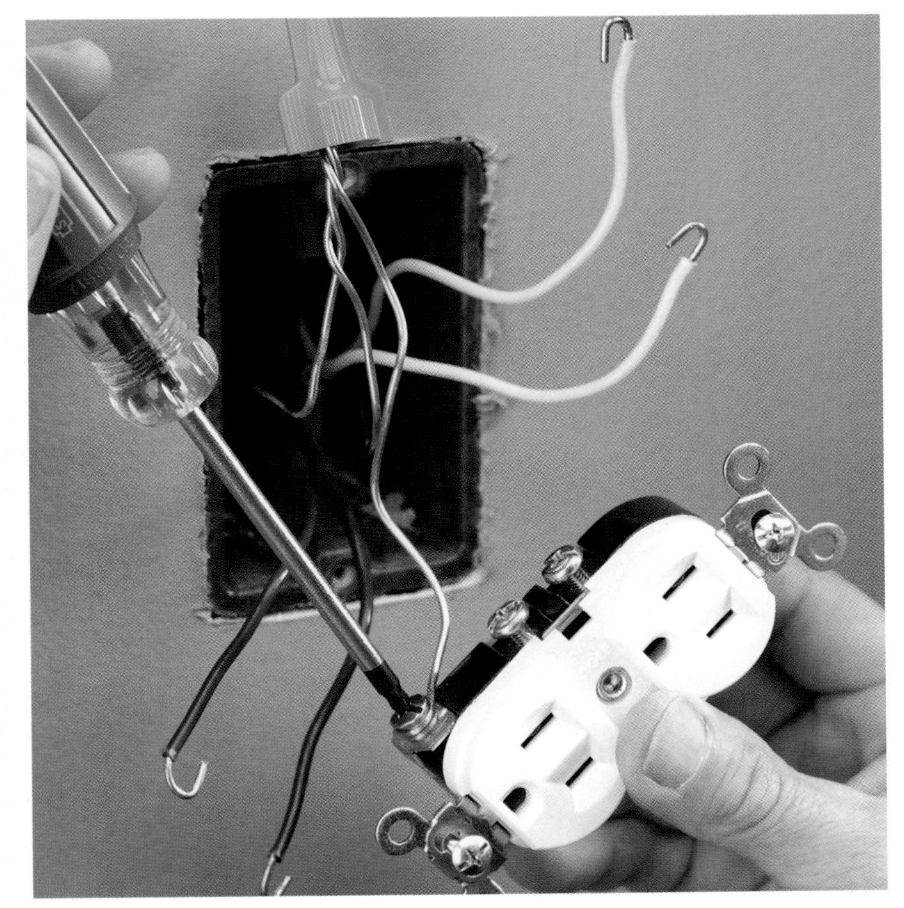

4 Remove the ground wire from the receptacle grounding screw and discard the receptacle. This wire will normally be the bare wire or sometimes green. If there is more than a single cable in the box, the ground wires will be spliced together in the back of the box with one wire (a pigtail) coming from the splice to connect to the green grounding screw. You are not allowed to have more than one wire under one screw. The twisted ground leads need a mechanical connection such as a wire nut or crimp. Without a mechanical connector, the ground wires have a habit of unwinding and pulling apart.

5 Bring in the new receptacle. Attach the ground wire to the receptacle's green ground screw. The wire end should already be in a half loop. Simply hook it over the screw and tighten the screw clockwise. Connect the white wires to the silver screws. As before, the wires should already be in a half loop. If they are not, bend a loop with a long-nosed pliers (See page 18).

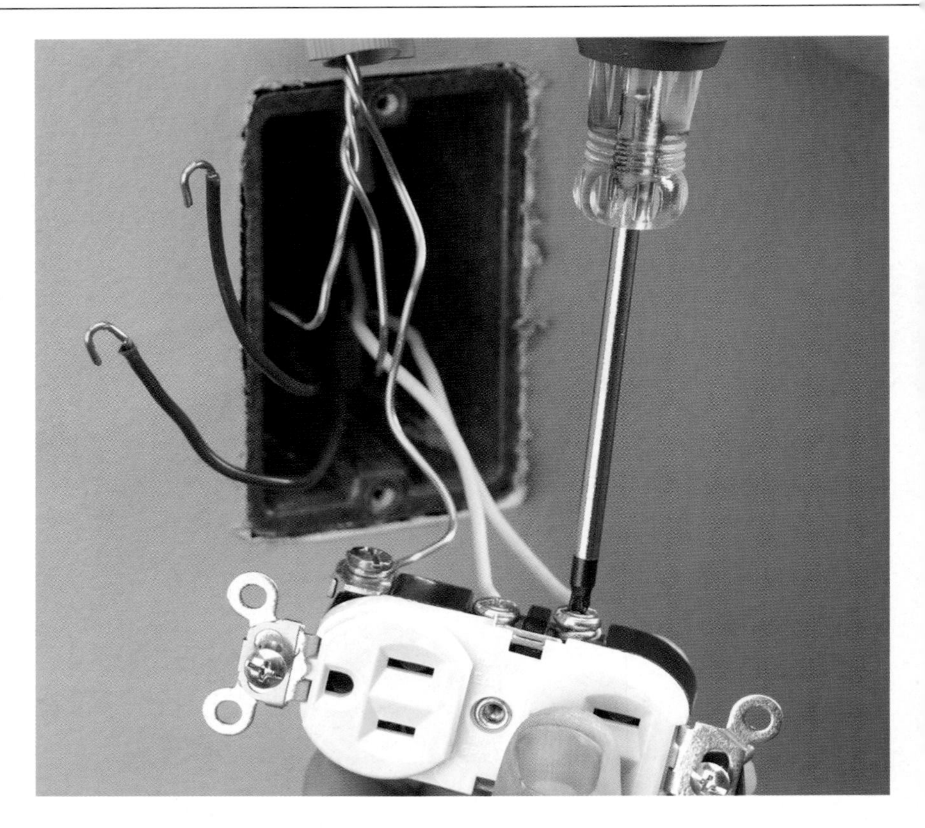

6 Connect the black wires to the brass or bronze-screw terminals on the receptacle. If you are wiring a switched receptacle (See page 91), arrange the wires so that the black wire from one cable is aligned with the white from the same cable (that is, both on the lower or both on the upper screws).

Tip: To provide some protection from the live screw terminal once the power is restored, you can place some black electrical tape over the screwheads and connections before inserting the receptacle into the box (See page 14).

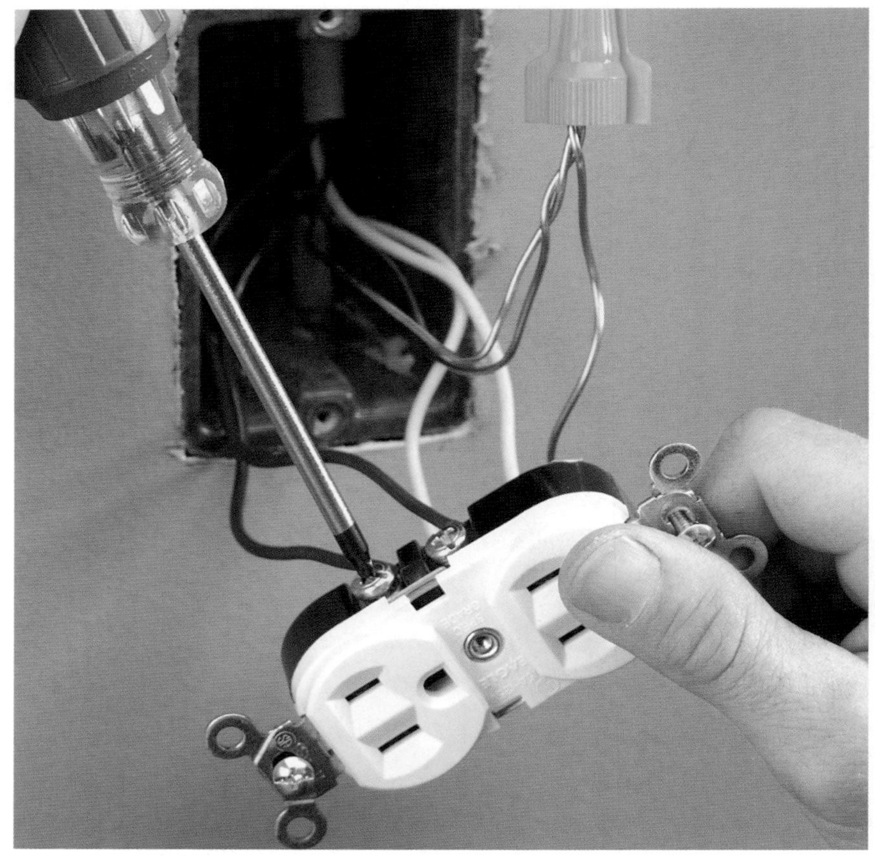

7 Push the wires neatly back into the box with your fingers. First, prebend the wires in the direction you want them to fold into the box. If you did it right, the wires should accordion neatly back into the box in a "Z" pattern. Push the receptacle back into the box and screw it in via the top and bottom attachment screws that are hanging from the receptacle's drywall ears. As you tighten the screws clockwise, note that you can shift the receptacle left and right to a slight degree. This allows you to plumb and center the receptacle.

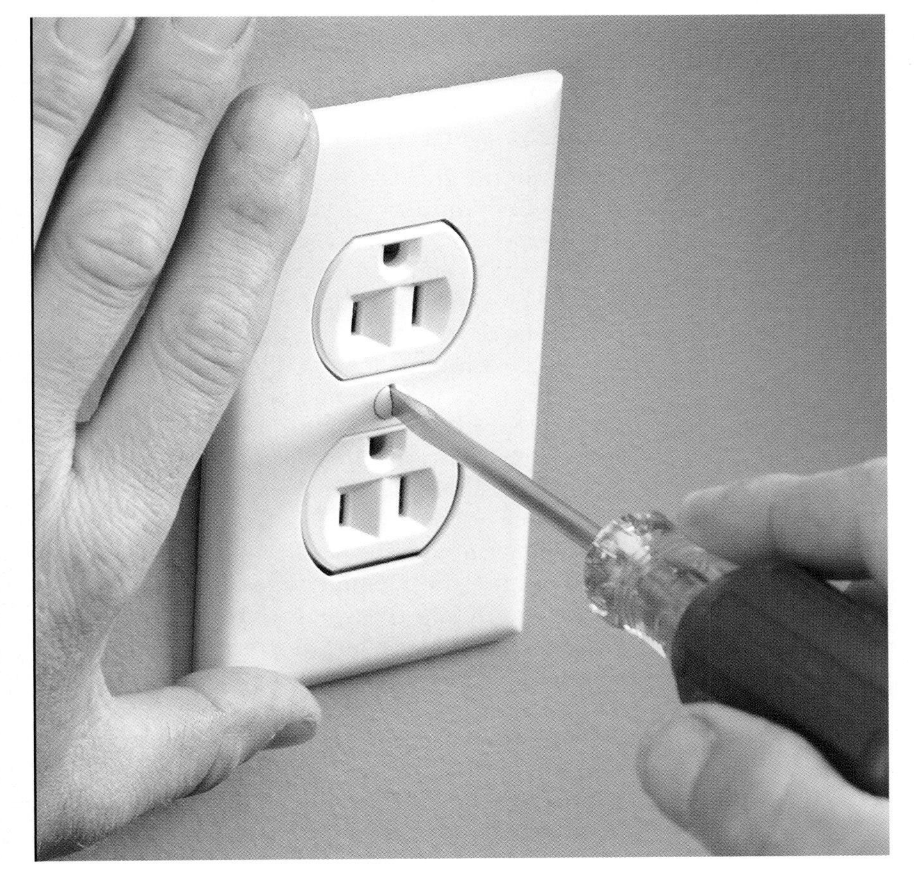

8 Reattach the receptacle cover and you are done. Reapply power and check your wiring with a plug-in checker or multimeter (See pages 26 to 28).

GFCI Receptacles

Ground-fault protection is the law of the land—and for good reason. GFCI (Ground Fault Circuit Interrupter) receptacles, commonly used for bathroom receptacles, have saved many lives and could save even more if they were more widely used. You can also provide GFCI protection to a circuit by installing a GFCI breaker in the service panel. The old movie scene of a radio dropping into the tub to electrocute the ill-fated bather could not happen in a bathroom properly wired with GFCI protection.

Old hair dryers are especially dangerous in wet areas since they have no fault protection built into their design. New hair dryers do have protection; it is in the little box at the plug-in.

Working with power tools, especially outdoors, is one of the most dangerous applications for electrical power. Whether using an old drill in the garage (concrete floor) or working outside on the swing set (earth floor), your feet are on conductive material. If the tool has a hot-wire-to-frame fault (short circuit), current will flow from the tool into your hand, making the muscles contract, which in turn tightens your grip and makes it functionally impossible for you to release the tool. The current flow continues through your arm, body, heart, and finally through your legs to the earth. If this happens on a ground-fault protected circuit, you will feel like someone jabbed you with a needle. Immediately thereafter the GFCI will open the circuit and the current will stop.

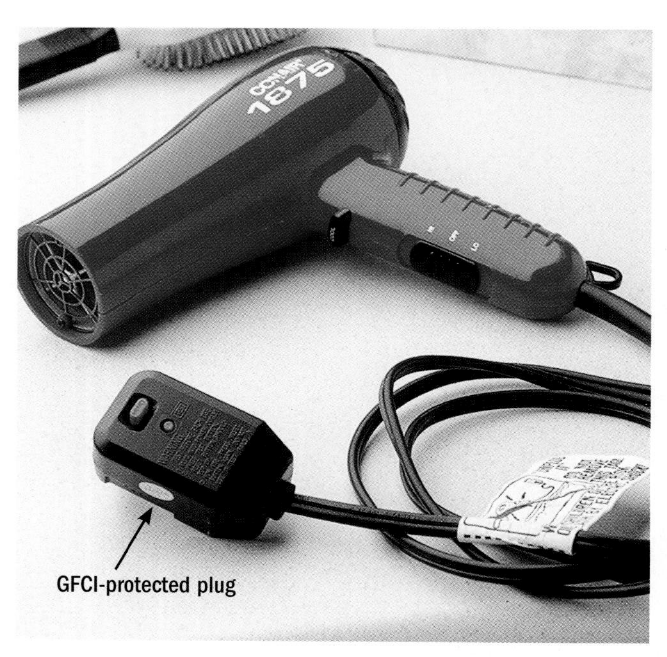

Many common household appliances now come with GFCI protection. The GFCI unit is usually built directly into the plug, as with the hair dryer shown here.

To make full use of these life-saving devices, you need to know everything about them. This chapter will illustrate the many uses GFCIs have; where to install them, and where not to, how they work and how GFCI testers work.

How GFCIs work

GFCIs are not the grand mystery most people conceive them to be. They are actually very simple devices. General-purpose, 120-volt household circuits have current flowing to and from the load on two insulated wires: the white and the black. Power is brought to the load on the black wire, flows through the load and then returns via the white. As long as these two currents are equal, the GFCI is happy and provides power like a standard receptacle. But if some of the return current is missing, the GFCI will immediately open the circuit.

The comparison is the primary factor. A GFCI has a comparator circuit that monitors the amount of electricity flowing through the black wire and compares it to the amount returning. Both wires, black and white, are wound around the comparator's toroidal coil. As long as the currents are equal, the magnetic lines of force around the toroidal coil cancel each other out and no difference current is generated. As soon as one wire shows less current than the other, one wire's magnetic lines of force will exceed the others and a *difference current* is generated. When the difference current exceeds a specific amount, the GFCI is

GFCI CIRCUIT BREAKERS

The circuit-breaker type of GFCI fits into the main service panel just like a standard breaker. However, it will have an extra white wire that connects to the neutral bus. The neutral for the GFCI circuit will connect into the breaker—it will not connect to the neutral bus. The hot wire will connect into the breaker like all breakers do. On top of the GFCI breaker will be a TEST button (no RESET). Once installed properly, pressing the button places a preset current imbalance on the line to verify that the breaker will trip off as it should. When tripped, the breaker arm goes to the half-off position and the circuit loses power.

Once tripped, the GFCI circuit breaker will not reset unless the breaker is first turned all the way off before it is turned back on again. Many no-power service calls are made to electricians when the only problem was the owner did not turn the breaker all the way off before turning it back on.

The disadvantages of the circuit-breaker type of GFCI compared to the receptacle type is in cost and inconvenience. GFCI breakers are considerably more expensive than receptacles. The inconvenience part is that you'll need to traipse all the way to the service panel to reset the breaker. But they do offer a big advantage in durability. They simply last longer than receptacle GFCIs and have the advantage of being inside the panel and not out in the weather when protecting outside outlets.

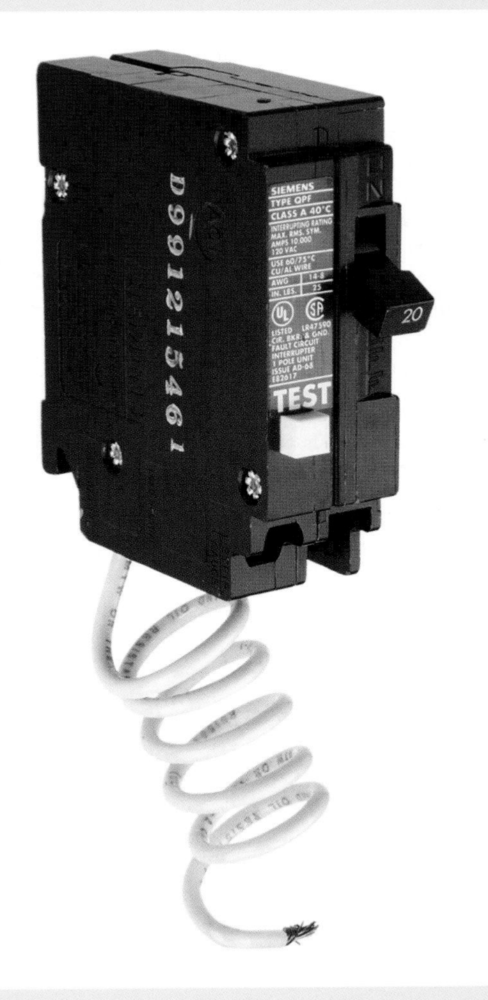

Installing GFCI protection at the service panel protects every outlet on the circuit, so standard receptacles can be installed throughout, even in wet or outdoor locations (as long as the receptacles have a weathertight cover).

Simply push the TEST button and the breaker will emit a current imbalance that will trip the breaker, confirming that it works. Unlike GFCI receptacles, GFCI breakers do not have a RESET button. You simply flip them all the way off, then back on, as when resetting any circuit breaker.

tripped. If everything is operating properly, the two currents should always be equal. If, however, some of the current is missing, the electrons must be going through something other than the load—such as a hapless tool user—and to ground. This current can be as low as .006 amp and the GFCI will still open the circuit. What's more, the tool doesn't need to be grounded for the ground-fault system to work.

GFCI's aren't foolproof. The tool you are using can be connected to a ground-fault circuit and you can still be electrocuted. For a GFCI to work, a ground-fault must occur. That is, electrical current must flow out of the normal circuit path to ground to create the current imbalance that trips the circuit. The current coming to the tool in the black wire cannot equal the current flowing back in the white wire. If you place your body between the black and white wires without having any current go to ground, the GFCI will not trip because, as far as it's concerned, the volume of electrons leaving is equal to the amount coming back—the current is simply going through the resistance within your body before returning. And you may not live to tell of your marvelous discovery.

So, why doesn't the circuit breaker at the panel trip and save your life if there is a ground-fault? Simply put: it is not designed to. A circuit breaker is not designed to trip soon enough or to be that current-sensitive. Breakers made for general-purpose receptacles are internally set to trip when the current exceeds 15 or 20 amps—many times more than it takes to produce death. A breaker, or even a fuse, is designed to protect the wiring within the household against excessive current—it is not designed for life protection. Having GFCI protection doesn't give you license to behave carelessly with impunity. Even with GFCI protection, do not operate any tool in wet conditions or place it under water.

GFCI types

GFCIs receptacles come in many different configurations. However, the two most common around the home will be types resembling either a receptacle or a single-pole 120-volt circuit breaker—both available in 15- and 20-amp designs. Less common are 30-, 40-, 50- and even 60-amp GFCI breakers, although they do exist. Look for these as double-pole breakers in spas and whirlpools.

Due to their low cost and ease of installation, receptacle GFCIs are the most common GFCI protection devices. They obtain power from a standard circuit breaker in the main panel and the GFCIs are placed at their point-of-use, such as the kitchen and bath. Many people prefer to use receptacle GFCIs inside the house and circuit breaker types for the outside power.

GFCI receptacle quality

The most common complaint concerning GFCI receptacles is their short life span. Though some do last a long time, many are bad upon installation and others last only a few years. A good number of professionals have had so much trouble with residential grade GFCIs that they no longer install them. They are made cheaply to sell in the consumer market. However, better grade GFCI receptacles are available. Look for SPEC grade, commercial grade, and hospital grade. These are much higher quality units for just a few dollars more. They are also available in more colors, including brown, ivory, white, gray and black.

Clearly label any standard receptacles that are downstream from either a multi-location protecting GFCI receptacle or a GFCI circuit breaker. GFCI receptacles are sold with special labels for this purpose.

Use a no-plug GFCI to add GFCI protection to any circuit that requires protection, but should not have outlets midstream. A hot tub, pool pump or sauna heater are a few examples.

Where to use (and not use) GFCI receptacles

So, if GFCIs are so great why don't we use them on every receptacle in the home and never have to worry about being electrocuted? Well, as you might have suspected by now, if GFCIs trip with current imbalances as low as .006 amp, they might just trip when they are not supposed to. Utility lines occasionally have noise and power spikes that come into the house and can trip a ground-fault interrupter. Tools and appliances that are especially noisy will trip a GFCI as well. Electric razors are famous for it. So you do not want to have any circuit GFCI-protected that cannot afford to be without power. Freezers, refrigerators, sump pumps, and medical equipment are a few examples of appliances you may not want on a circuit that is GFCI protected. In addition, lights, unless required by code because they are in specific areas, should never be on a GFCI circuit. If the GFCI trips, you'll be left in the dark trying to find your way out of a dark, wet bathroom.

GFCIs cannot be used for ranges, ovens, cooking appliances, clothes dryers and other appliances with grounded neutrals connected to the frame of the appliance.

There are certain locations throughout the house and residence where the NEC and common sense require that GFCIs be used. For example, every small appliance outlet along the kitchen counter (the 6-foot rule is out) and at a wet bar. Bathrooms are always wet, so all receptacles in the bathroom need GFCI protection. The overhead bathroom fan, light, or combination thereof, will need GFCI protection when they're mounted above the bath or in a shower enclosure. In addition, the unit the GFCI protects should be rated for wet locations. Outside receptacles and those in outbuildings need GFCI protection. Garages, crawlspaces, boathouses, areas around swimming pools, spas and hot tubs, and unfinished basements all need GFCI protection. Spas, hot tubs, and swimming pools get quite complicated when it comes to GFCI protection because of the obvious danger involved. Your exact situation should be looked at by a licensed master electrician.

There are exceptions to the requirements: For example, a specific piece of plug-and-cord equipment in the garage that will always be in the same location (such as a freezer that is not easily moved) that you want to operate without worrying about false tripping and losing

MULTI-LOCATION PROTECTION

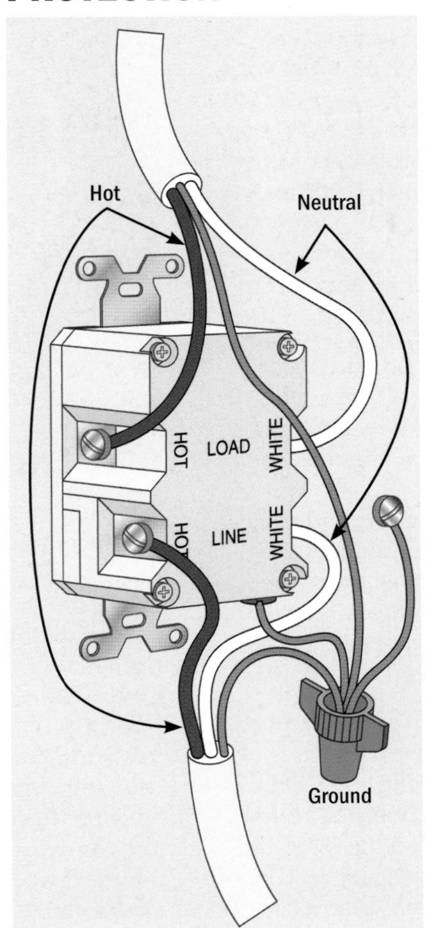

SINGLE LOCATION PROTECTION

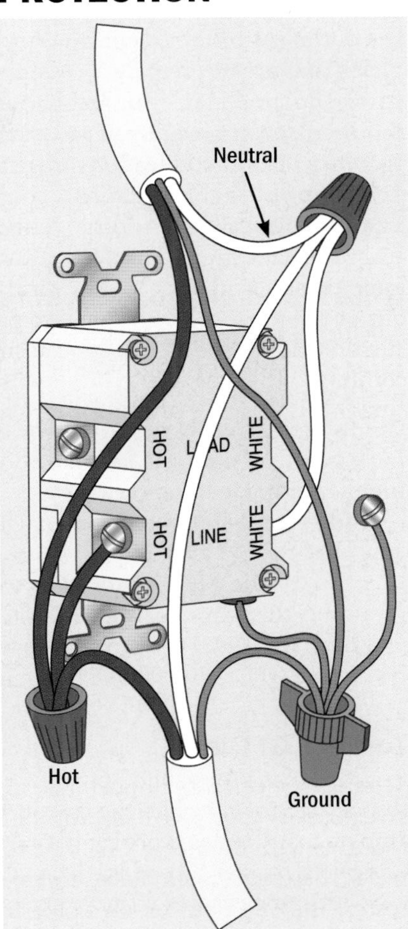

There are basically two ways to wire a GFCI outlet: for a single location or for multiple locations. With the single-location method, only the receptacle itself is protected from electric shock. In multi-location wiring configurations, the GFCI receptacle will also sense uneven electrical flow at any point in the circuit further down the line.

SAFETY TIP

You may find that when you go in to buy a GFCI receptacle, they will be out of stock of 15-amp configurations and offer you a 20-amp at no extra charge. I think they do this on purpose to keep their stock down. If this happens to you please remember you cannot put a 20-amp receptacle on a 14-gauge, 15-amp circuit. They can only be on 12-gauge, 20-amp circuits.

power. Simply install a single receptacle (See page 88) for one appliance or a duplex for two, so only the appliance or appliances in question can be plugged into the outlet. Another exception is presented by receptacles that are not readily accessible, such as outlets on garage door openers. But just because GFCIs are not required doesn't mean you can't install them. In fact, they're a very good idea for garage door openers. Why? To trip in case lightning surges come down the line. Lightning loves garage door openers.

GFCI's and old-house wiring

GFCIs are required to be installed whenever a receptacle, grounded or ungrounded, goes bad and needs replacement, if the receptacle is in a location where GFCIs are currently required. For example, if a receptacle goes bad over the kitchen counter, the replacement receptacle must be a GFCI.

Code allows GFCIs to be used without grounds. It's true that the old wiring won't have a grounding wire to attach to the GFCI, but a GFCI works whether the ground is there or not. If a GFCI feeds ungrounded outlets from its LOAD terminals, those receptacles must be labeled GFCI PROTECTED and NONGROUNDED.

Testing GFCIs

Testing is of primary importance with GFCIs since their sole purpose is to save lives. All GFCIs should be tested monthly with their own TEST button and the receptacles they protect should be tested with a plug-in GFCI tester. The TEST button on a plug-in tester puts a current imbalance on the line—the result of which should trip the GFCI. An audible click will be heard. GFCIs are not toys. Do not allow children to play with the TEST and RESET buttons just to hear them click—eventually the button will fail and the outlet will be ruined.

Besides having the push button for testing the life-protection circuitry, most GFCI testers also have light indicators to analyze the wiring attached to the unit itself. This is also an important test because sometimes a GFCI may test right even though it is wired wrong. In situations like this, the manufacturer will not warranty the unit.

TIP: Never buy a new house or even an old one without taking a GFCI tester with you to verify that the GFCI units are working properly. If you find the problem before the sale, the seller will have to fix the problem. If you find the problem after the sale, you may have to fix it yourself.

The test buttons on a GFCI breaker, a GFCI receptacle, and a GFCI tester all work differently. The tester places leakage current to the bare wire, grounding system. Therefore, if the ground is missing, the GFCI may not trip when the TEST button on the little plug-in tester is pressed. When the TEST button on the breaker is pressed, it places a leakage current from the line-side hot directly to the neutral bus. Therefore, a GFCI breaker only needs to have its pigtailed wire connected to the grounding bus for it to be tested. A GFCI receptacle places leakage current from load-side hot to line-side neutral to simulate a fault condition. Therefore, the sensor sees a portion of the current missing and opens the circuit.

When the test button opens the circuit, the circuit is opened differently when comparing the breaker to the receptacle. A receptacle GFCI will open both the neutral and line terminals. Therefore, even if the hot and neutral wires are reversed on the GFCI, it doesn't make any difference since both lines are opened. However, the GFCI breaker only opens the hot line—the neutral stays intact. If the breaker has been wired backwards, the intact line is now the hot line and current can still go to the load.

GFCI EXTENSION CORDS

Whether you are a working pro or an amateur helping someone out, you are required to be using GFCI protection the minute you plug that extension cord into someone else's outlet. It's true that OSHA or the GFCI police will probably not visit you, even though they may, but safety has precedence. Even if the job is just a simple renovation for your Aunt Bessy, where you are just adding a room or two, all personnel must be using circuitry with ground-fault protection. So what do you do if the wiring is really old, and there are no GFCIs in its electrical system? Simple: bring your own—use GFCIs that come already built into extension cords (remember, GFCIs do not need a ground to work—only a current imbalance). These come premade from manufacturers in many different varieties.

Installing GFCI Receptacles

GFCI receptacles are quite easy to install. But follow these rules:

- The outlet box the GFCI goes in must be a deep box, otherwise there will not be enough room for both the box and the wiring.
- Never install a 20-amp GFCI on a 15-amp circuit.
- Always be sure that the LINE and LOAD are not switched. LINE always connects to the incoming feeder cable. If there is more than one cable in the box then you will have to measure each cable, black to white, to determine which is the feeder.
- The LOAD terminals are always connected to any downstream receptacles that need to be ground-fault protected.
- If a second cable goes to a light or another receptacle that is not ground-fault protected, then it must splice onto the feeder cable before the feeder connects to the LINE terminals of the GFCI receptacle. To do this, attach a pigtail to the splice of both the black and white conductor splices, and use the pigtail to jump to the LINE terminals of the GFCI receptacle.

HOW TO INSTALL A SINGLE-LOCATION PROTECTION GFCI

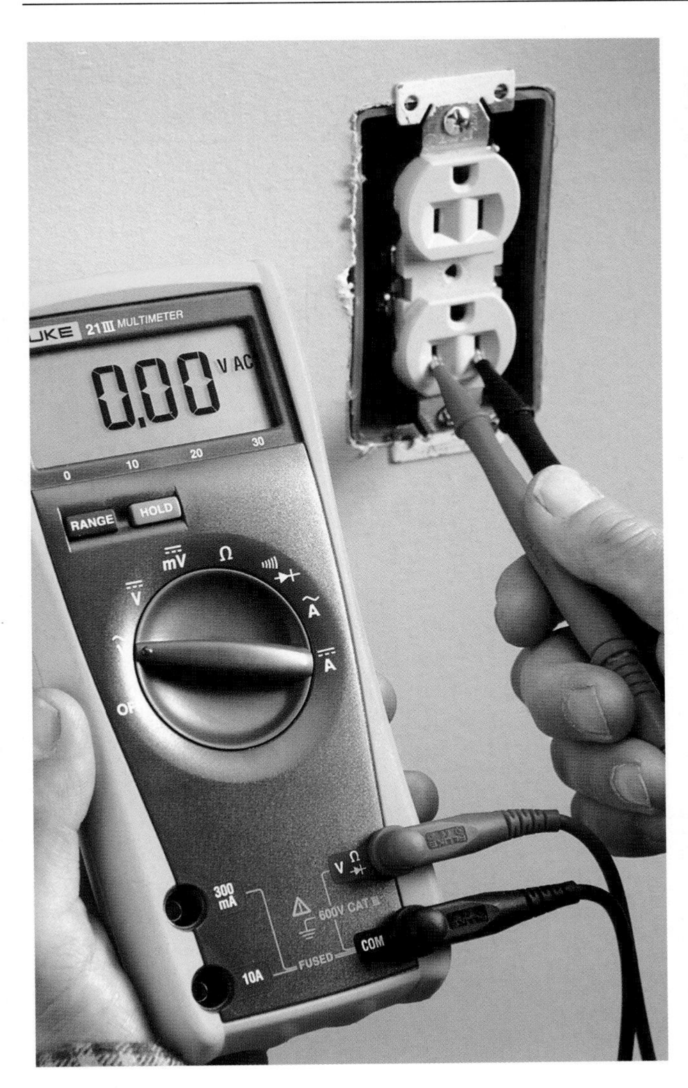

1 Remove the electricity from the circuit you are working on by turning off the breaker or pulling out the fuse. Verify loss of power with a multimeter (See pages 26 to 28).

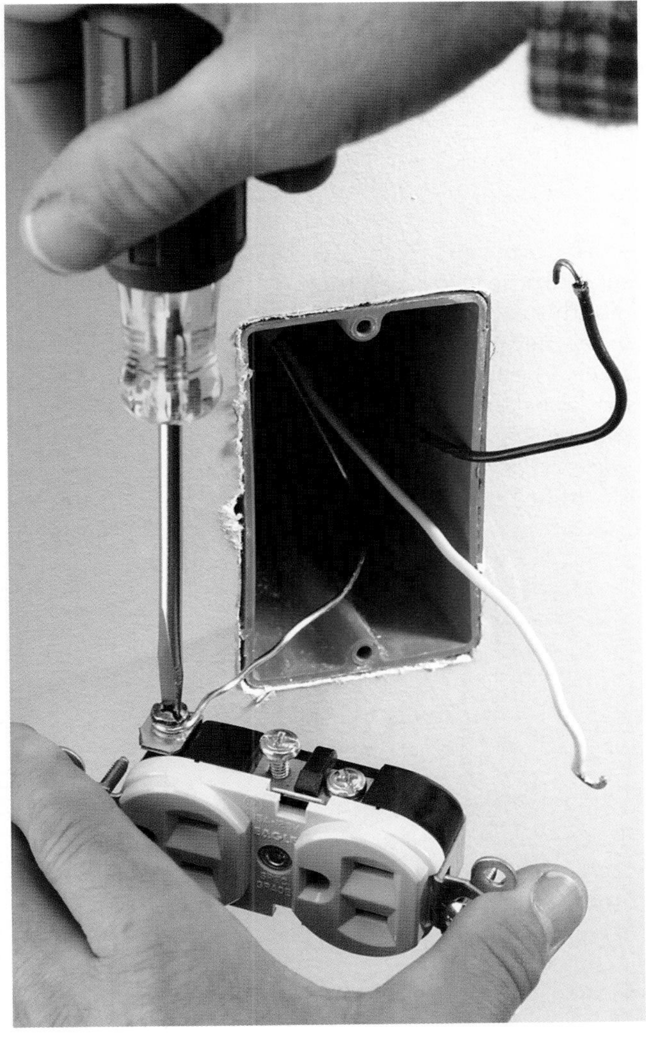

2 Remove the old receptacle. If wires are not coded, label each wire as you remove it.

HOW TO INSTALL A SINGLE-LOCATION PROTECTION GFCI (CONTINUED)

3 All attachments to the GFCI itself are done with the stripped wire end formed into a half loop then inserted over the screw and tightened down. The incoming wires are black, white, and ground. Attach the black wire to the LINE brass-colored screw. Attach the white wire to the LINE silver-colored screw. If you're installing the receptacle in a new box, bring the cable into box, cut the cable to length (around 6 to 8 inches after it comes into box), strip off the sheathing leaving around ½ in. where the sheath enters the box. Next, strip about ½ in. of insulation off each conductor and continue with the installation.

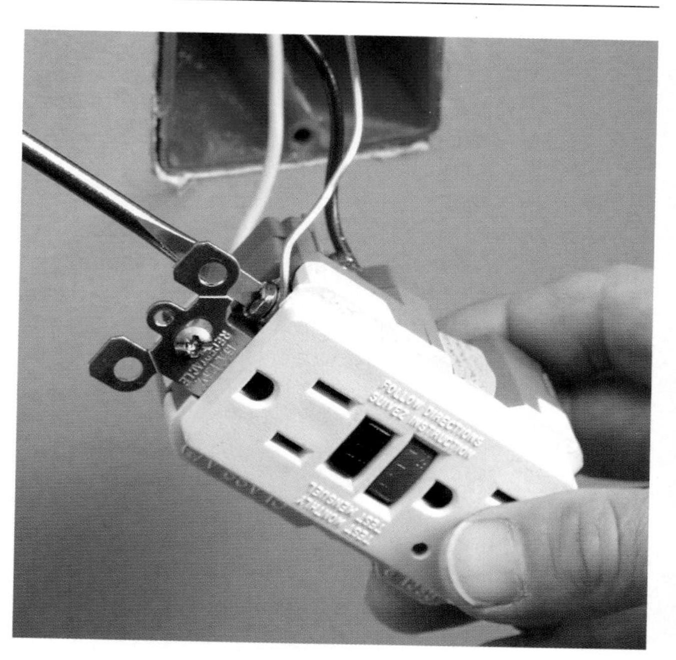

4 Attach the bare ground wire to the green grounding-screw terminal on the GFCI receptacle (See wiring diagram "Single location protection" on page 101).

5 When splicing is done, push the wires neatly back into the box with your fingers. First, prebend the wires in the direction you want them to fold into the box. If you did it right, the wires should accordion neatly back into the box in a "Z" pattern. Attach the receptacle to the box.

6 Attach the coverplate to the GFCI, turn power on and press the RESET button (the receptacle won't work until the button is pressed). Then, make sure the receptacle is good by pressing the TEST button, which should trip and remove power from the receptacle. It's also a good idea to test with a plug-in tester.

HOW TO INSTALL A MULTIPLE-LOCATION PROTECTION GFCI RECEPTACLE

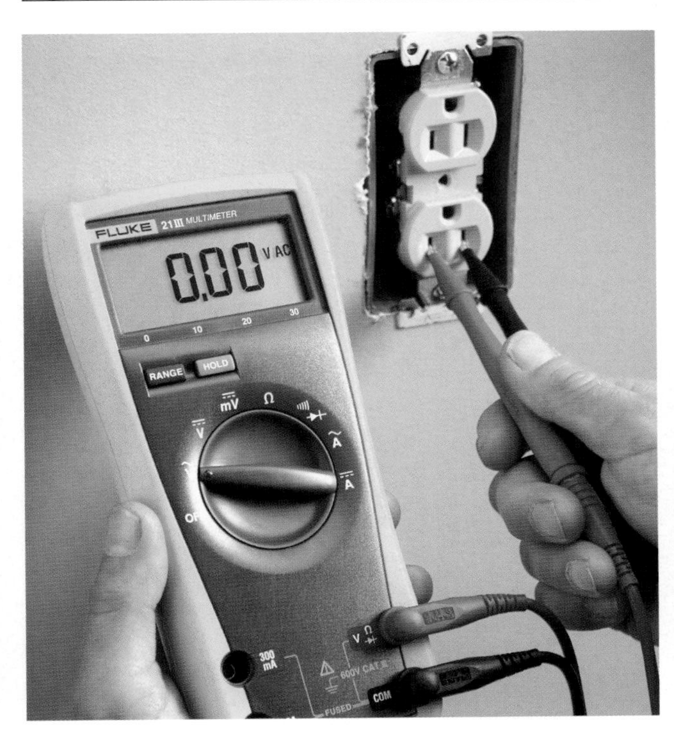

1 Remove the electricity from the circuit you are working on by turning off the breaker or pulling out the fuse. Verify loss of power with a multimeter.

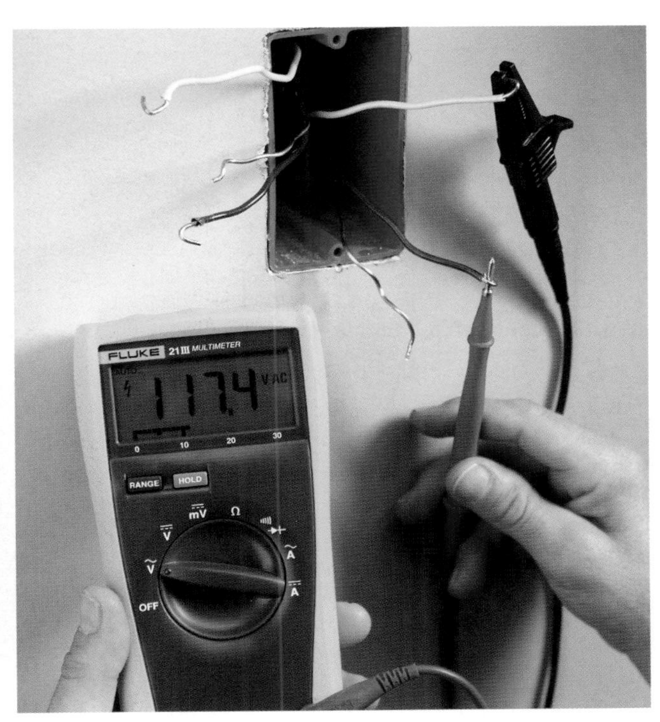

2 If you don't know already, determine which incoming wire is the feeder (LINE) and which wire is the LOAD. This is done with a multimeter. Separate the cables in the box so none of the exposed wires are touching. With power on, touch the probes of the multimeter to the black and white wire of one of the cables, and then to the wires of the other cable. The cable that reads approximately 120 volts is the LINE.

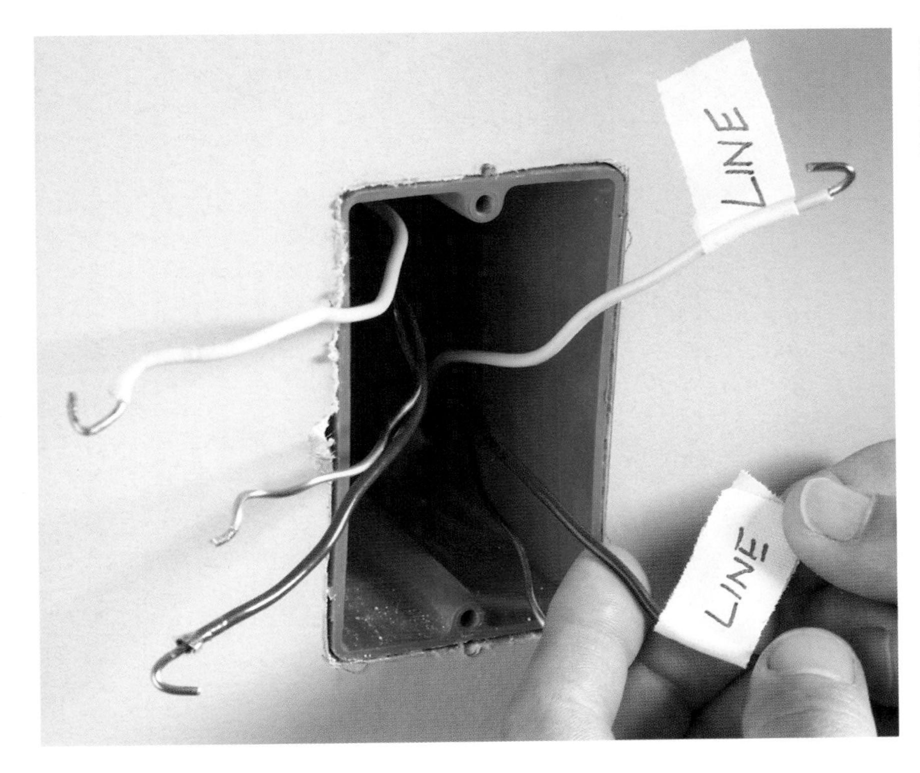

3 With the power back off, label the LINE wires so you don't mistake them for the LOAD wires. Wrap a piece of tape around each wire to make the labels.

HOW TO INSTALL A MULTIPLE-LOCATION PROTECTION GFCI RECEPTACLE (CONTINUED)

4 Attach the black LINE wire to the brass LINE terminal on the GFCI. Attach the white LINE wire to the silver-screw terminal. On most GFCI receptacles, the terminals that accept the LINE wires are open and the terminals that accept the outgoing LOAD wires are concealed by preattached tape to prevent mistakes. Once the LINE wires are attached, go ahead and remove the tape to expose the LOAD terminals.

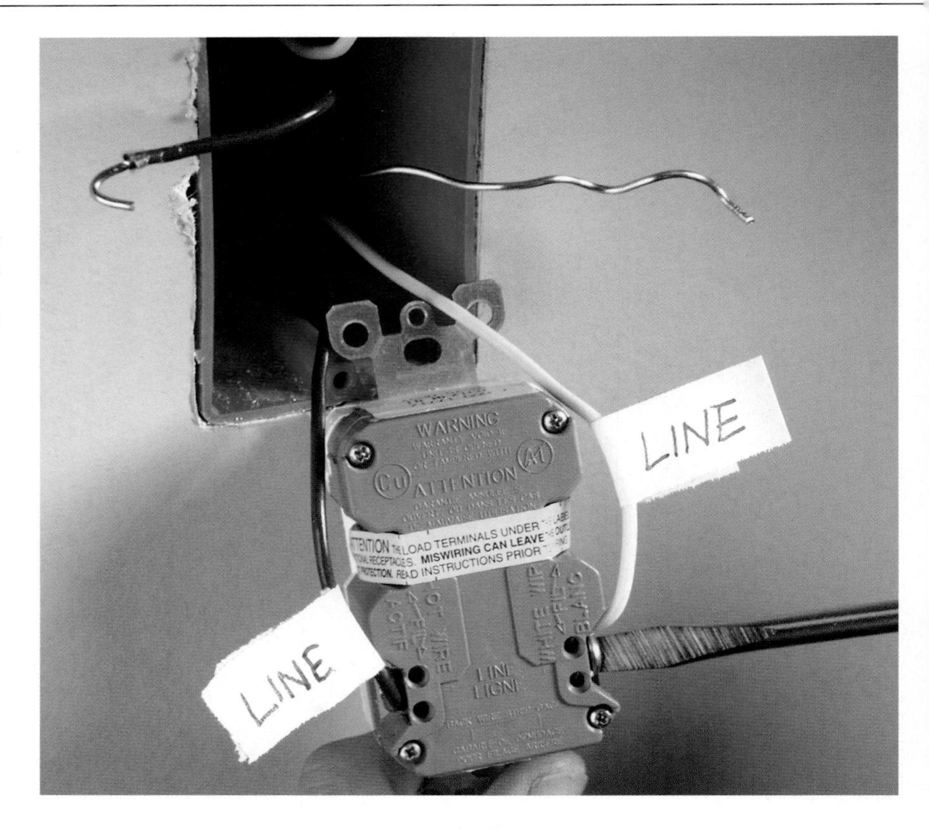

5 Attach the black LOAD wire (the one leading to the protected locations) to the brass LOAD terminal on the GFCI. Then attach the white LOAD wire to the LOAD terminal.

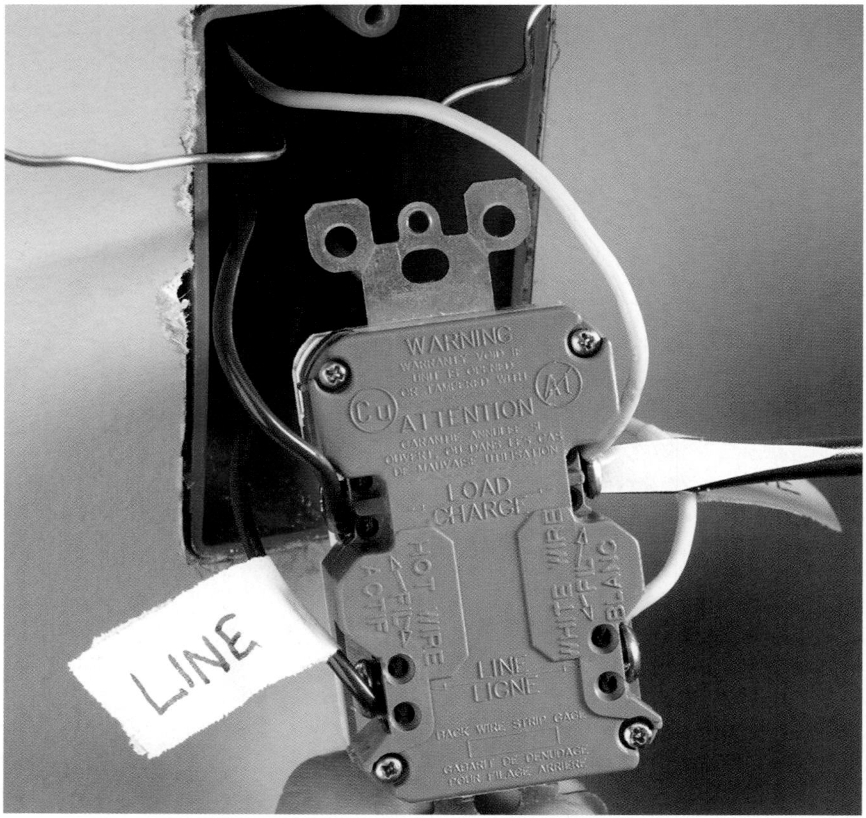

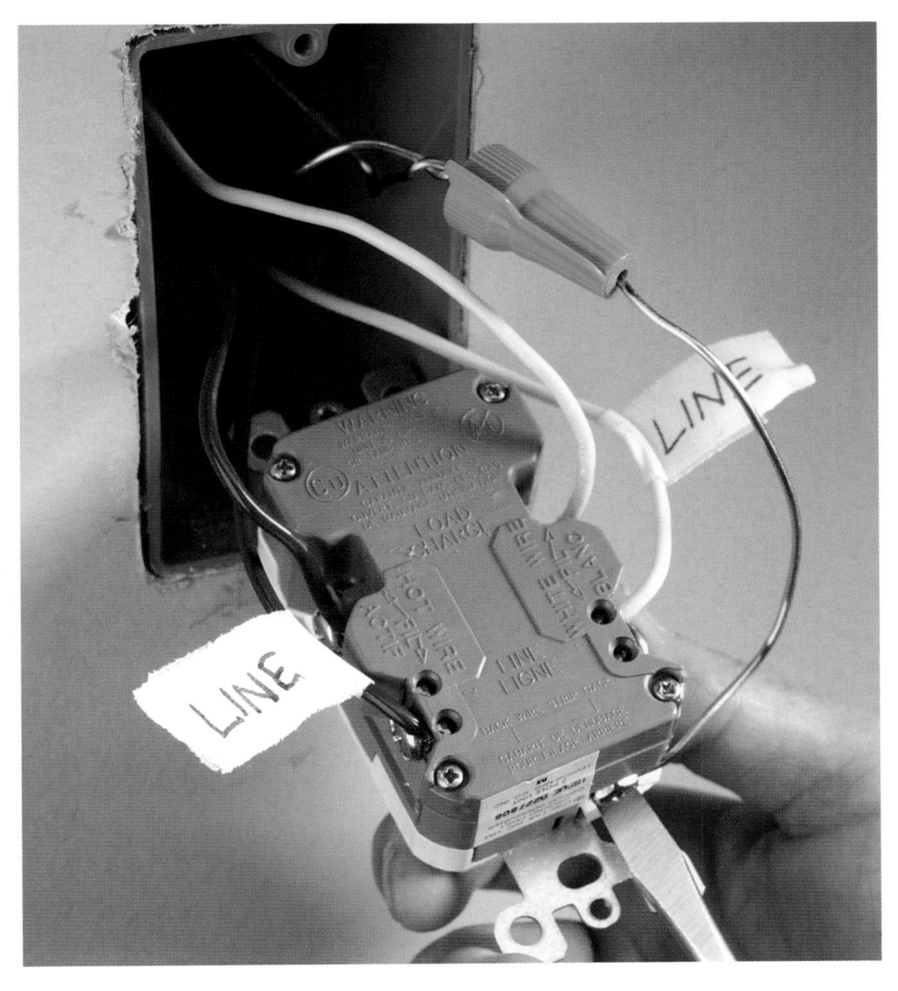

6 Splice both ground wires together with a wire connector and run a pigtail to the grounding screw on the GFCI. In the photo above, we used a grounding connector with a hole in the top so we could splice one of the bare grounds to the other, cutting one wire shorter and running the other out the top and to the screw terminal. This eliminates the need to cut a separate pigtail wire.

7 When splicing is done, push the wires neatly back into the box with your fingers. First, prebend the wires in the direction you want them to fold into the box. If you did it right, the wires should accordion neatly back into the box in a "Z" pattern. Attach the receptacle to the box.

8 Attach the coverplate to the GFCI, turn power on and press the RESET button (the receptacle won't work until the button is pressed). Then, make sure the receptacle is good by pressing the TEST button, which should trip and remove power from the receptacle. It's also a good idea to test with a plug-in tester.

HOW TO INSTALL A SINGLE-LOCATION PROTECTION GFCI IN MID-CIRCUIT

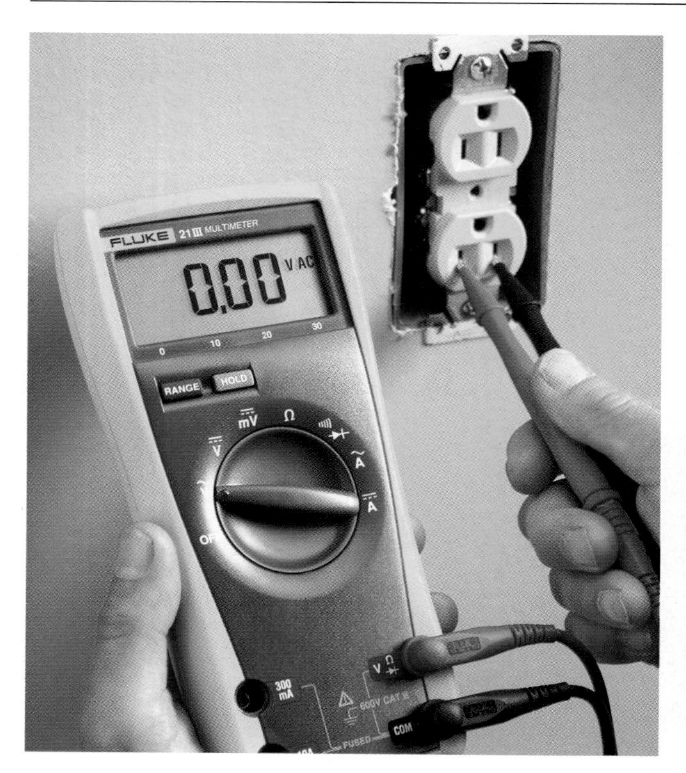

1 Remove the electricity from the circuit you are working on by turning off the breaker or pulling out the fuse. Verify loss of power with a multimeter (See pages 26 to 28).

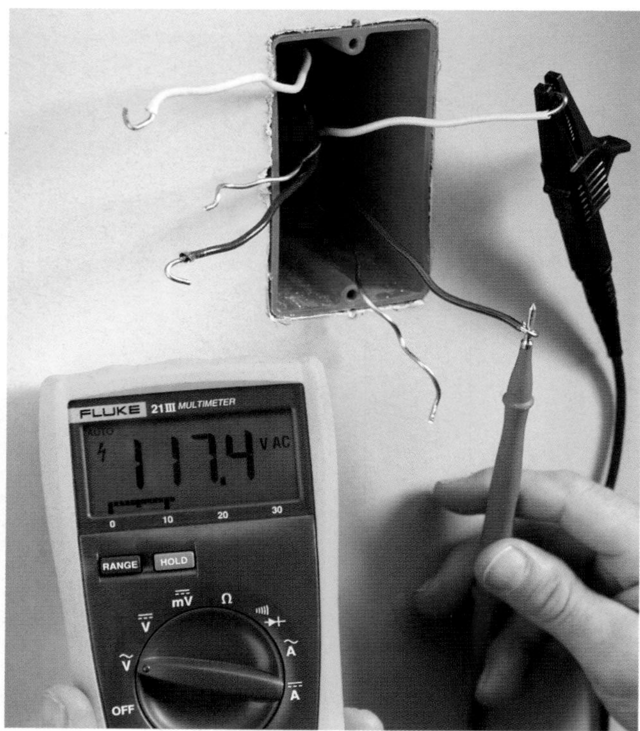

2 If you don't know already, determine which incoming wire is the feeder (LINE) and which wire is the LOAD. This is done with a multimeter. Separate the cables in the box so none of the exposed wires are touching. With power on, touch the probes of the multimeter to the black and white wire of one of the cables, and then to the wires of the other cable. The cable that reads approximately 120 volts is the LINE.

3 With the power back off, label the LINE wires so you don't mistake them for the LOAD wires. Wrap a piece of tape around each wire to make the labels.

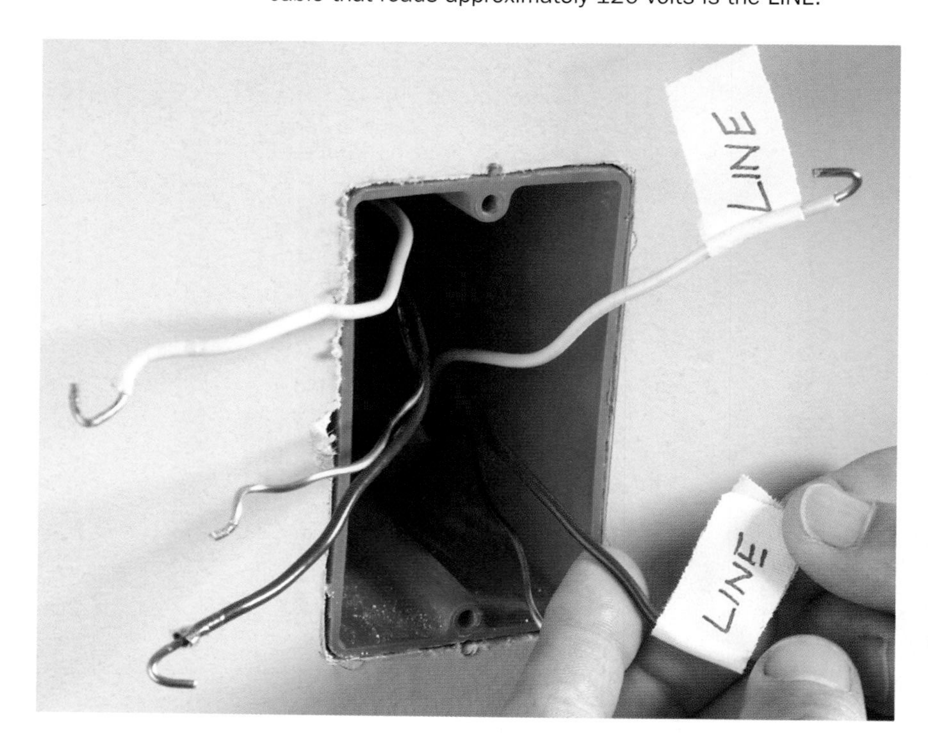

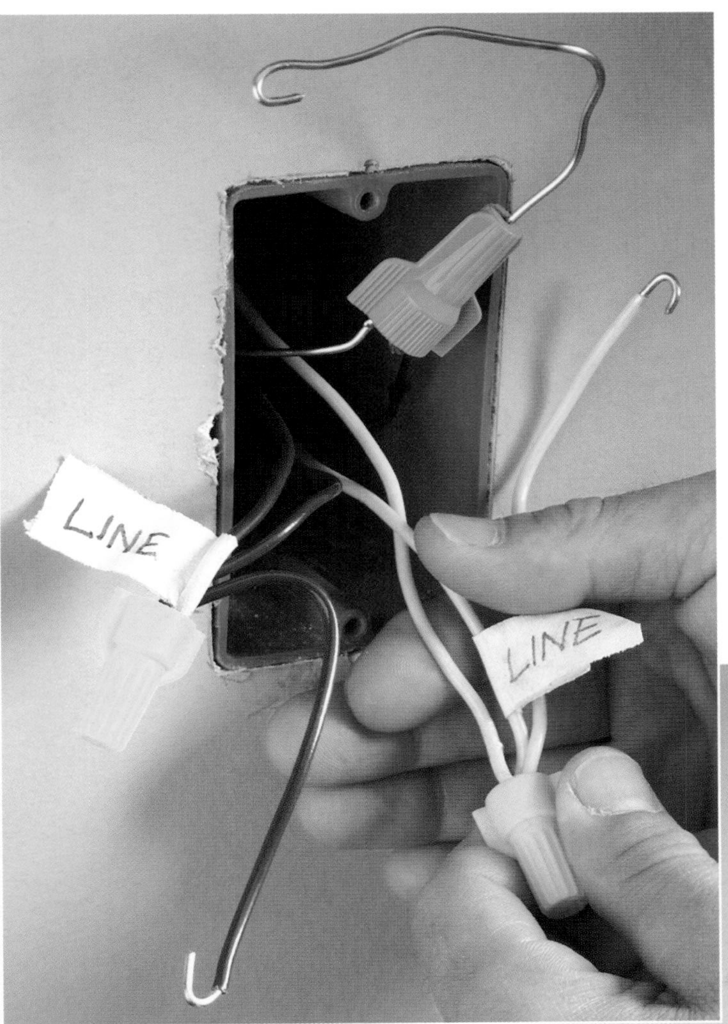

4 Splice the two black wires together along with a black pigtail. Cap the splice. Splice the two white wires together along with a white pigtail. Cap the splice.

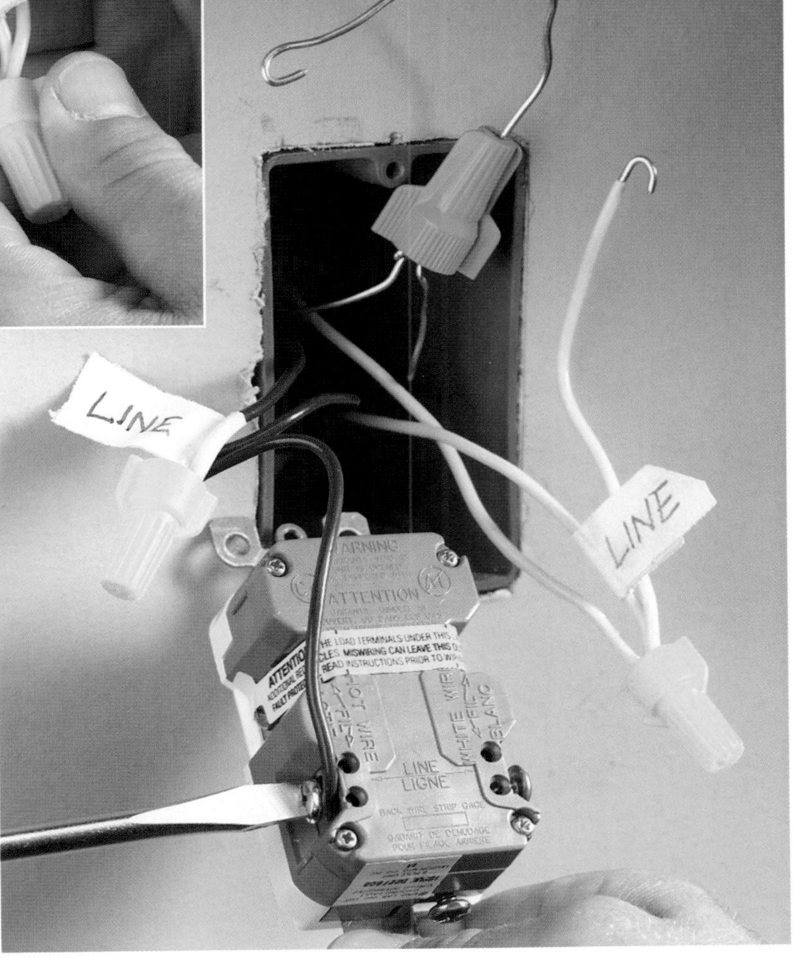

5 Connect the black pigtail to the LINE terminal brass-colored screw that says "hot" or "black."

HOW TO INSTALL A SINGLE-LOCATION PROTECTION GFCI IN MID-CIRCUIT (CONTINUED)

6 Attach the white pigtail to the silver-colored LINE screw that says "white" or "neutral."

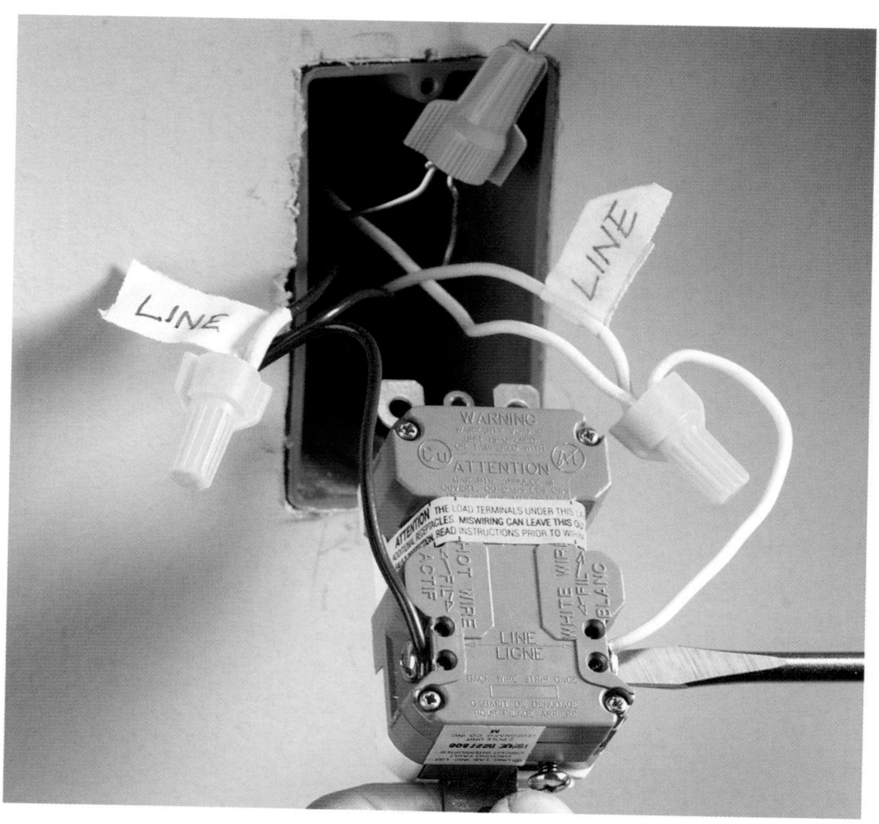

7 When splicing is done, push the wires neatly back into the box with your fingers. First, prebend the wires in the direction you want them to fold into the box. If you did it right, the wires should accordion neatly back into the box in a "Z" pattern. Attach the receptacle to the box.

8 Attach the coverplate to the GFCI, turn power on and press the RESET button (the receptacle won't work until the button is pressed). Then, make sure the receptacle is good by pressing the TEST button, which should trip and remove power from the receptacle. It's also a good idea to test with a plug-in tester.

HOME WIRING PROJECTS

Armed with a clear understanding of his electrical system and the tools and materials used to install and maintain it, there are few home wiring projects that the ambitious home handyman will shy away from. Some are quick and easy, others are more complex and can be disruptive to your day-to-day living if not managed properly. In either case, the project should begin with a plan and a permit. Do some investigative work so you know exactly what you're getting into: What kind of wires and boxes are used in the existing circuit you plan to work on? What is the current load on that circuit? Does your main service panel have the space and capacity for you to add new circuits? The first part of this book is filled with information you'll need in order to know which questions to ask and what the answers mean. Read it.

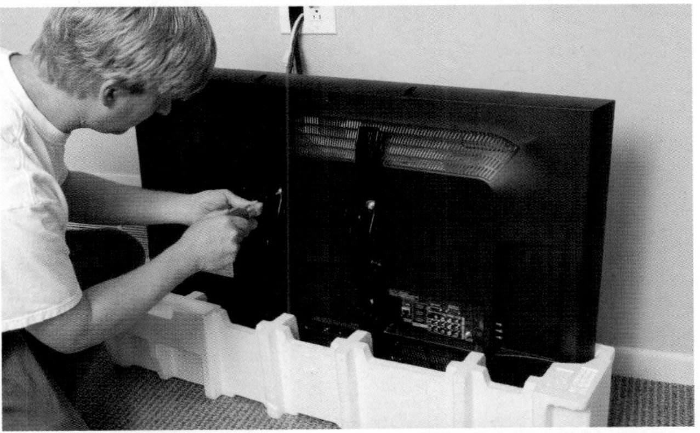

Once you have your plan in place, pay a visit to your local building department. Any project that involves making changes to your electrical system will require a permit and an inspection. The inspector will need to know all about your existing system, as well as how you plan to execute your project: What type and size wire will you use? Where will the connections be made? What other loads are on the circuit currently? Essentially, he needs to be assured that you know what you're doing before he will issue a permit. And even then he may require that you use a licensed electrician to make the final hookups.

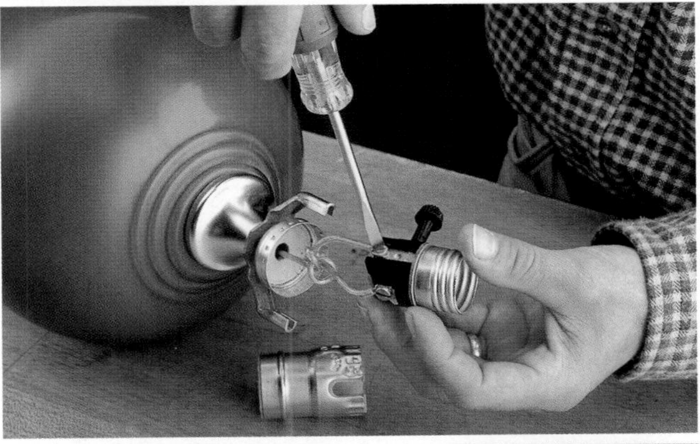

The typical wiring project sequence is to run new cable (if needed), then install and hook up the load fixtures. The connections should not be made at the power source until the work has been inspected and approved. And make sure to leave the wiring as accessible as possible so the inspector can see what you've done.

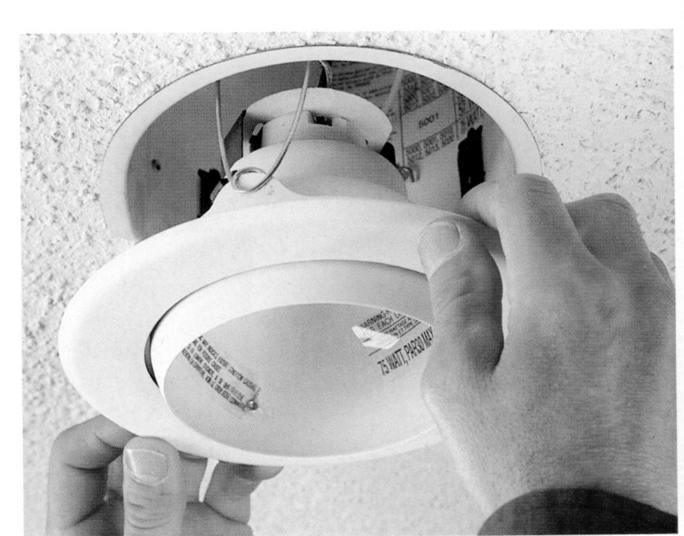

Getting Power to your Project

Most home wiring projects will require you to run new cable at some point. Whether you're adding an entire new circuit, adding a receptacle or switch to an existing circuit or replacing the cable in an existing circuit, you'll need to find a way to route the new wires through your home, preferably without removing all the wall surfaces in the work area. Running cable can be a tricky, frustrating endeavor but there are a few tricks that can help. Above all, however, make sure that the new cable is installed safely and conforms to all wiring codes.

TIPS FOR RUNNING CABLE

INSTALL PROTECTOR PLATES

A metal protector plate must be installed over each spot where there isn't at least 1¼ in. of wood protecting the cable from damage by nails or screws.

MAKE SMOOTH TURNS

Make a smooth curve when bending cable. Do not make sharp corners, which can crimp and damage the wires.

CUT A BASEBOARD CHANNEL

Routing cable behind baseboard and door casing is a simple method for adding new cable within a finished room. Carefully remove the baseboard or casing so it can be re-installed. Remove enough wall surface behind the trim pieces so you can work, but make sure the trim will cover the work area. You won't need to patch holes in the wall surfaces that are covered by trim pieces. Create a route for the cable, cutting notches in the wall studs that the cable must cross. Once the cable is in place, cover each notch with a metal protective plate. Re-install the trim pieces. You may need to fill gaps between the trim pieces and framing members caused by wall surface removal, using scrap lumber spacers.

GAINING ACCESS

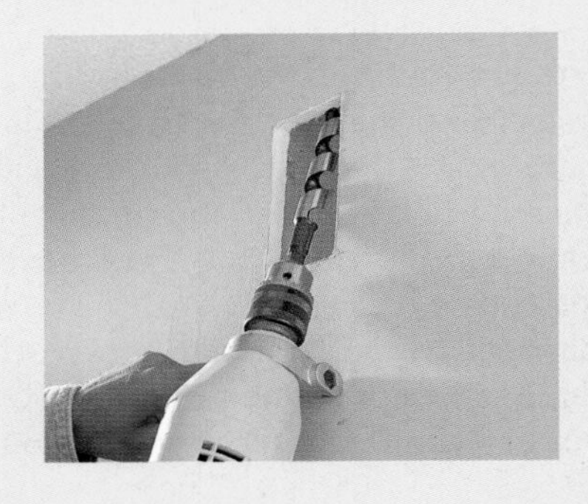

MAKE A CUTOUT FOR WALL-TO-CEILING ACCESS

To route cable from one finished room to the room above, cut a 3 × 5-in. opening in the wall surface near the ceiling. Drill through the top plate using a long auger bit at as steep an angle as possible. If you need to route the cable into the ceiling, cut another 3 × 5 in. opening in the ceiling near the wall. You may need to drill another hole to make a path for the cable into the joist cavity. Patch the wall and ceiling with wallboard.

CREATING WALL-TO-FLOOR ACCESS

To route cable from one finished room to the room below, cut a 3 × 5-in. hole in the wall surface near the floor, behind the baseboard if possible. Drill through the bottom plate using a long auger bit at as steep an angle as possible.

FISH TAPES

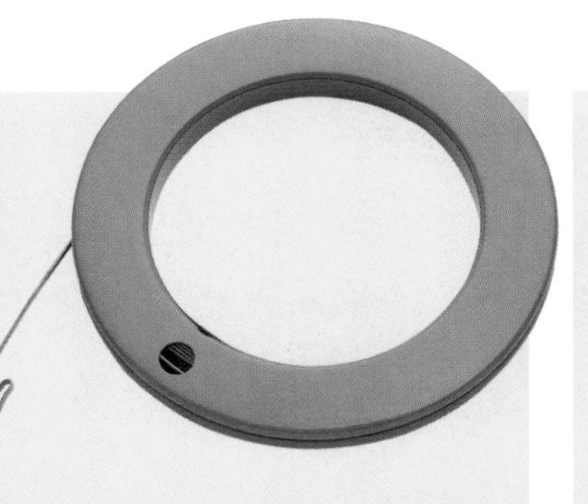

A fish tape is a coil of semi-rigid tempered steel that's used to pull cable through walls, floors and ceilings. The end of the tape is inserted into an opening then guided through the interior of a wall, floor or ceiling until the end reaches the destination (or a manageable point en route to the destination). This is not as easy as it sounds: although the tape, when unrolled, is semi-rigid it can still bend easily and has a tendency to try and revert to a coil. Once the tape has been run from point to point, attach the cable you're running to the end (See photos, below) then retract the tape to pull the cable.

THE TRADITIONAL WAY TO HOOK UP A FISH TAPE

Remove about 3 in. of sheathing from the end of the cable. Insert the wires through the hook at the end of the fish tape, then bend them back onto the cable. Begin wrapping electrical tape on the fish tape above the hook (right photo). Continue wrapping electrical tape tightly around the fish tape and wires and onto at least 2 in. of cable past the connection (left photo). Make the joint as thin and smooth as you can.

A SLICK OPTION FOR HOOKING UP A FISH TAPE

Cut the looped end of the tape off (the loops catch in wall cavities and increase the thickness of the connection). Insert the cut end of the tape directly into the cable sheathing. Bind the tape to the cable with electrical tape.

DRILLING FROM ABOVE A WALL

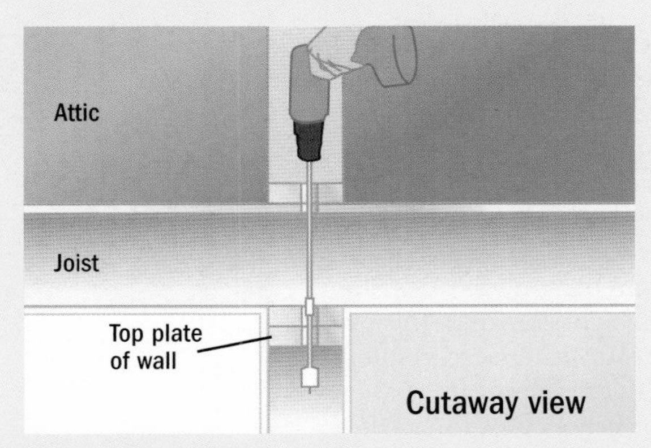

Routing cable through a wall is much easier if you have access to the attic space above the wall. Measure carefully from a structural member common to both levels to determine where to drill. This same method is used when drilling up into the wall cavity from the basement below the wall.

ROUTING CABLE THROUGH OFFSET WALLS

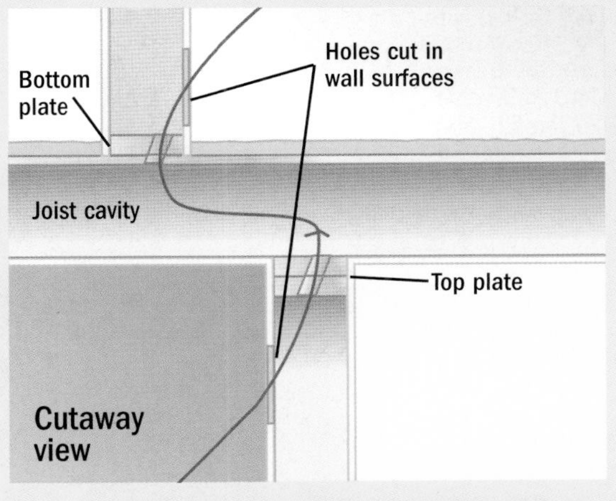

Routing cable through offset walls in finished rooms is difficult. You will need two fish tapes and a helper. Cut holes in appropriate wall surfaces and drill holes in the bottom and top plates of the walls. Have your helper run one fish tape down through the holes in the room above. Push the other fish tape up through the holes in the lower room and catch the first fish tape with the hook on yours. Pull your fish tape until the hook from the other fish tape emerges from the holes. Attach cable to the fish tape and have your helper pull it to the room above.

Replacing a Ceiling Light

Replacing an out-of-date or poorly functioning ceiling light is a relatively simple home wiring job. In general, light fixtures that mount directly to the ceiling are easier to remove and replace than hanging fixtures like the light shown in this project. In either case, though, it's very important that the ceiling box be attached securely and equipped to support the weight of the fixture (See pages 59 to 63). You'll also need to inspect the wiring on the old fixture to determine if the power feed is coming to the light first, then to the switch, or if it's the other way around (See the illustrations at the bottom of this page).

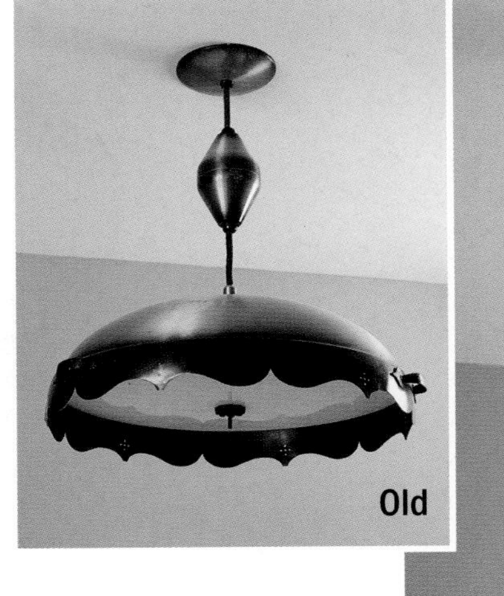

Replacing an old or troublesome ceiling light fixture is a quick and easy way to make a room look fresh and updated.

New

IDENTIFY THE ORIGINAL WIRING CONFIGURATION

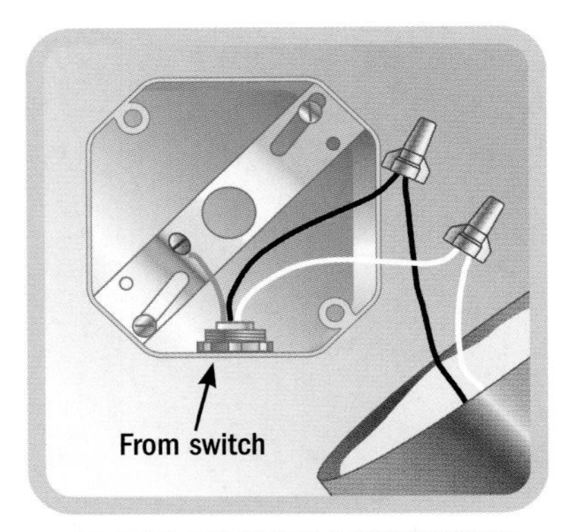

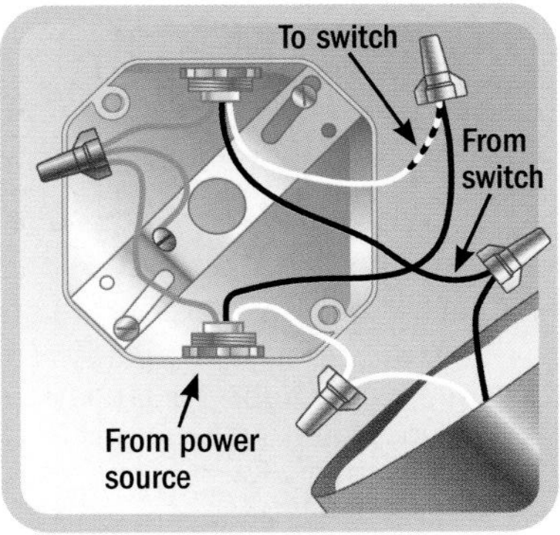

Before removing the original ceiling light, inspect the wiring to find out if the fixture is wired to receive power directly from the power source (top illustration) or if the power goes to the switch box first (bottom illustration). If there are multiple cables entering the light fixture box, it probably means that the current bypasses the fixture when it enters the box and heads directly to the switch via a tagged white wire. If the switch is turned on, the current goes through the switch and returns back to the light fixture via the black wire. In this situation, connect the black wire from the new light fixture to the black wire that's paired with the tagged white wire (called a switch loop). The black (hot) lead from the power source is connected to the tagged wire, and the white neutral from the source is connected to the white wire on the fixture.

WIRING DIAGRAM CEILING LIGHT

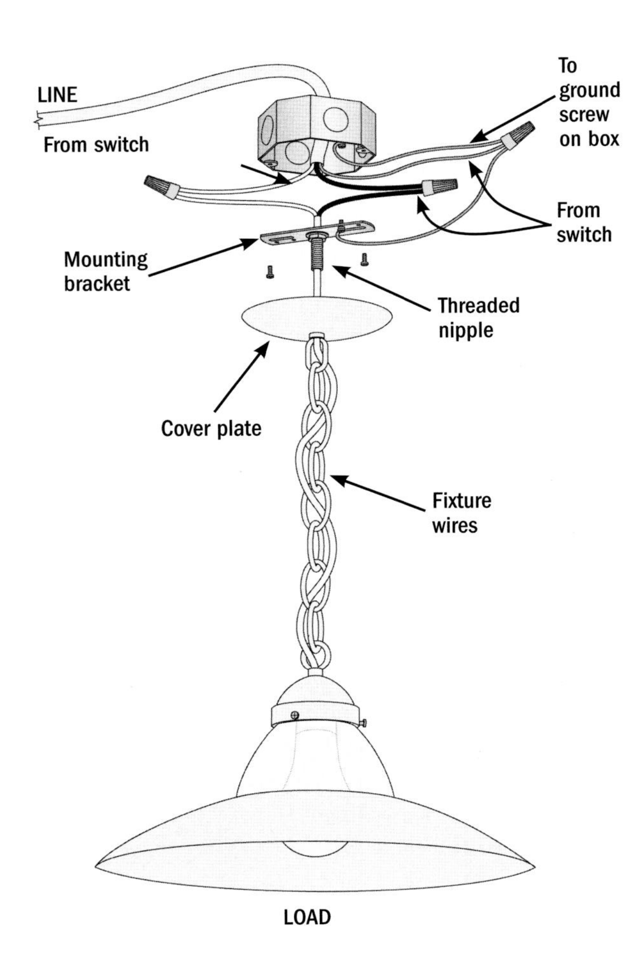

HOW TO REPLACE A CEILING LIGHT

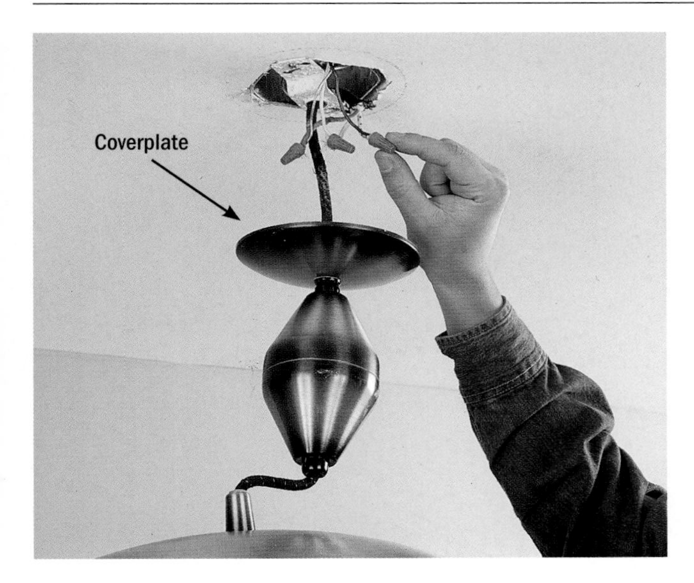

1 Shut off power to the electrical circuit at the main service panel. Remove diffusers, shades and bulbs to provide access to the coverplate of the old light fixture. Remove the coverplate (either by removing mounting screws or loosening the retaining nut that's attached to a threaded nipple that projects from the mounting strap on the electrical box in the ceiling). Gently draw the fixture away from the box to expose the wire connectors. Test with a multimeter to make sure there is no current flowing to the fixture.

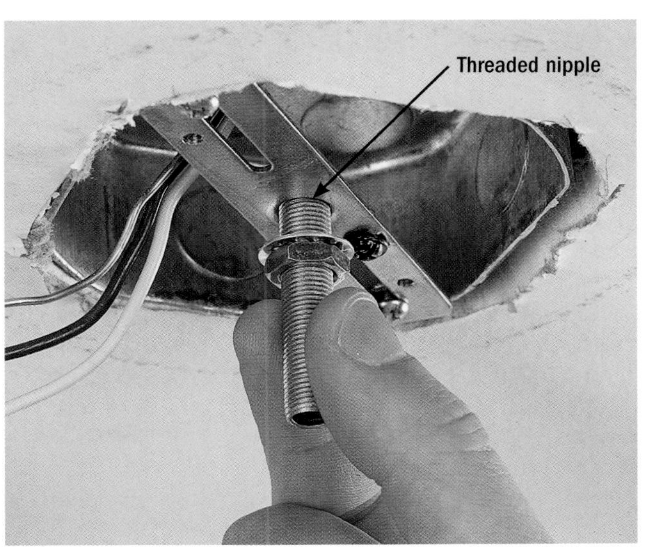

2 Disconnect the wires and ground, if any—older homes may not have a ground. If supply wires are not color coded, label the hot lead by wrapping it with a small piece of electrical tape. Attach the mounting bracket provided with your new light to the electrical box using the box mounting screws. Make sure the existing box is large enough to house the new light fixture wiring. Also attach the threaded nipple into the threaded hole in the mounting bracket.

3 Assemble the new fixture as required. Most light fixtures, especially more complex units intended for the kitchen, require a significant amount of assembly and wire threading before they can be hooked up. Assemble the new unit as completely as you can (it's much easier to do this now than after it's partially hanging from the ceiling) but don't install globes, diffusers or bulbs yet.

4 With a helper supporting heavier fixtures, thread the fixture wires up through the nipple in the mounting bracket, then secure the lock washer or retaining nut that secures the fixture to the ceiling. Adjust any chains or cables as directed to set the height of pendant-style fixtures, then trim the wires back so 6 to 8 in. are free in the electrical box. Strip insulation at the ends to expose ½ in. of bare wire, then make hot, neutral and ground connections with wire connectors as directed. Attach the coverplate to the electrical box, then secure the new coverplate. Install bulbs and diffusers. Turn power on and test.

Now available in a wider range of design styles, fluorescent light fixtures have made their way from basements and garages into the main living areas of the home.

Installing a Fluorescent Light Fixture

Once relegated to basements, garages and commercial buildings, fluorescent light fixtures are becoming increasingly popular in all areas of the home. The main reason is efficiency: fluorescent bulbs are much more economical than incandescent bulbs, which convert a lot of electricity into wasted and unwanted heat. The drawbacks to fluorescent fixtures have typically been the cool, unnatural quality of the light they emit, the low buzz that comes from the ballast (especially older ballasts) and the lack of design options. The light quality issue can be addressed, however, by choosing natural light (sometimes called "daylight") bulbs. They cost a bit more, but are a better choice for living spaces. The buzzing can usually be eliminated (or at least reduced) by changing the ballast. The aesthetic issues are improving as the number of troffer and diffuser options has expanded. Most fixtures for the home are either 2 ft. or 4 ft. long.

Even though the wiring connections for a fluorescent light fixture are made in the wireway inside the fixture body, most codes will still require that the power cable enters the fixture from a ceiling outlet box installed at the fixture location (See page 60). On small fluorescent fixtures, you may need to make the wire connections in the outlet box to have enough room.

FLUORESCENT LIGHTS IN SUSPENDED CEILINGS

A 4-ft.-long fluorescent light fixture fits perfectly into a 2 × 4-ft. panel opening in a suspended ceiling. The lightweight fixture can be supported by the gridwork for the ceiling if the cross-tees of the grid are well supported, but it's always a good idea to employ supplementary support (most often a couple of wires attached to the ceiling joists). After the fixture is installed, a 2 × 4-ft. diffuser panel is inserted into the grid in place of a ceiling panel.

HOW TO INSTALL A FLUORESCENT LIGHT FIXTURE

1 Turn power off. Run the feed cable from the switch through a hole in the ceiling at the ceiling outlet box location (try to keep the hole narrower than the fixture). Thread the cable through a knockout in the top of the fixture and a cable clamp (don't fully tighten the clamp yet). Attach the fixture to the ceiling by driving screws up through the top of the unit and into ceilings joists (you can use toggle bolts or molly bolts, but always try to plan the fixture position so you can attach it directly to the ceiling joists).

2 Once the fixture body is secured to the ceiling, go ahead and tighten the cable clamp. Make sure you have enough cable entering the fixture to make your connections. Strip ½ in. of insulation from each of the conductors.

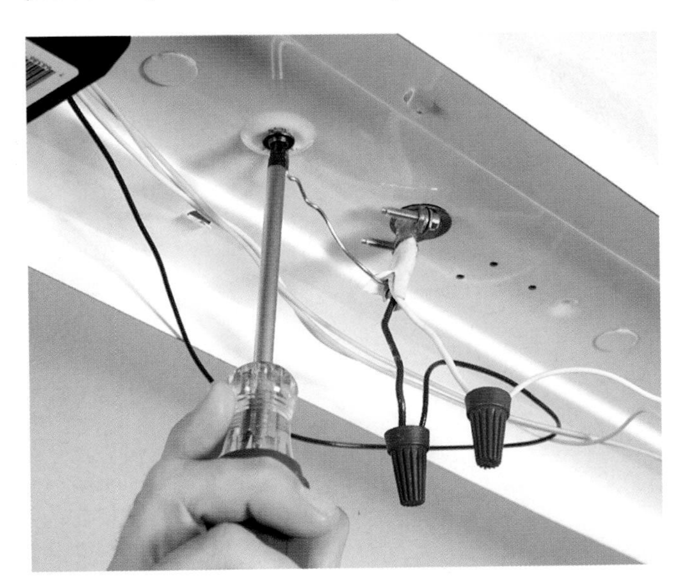

3 Make the wire connections, twisting the white neutral together with the white fixture wire and the black hot together with the black fixture wire. Make a loop in the end of the bare copper ground and attach it to the grounding screw on the fixture body.

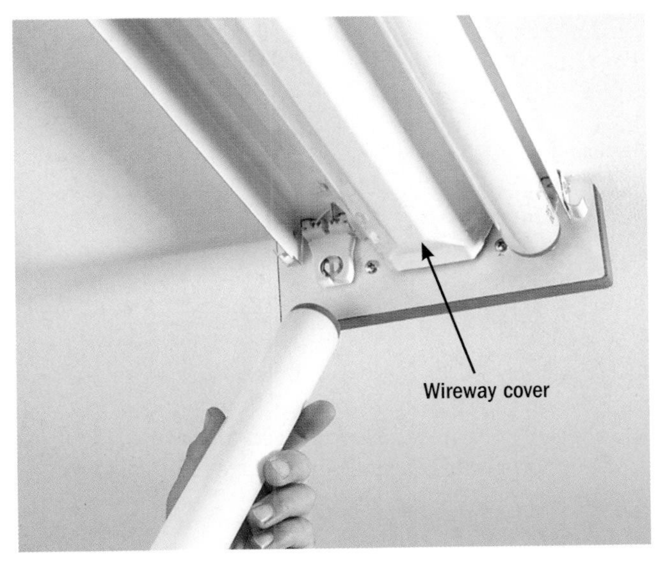

4 Attach the wireway cover to the fixture according to the manufacturer's instructions. Complete any other assembly requirements (the model above came equipped with decorative oak end panels that needed to be attached). Install fluorescent light bulbs, then turn on the power and test. On models with concealed bulbs, install the diffuser or lens.

Installing Recessed (Canister) Lights

Recessed lights, commonly called "canister lights," are most often installed in series to provide directed task lighting in much the same manner as track lighting. They also can be installed in areas where clearance is needed near the ceiling (for example, near floor-to-ceiling bookcases with swinging upper cabinet doors) or anywhere you want to give a more contemporary sense to the room.

If you're installing recessed lights over a kitchen countertop, the standard rule is to space them 18 in. apart, directly above the front edge of the countertop. Before purchasing the fixtures, make sure you have enough depth in the ceiling cavity to accommodate the canisters (if the depth is limited, look for lights with low-profile housings). If the ceiling above is insulated, the best bet is to buy lights with housings that are rated for insulation contact (See next page). And make sure the units you buy have trim kits that meet your design needs.

Recessed lights cast a cone of light downward, making them a popular choice for task lighting and display lighting. Trim kits with a pivoting, parabolic "eye" allow you to direct the light with greater accuracy.

WIRING DIAGRAM: CANISTER LIGHTS IN SERIES

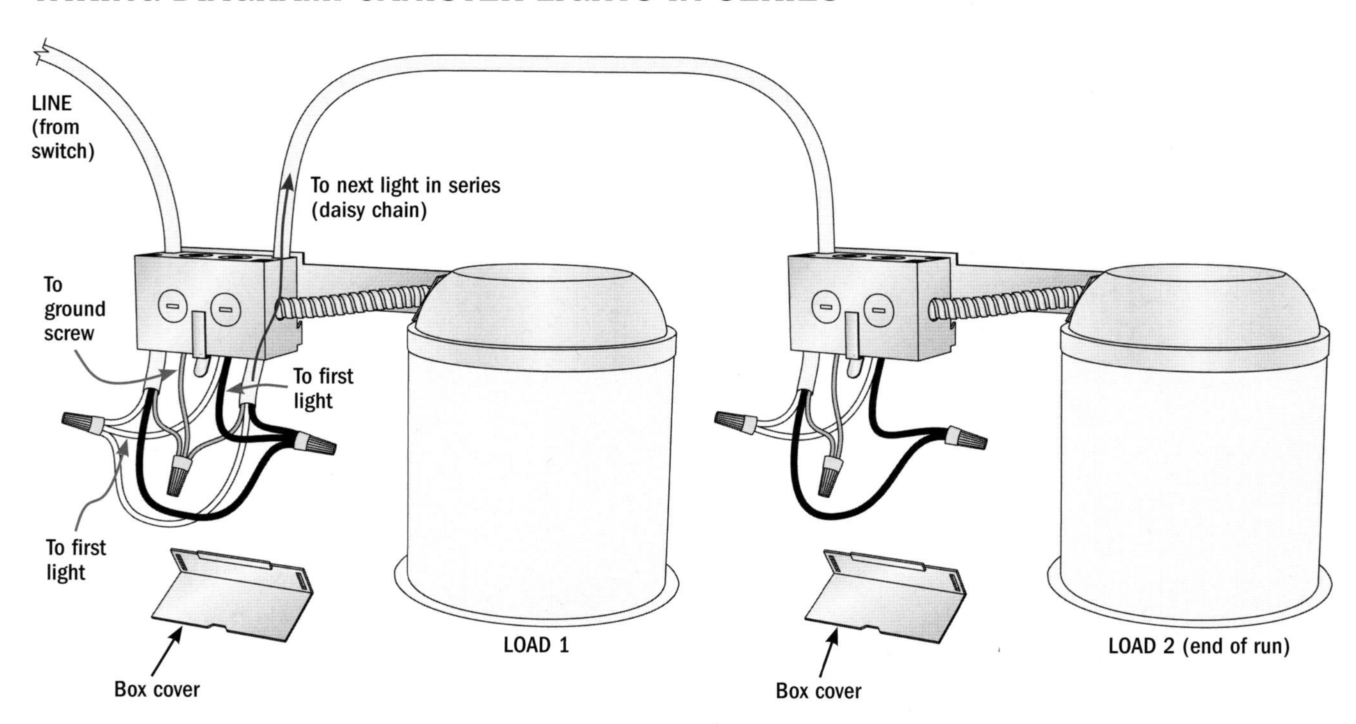

Canister lights wired in series usually are installed so all lights in the area are controlled by the same switch. From the switch, run cable (14/2 NM w/ground in most cases) to the fixture box for the first light in the series. Also run cable from the second light in the series to the first box. Twist the black leads from both cables together, along with the black fixture wire. Do the same with the white wires. Also twist a ground pigtail with the incoming and outgoing grounds, then run the pigtail to the ground screw on the metal fixture box. Wire each intermittent light in this manner until you reach the end of the run, where you simply connect black to black and white to white, then ground to the box.

INSULATION CONTACT (I.C.) RATINGS

Non-I.C.-rated (or "T" type) canister lights need at least 3 in. of free air space on all sides, or heat buildup will cause the fixture to shut off. Fiberglass insulation can simply be cut back, but if you have loose insulation you'll need to create an insulation dam by tacking a board into the joist cavity on each side of the unit.

I.C.-rated (or "ICT" type) canister lights have an internal thermal protection feature so you can insulate up and around the light fixture canister without creating heat buildup issues.

HOW TO A INSTALL A RECESSED (CANISTER) LIGHT FIXTURE WITH ACCESS FROM ABOVE

1 If the ceiling joists in the installation area are accessible from above (as in an attic), make the cutout in the ceiling for the light then position the unit over the hole and attach it to the joists with the accompanying support braces. When working on uncovered ceiling joists, lay a large plywood scrap across the joists to create a kneeling surface and prevent you from stepping or falling through the ceiling.

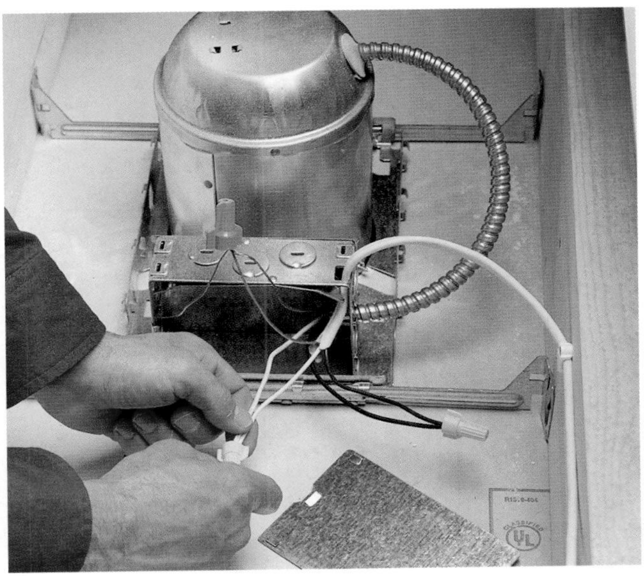

2 Run the feeder cable into the fixture box, securing it with a cable clamp. Make sure the installation of the circuit cable conforms to your local codes: in many cases, conduit or armored cable are required for attic installations. Make the wiring hookups (See previous page) then install the trim kit as shown in Step 4, next page.

HOW TO RETROFIT A RECESSED (CANISTER) LIGHT FIXTURE

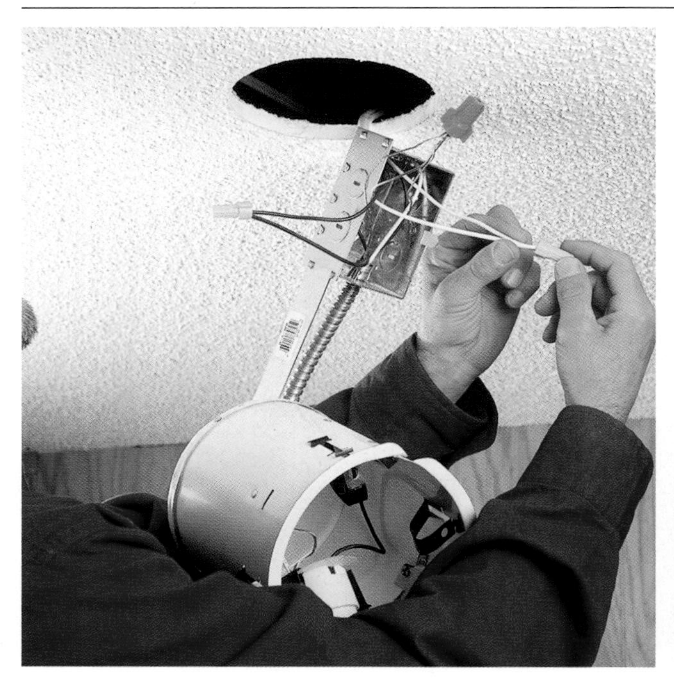

1 If you are unable to access the ceiling joists from above (as shown on the previous page), you'll need to retrofit the canister lights into the ceiling. Before installing the lights, fish power supply cable from the switch to the joist cavity above the location for the first canister. With the power off, make the wiring connections as shown on page 118.

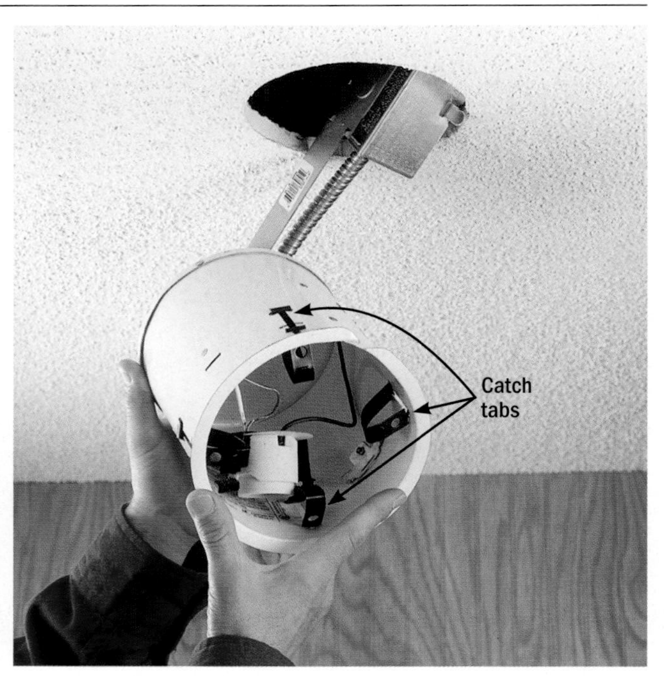

2 Once the connections are made, attach the cover to the fixture box then insert the box up through the cutout in the ceiling. Make sure the catch tabs inside the canister are oriented so they can be pressed through the canister to support the unit after it is in place.

3 With the canister flanges flush against the ceiling, press the catch tabs through the tab slots to force the tabs down against the top surface of the ceiling, locking the canister in place.

4 Mount the trim kit—most are suspended with springs from slots inside the canister. Screw a light bulb into the socket in the canister light and test to make sure the light functions.

Installing track lighting is a very easy home wiring project that brings adjustable task and display lighting into any room. Track light kits are installed frequently in kitchens above countertops and islands, as well as in living areas to project light onto a favorite room feature or artwork.

Installing Track Lighting

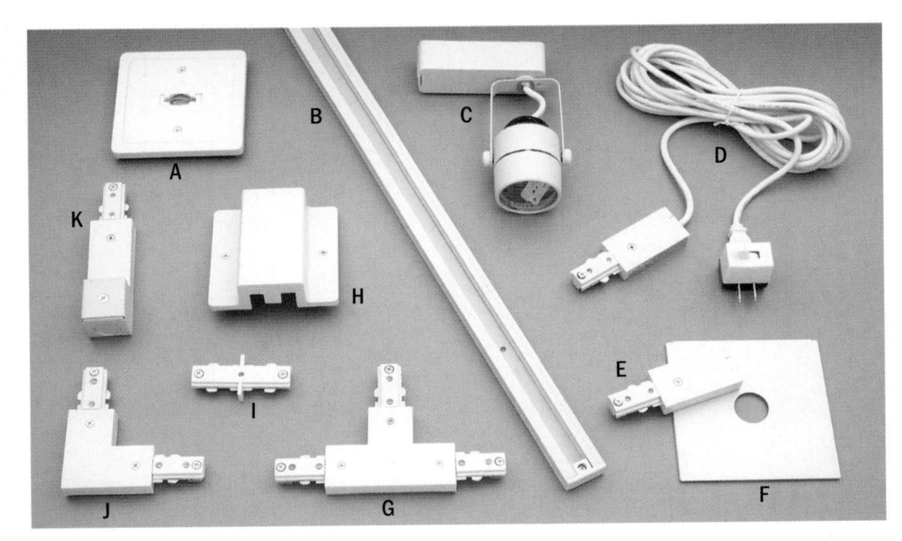

Parts of a track lighting system include: (A) "Monopoint" mounting plate for installing a single pivoting fixture without track; (B) track section; (C) track light fixture with track head; (D) track end with plug-in cord to bring power to track from wall receptacle—may not be compatible with some systems; (E) end connector; (F) mounting plate; (G) "T" connector; (H) floating feed connector; (I) straight connector; (J) "L" connector; (K) track end with conduit knockout.

Track lighting is a perfect solution if you want to introduce task or display lighting into a room with very little mess and fuss. The tracks work like trolley tracks, carrying current through conductors inside each track section so you can adjust the track fixtures simply by removing them then snapping and twisting them back into a new location on the tracks. The parts are sold separately and as kits in a variety of colors and styles. Some can even be powered from a wall receptacle, but the preferred installation method is to hard-wire a 120-volt feeder line from a wall switch.

HOW TO INSTALL TRACK LIGHTS

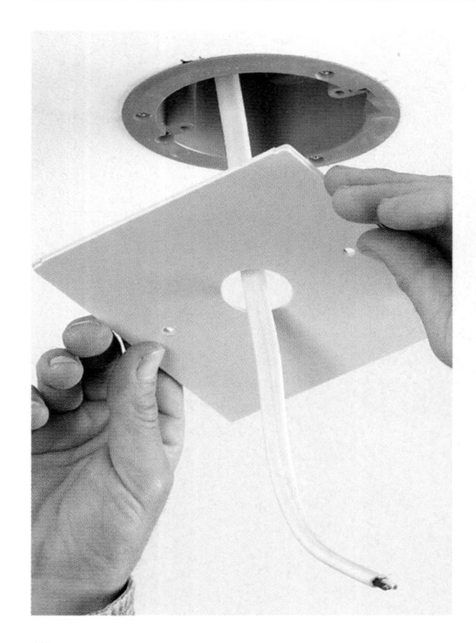

1 Run power cable from the power source to a ceiling box at the end of the installation area. With power off, feed the cable through the hole in the center of the cover plate then attach the plate to the ceiling box with screws (drill or punch out holes in the plate at the screw hole locations in the box.

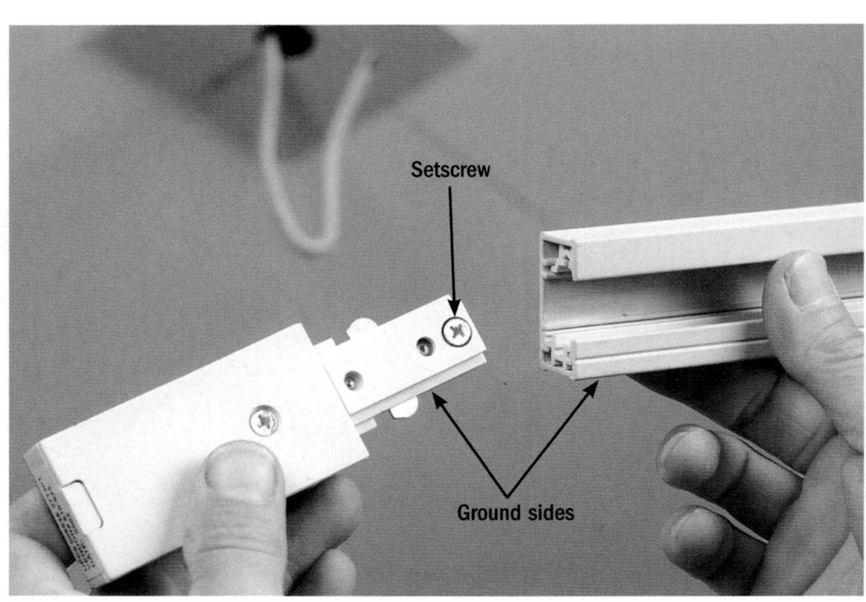

2 Attach an end connector to a section of track (choose the correct end connector: some have a knockout for a conduit feed and some have a hole in the top of the connector cover plate for feeding in the insulated wire from the 120-volt circuit). Assemble the parts so the "ground"sides are aligned (the tabs and slots are profiled so they'll only fit together if they're aligned correctly). Tighten the setscrew on the end connector to secure the connection.

3 Working on the floor or another large flat surface, assemble the track parts using L-connectors, T-connectors and straight connectors as your layout determines. Do not cut the track sections to length: they're typically available in 2-, 4- and 8-ft. lengths so you can piece them together without cutting. Attach an end cap at the end of the track line.

4 With a helper, hold the track assembly against the ceiling in the exact installation area. The top surface of the track contains predrilled mounting holes. Mark the hole locations on the ceiling so you can drill guide holes for the toggle bolts that will support the track. Remove the track and drill the guide holes at the mounting hole locations. Size the holes to match the width of the toggles (we used 3⁄16-in.-dia. × 2-in.-long bolts that require a 5⁄8-in.-dia. guide hole to accept the toggle nut).

5 Thread the bolts through the mounting holes in the tracks and twist the toggles onto the bolt ends. Remove the cover plate on the bottom of the end connector, then raise the track assembly, slipping the power cable through the hole in the top of the end connector. Insert the toggles into the guide holes and tighten the bolts just far enough to keep the track stationary.

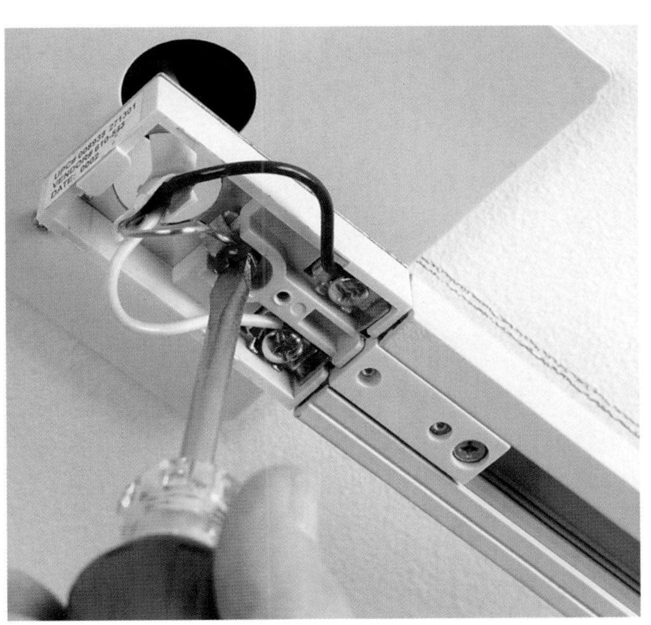

6 Strip ¾ in. of insulation from the end of each insulated wire and form loops at the ends with a long-nosed pliers. Also make a loop on the bare copper ground wire. Connect the wires to the screw terminals: black to the brass screw; white to the silver screw; copper ground to the ground screw (usually green).

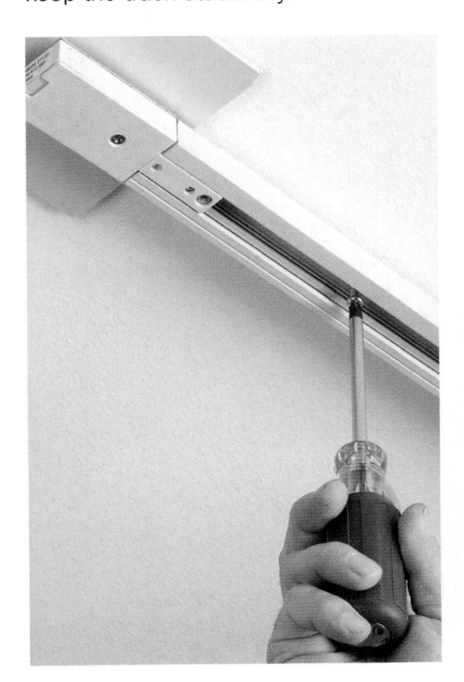

7 Feed any excess wire back up through the hole in the end connector, then attach the cover plate to the end connector. Finish tightening the mounting screws until the track is flush and secure against the ceiling.

8 Remove the lenses from track light fixtures and install light bulbs (usually halogen) as directed by the manufacturer. Replace the lenses. Insert each track head into the track slot then lock it in place with the locking tab on the head. Twist the head so the sides are flush with the track. To change the position of a fixture, simply release the locking tab and reposition the fixture in the track. Turn on the power and test the lights.

Installing Motion Detector Lights

Motion detector lights improve the security of your home by discouraging intruders and illuminating walkways and entry areas.

Replacing an ordinary exterior light with a motion detector security light is a good step toward discouraging unwanted visitors and generally making the entry points to your home safer. Before purchasing a motion detector light to replace an existing light, check the shape of the wall box so you can buy a unit that will fit it. If you're installing a motion detector light where no light exists, you'll need to bring power service to a wall box in the area. It's best to locate the switch indoors so the light can't be shut off from outside. Also, try to locate new lights so the bulbs are high enough to be out of easy reach (otherwise, intruders can simply unscrew the bulbs). But don't locate the light higher than 12 ft. above the ground or its range and sensitivity will decrease. Follow the manufacturer's suggestions for adjusting the position and sensitivity of the sensor.

HOW TO REPLACE AN OUTDOOR LIGHT WITH A MOTION DETECTOR LIGHT

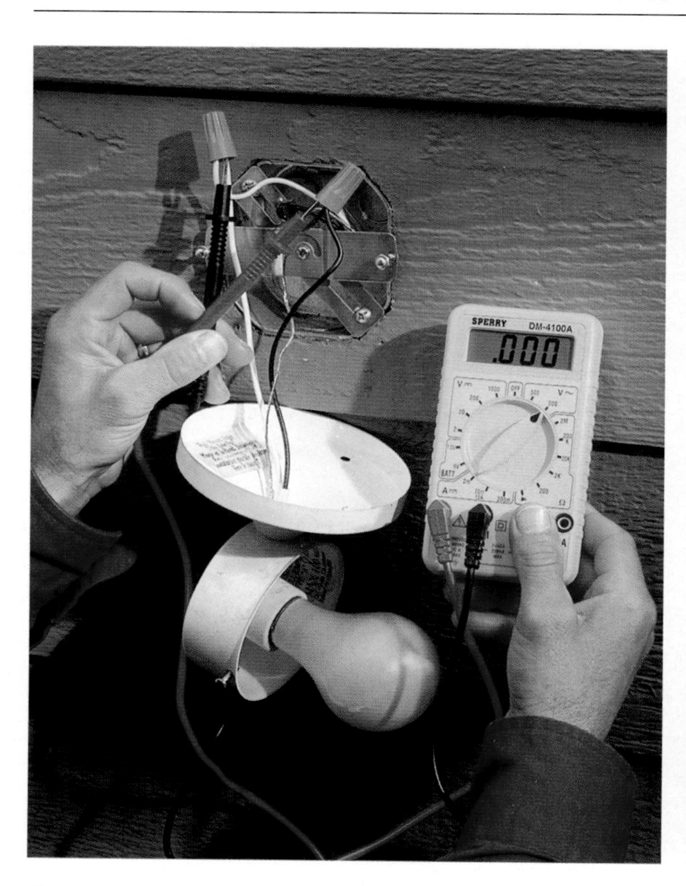

1 Shut off power and remove the fixture coverplate from the old exterior light. Touch the probes of a multimeter to the hot (black) and neutral (white) wire connections to verify that there is no current flow.

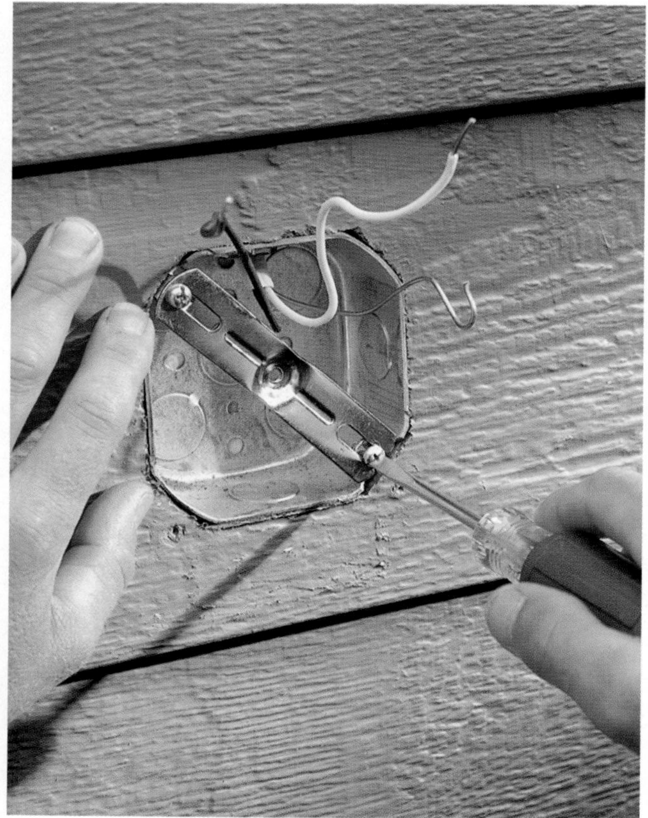

2 Disconnect the old wire connections and remove the mounting bracket (strap) from the box. Attach the mounting strap for the new light fixture to the box.

HOW TO REPLACE AN OUTDOOR LIGHT WITH A MOTION DETECTOR LIGHT (CONTINUED)

3 Support the new light fixture with an S-hook (usually included) or wire hung from the mounting strap. Run a pigtail from the incoming ground wire to the grounding terminal on the fixture, and run another pigtail to the grounding screw on the box (if it's metal). Make the wiring connections: black to black, white to white, using wire connectors.

4 Fold the wires neatly into the box, then secure the fixture to the box with the mounting screw. Make sure to insert the foam or rubber gasket between the fixture coverplate and the wall before securing the fixture. To seal the screw hole, apply a dab of silicone caulk to the screw before driving it. Install light bulbs then turn on power and test.

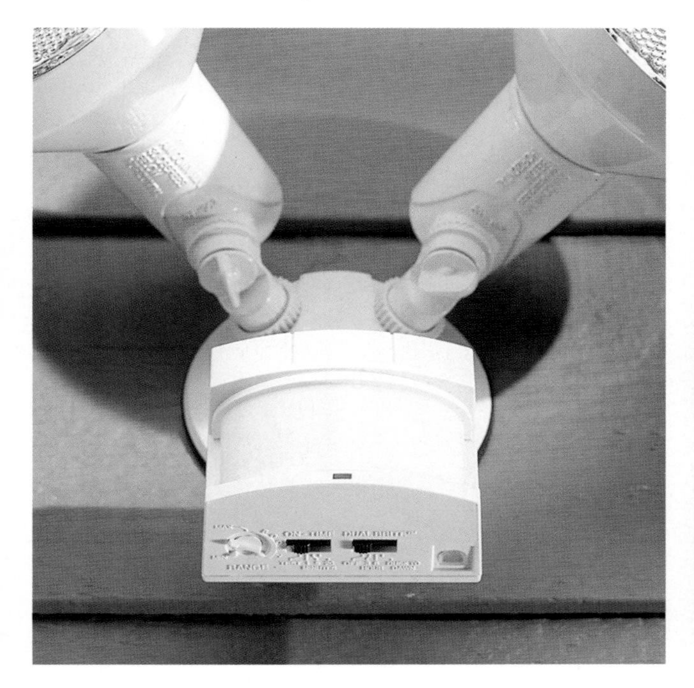

5 Set the light control settings on the base of the fixture. Most allow you to set the range so the sensor does not trigger from motion outside of the area you wish to secure. You can also set the duration of the time the light will stay on when triggered. Check the manual for other features of your light.

6 Adjust the position of the sensor so it aims at the area you wish to secure: the higher the sensor is aimed the greater the coverage range will be. You'll want to experiment with coverage areas once it is dark out. Lock the sensor in position by tightening the screw on the sensor clamp.

Repairing Lamps

More than any other kind of lighting fixtures, lamps break. They're knocked off tables, dragged by their cords, kicked and exposed to a host of stresses other lights don't undergo. But the fact that they're injury prone doesn't mean they're disposable. In fact, the electrical components of a lamp are very easy to remove and replace. So next time the dog crashes into a floor lamp and cracks the socket, don't haul it out to the curb and put a "Free" sign on it (the lamp, that is, not the dog): fix it.

Broken sockets, frayed or damaged cords and broken plugs are the most common ailments to affect the wiring of a lamp. In most cases, it's not worth trying to repair the damaged part of the lamp (in fact, it is a bad idea). Instead, find a replacement part at your local lamp supply store or electrical supply store and make the repair.

Knowing how to replace a lamp cord, plug or socket will give you the power to extend the life of your favorite lamp.

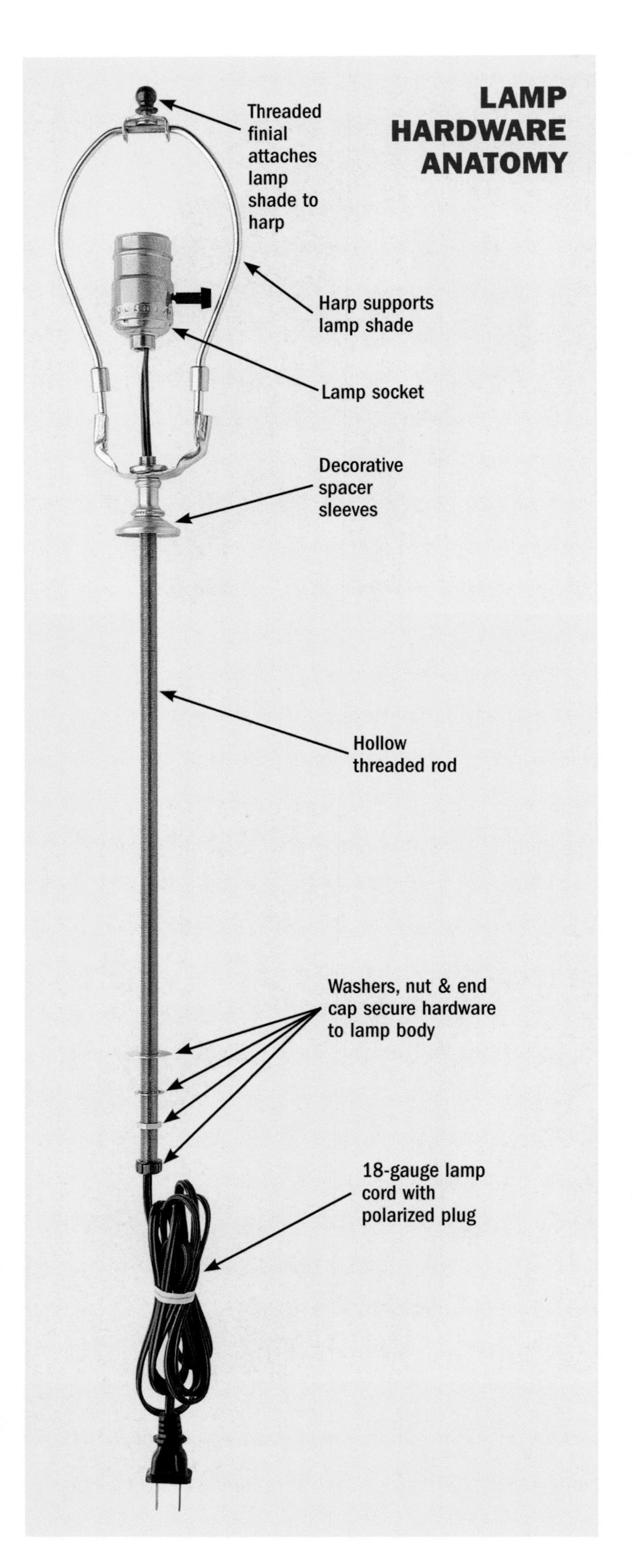

HOW TO REPLACE A LAMP SOCKET

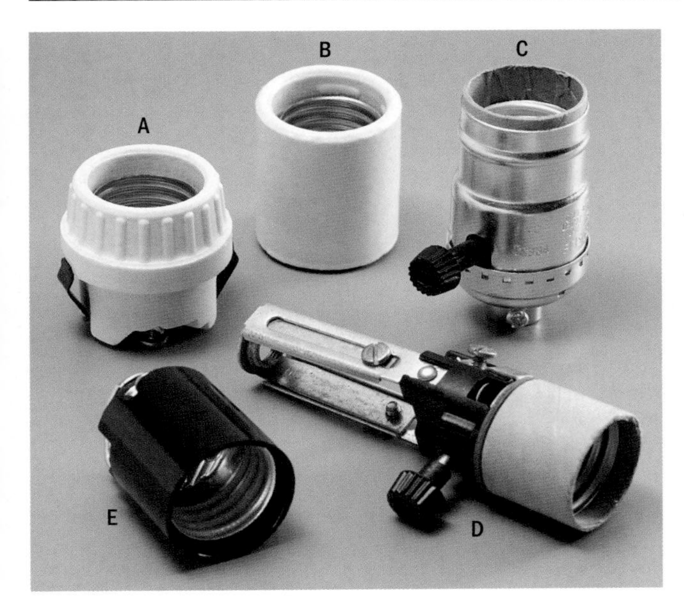

Common types of lamp sockets for lamp repair include: (A) snap-in style porcelain socket with torsion springs; (B) porcelain socket with mounting screws; (C) switched socket with setscrew for threaded tube connection; (D) adjustable-height socket with cardboard insulation and switch; (E) screw-on socket threads directly onto hollow threaded tube. Always try to replace the socket with the same type as the original.

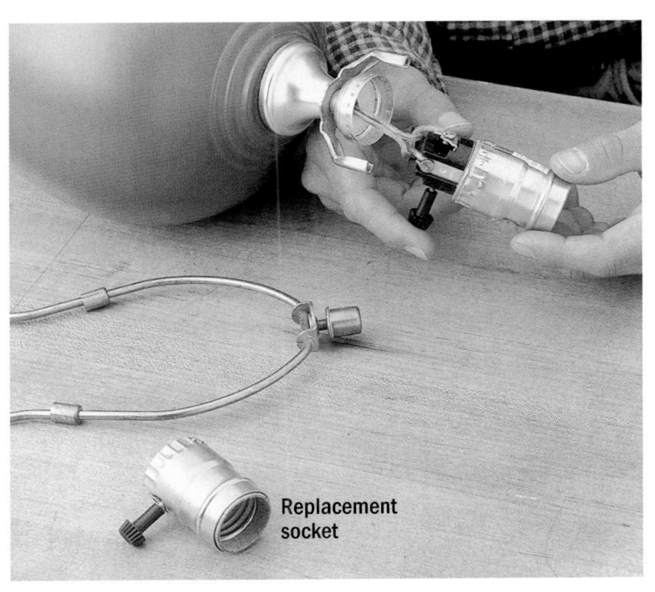

1 With the lamp unplugged, remove the harp then disconnect the old socket at the base. Disassemble the socket by squeezing the socket shell at the point where it joins the socket base (some shells will have the word "Press" printed on them to help you identify the correct spot to squeeze). Disconnect the lamp cord at the switch terminal screws then pull the cord back through the socket base (you may need to loosen a setscrew in the base or untie a knot in the cord to remove it).

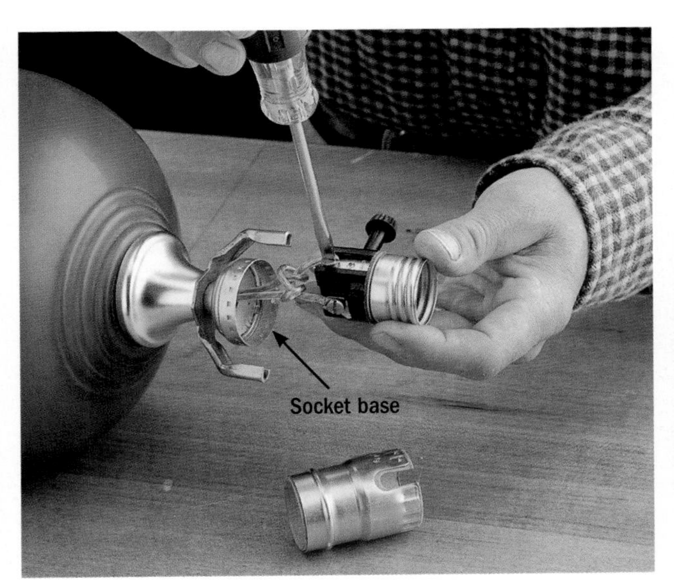

2 Thread the cord through the base of the new socket. Expose fresh wire by trimming the ends then stripping off ½ in. of insulation from each wire. Tie a loose knot (called an underwriter's knot) in the cord to keep it from slipping out through the socket base. Leave about 3 in. of free wire after the knot. Twist a loop into the end of each wire with a long-nosed pliers then connect the wires to the screw terminal on the new socket (the ridged, insulated wire goes to the silver screw).

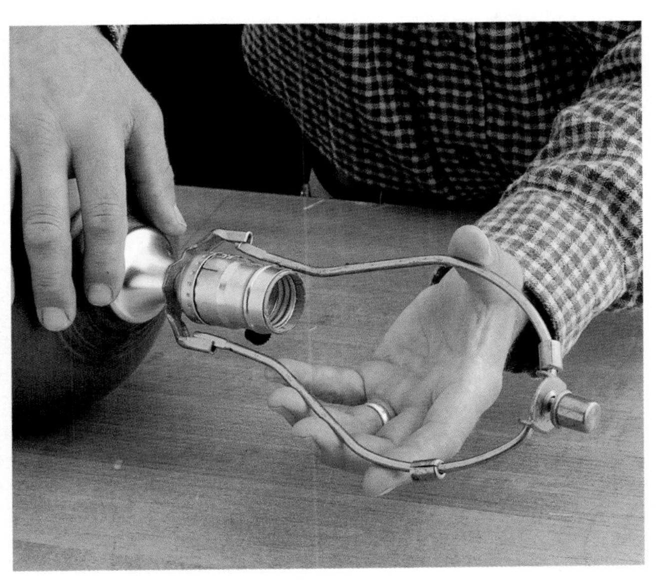

3 Slip the insulation and socket shell over the socket, then snap the shell and socket base together securely. Attach the socket and harp retainer to the neck of the lamp, insert a light bulb and test. Reattach the harp and lamp shade.

HOW TO REWIRE A LAMP

1 Remove the old socket and disconnect the old cord (See Step 1, previous page). Cut off the plug. Expose some wire on the ends of both cords, then loop and crimp them together. Wrap the cord ends with electrical tape, keeping the connection as narrow as possible.

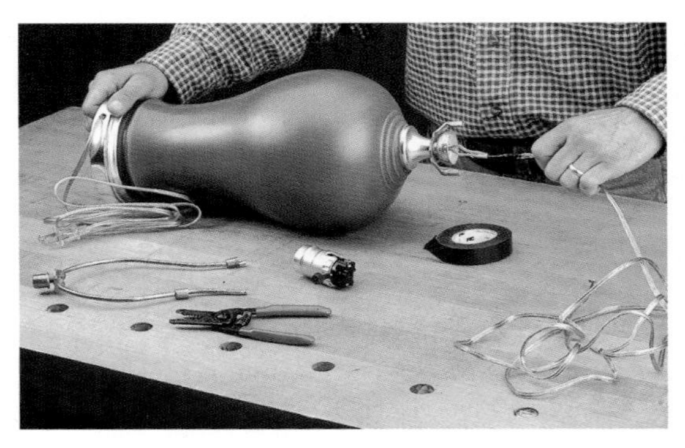

2 Fish the new cord up through the hollow threaded rod by pulling upward on the old cord. If the new cord does not have an integral molded plug, either attach the new plug end (see next page) or tie a loose knot in the end so you don't pull it too far into the tube.

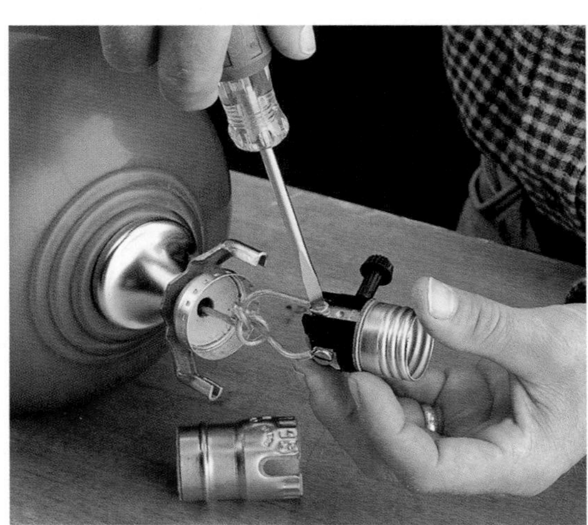

3 Tie a loose knot near the end of the new cord (separate the wires or strip the sheathing first), leaving about 3 inches of free wire exposed past the end of the socket base. Strip ½ to ¾ in. of insulation off the ends of the wires. Make terminal loops at the end of each wire with a long-nosed pliers. Connect the cord wires to the lamp socket at the screw terminals (the ridged insulated wire connects to the silver screw and leads back to the larger prong on the plug).

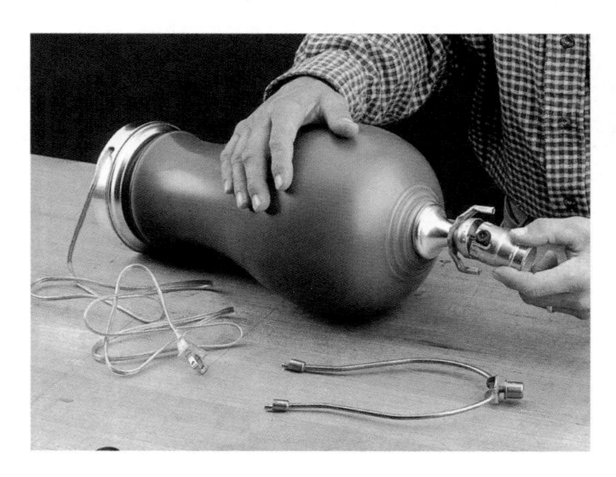

4 Assemble the socket and attach it to the lamp neck (See previous page). Reattach the harp.

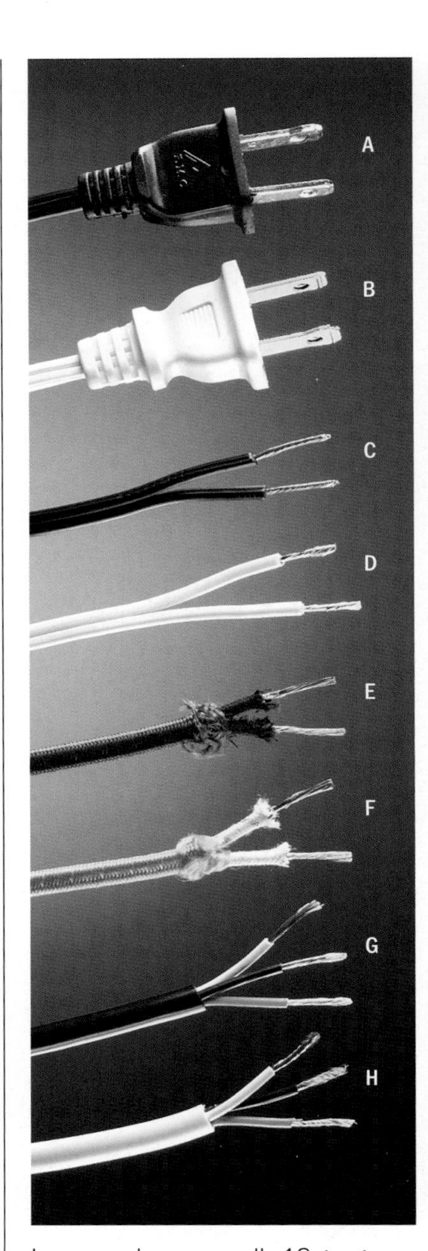

Lamp cords are usually 18-gauge wire made up of braided strands of fine copper. Many do not have a ground wire. You can choose a cord with an integral molded plug or add your own plug to lamp wire. If working on an old or antique lamp, you can find reproduction "antique" cord at lamp stores or electrical supply stores.

Cord types shown above (all 18-gauge) are: (A) black plastic with molded plug; (B) white plastic with molded plug; (C) black "zip cord"; (D) white "zip cord"; (E) "reproduction" cord with brown cloth wrap; (F) "reproduction" cord with gold cloth wrap; (G) black 3-wire cord with ground; (H) white 3-wire cord with ground.

Cord plugs are manufactured in particular sizes and configurations for particular reasons. If a plug fails or becomes damaged, the plug can usually be replaced easily. But it can be dangerous to replace a plug with one that is not an exact match for the original. Bring the old plug along when shopping for a replacement. If you can't find an exact match, bring the plug to a qualified electrical supply professional and have him or her help you find a suitable replacement.

Plug types shown above are: (A) snap-together plug with hinged top; (B) snap-together plug with insert and housing; (C) snap-together plug with sliding end cover; (D) screw-connect plug with rubber housing; (E) screw-together plug with plastic screw protector.

HOW TO ATTACH A SNAP-TOGETHER CORD PLUG

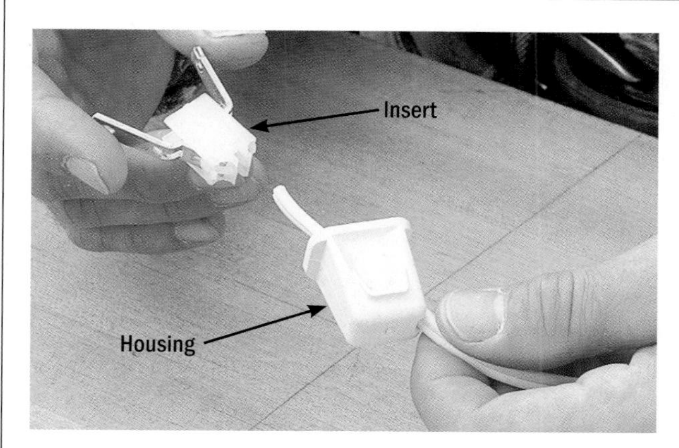

1 Cut the cord at the base of the old plug. Thread the cord through the entry hole in the snap-together housing. Spread the prongs to back the contact spurs out of the cord channel, then slide the cord end all the way into the channel. (You don't need to strip insulation off the cord.)

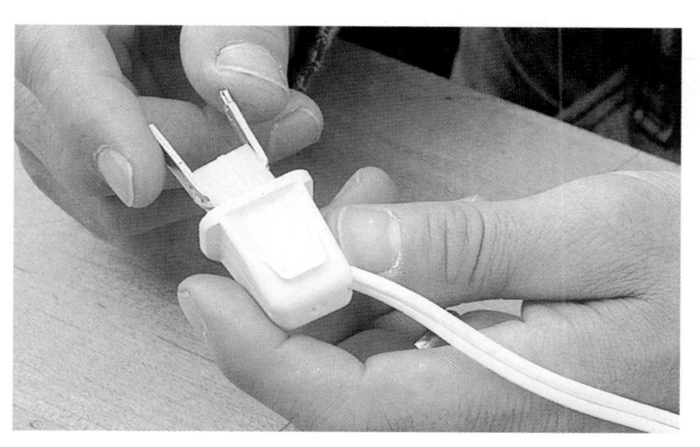

2 Press the prongs together, forcing the spurs to penetrate the cord sheathing and contact the wires. Slide the insert into the housing, backing the cord out of the entry hole, until the insert snaps into the housing.

HOW TO ATTACH A SCREW-CONNECT CORD PLUG

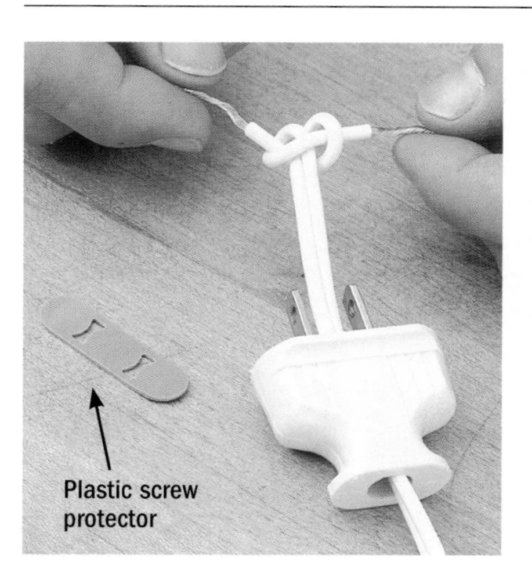

1 Feed the end of the cord through the entry hole in the back of the plug. Strip the end of each wire to expose ½ to 1 in. of bare wire. Tie the insulated wires into a loose knot and cinch the cord by tugging lightly against the plug.

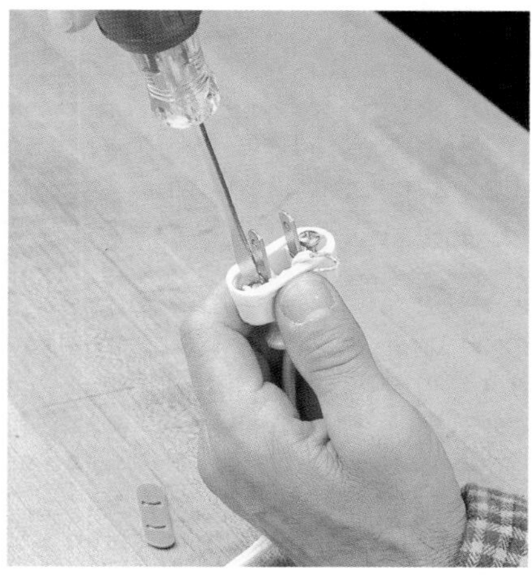

2 Twist loops into the ends of the wires with a long-nosed pliers, then attach the wires to the screw terminals inside the plug (if the plug is polarized, the ridged half goes to the wider plug side). Make sure all of the fine strands are tucked securely under the screw head. Tug gently on the cord to pull the excess cord wire out the back. Slide the plastic screw protector over the prongs.

A quality ceiling fan makes a room more comfortable and reduces heating and cooling costs. It can also contribute to the decor of a room. And when a light kit is added, you don't have to sacrifice your overhead light to get the benefits of a ceiling fan.

Installing a Ceiling Fan

Ceiling fans are becoming quite commonplace in today's houses as tools for improving air circulation. This, in turn, helps to reduce cooling and heating costs. And with their growing popularity, a much wider variety of styles and colors are manufactured now so the fan unit can become an integral part of the room décor—especially when combined with a ceiling light. For these reasons, it is not unusual for a single house to be equipped with several ceiling fans.

Ceiling fans typically have a blade span of 42, 52 or 56 in., although you can find them with spans as small as 32 in. The majority are sold with a light kit, but you can also buy the fan only (most of these will accept a light kit if you choose to add one later). Bear in mind that most light fixtures attached to a ceiling fan tend to wobble when the fan is operating, which can be a little unsettling to some people.

Even the most inexpensive ceiling fan models have 3-speed motors so you can adjust the speed of the blades. And most are reversible so you can set them to force the air down during cooling months or draw the air up during heating months.

When buying a ceiling fan, look for one with a 25-year or longer warranty: they generally have better quality bearings and a heavier-duty motor than the lower-end units. When considering which fan to purchase, pay attention to the weight of the unit. If the fan weighs more than 35 pounds, it cannot be attached directly to the junction box but must be supported independently, usually with a ceiling brace or a special mounting kit.

Another factor to consider is whether the light and fan are switch-operated or pull-chain operated. In the long run, you'll probably appreciate switches over pull chains: they're more convenient and less of a visual distraction. Pull chains also have a tendency to catch in the spinning blades. Even though most have breakaway chains so the motor isn't damaged, you may end up needing to replace the speed switch on the motor if the chain breaks off inside the switch housing.

Where to position a ceiling fan. The best spot to install a ceiling fan is in the center of the room. This positioning takes best advantage of the air circulation patterns for maximum air movement. The blades should be at least 30 in. away from the room walls, and at least 7 ft. up from the floor. To achieve this clearance, you'll need to flush-mount the unit directly to the ceiling in rooms with a ceiling less than 8 ft. high. In rooms with higher ceilings, you can install the unit with a down rod that drops from the ceiling. You'll also want to use a down rod in rooms with a sloped ceiling so the motor and blades can be in a horizontal position while the mounting hardware is attached directly to the sloped ceiling joists.

The switch outlet box. The switch outlet box can be either a double- or a single-gang box, depending

WIRING DIAGRAM: CEILING FAN WITH LIGHT KIT

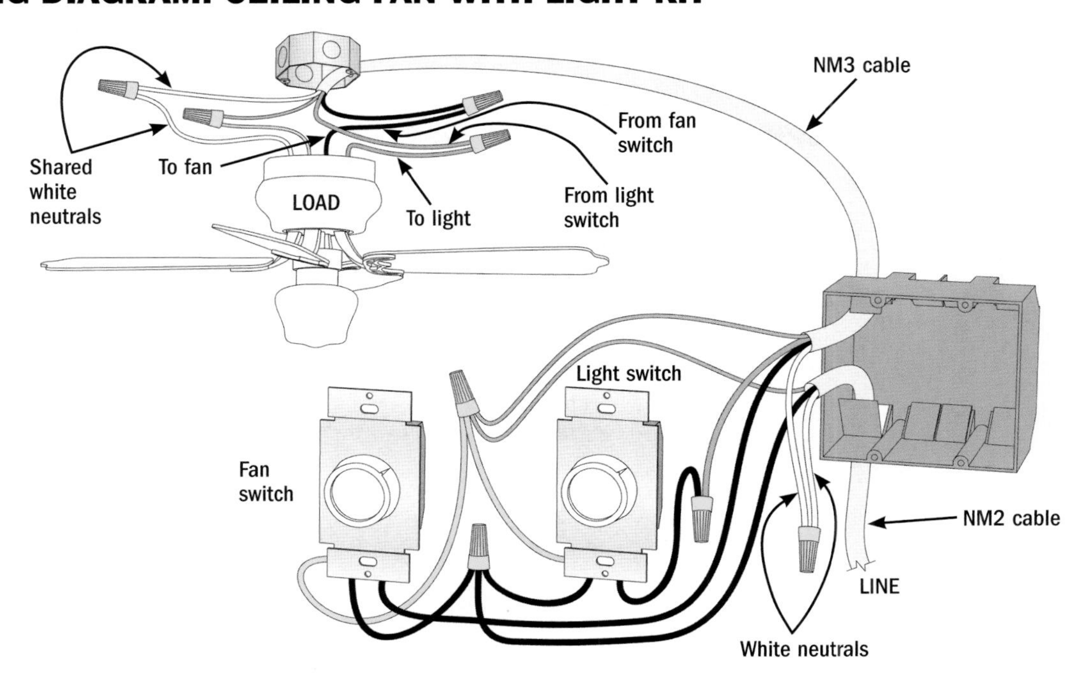

on whether you are wiring a single switch or separate switches for the fan and the light. In either case, the box should be deep, with plenty of splicing room in case you want to add a dimmer for the lights or a speed-controller for the fan. Both occupy a lot of room. Obviously, if you are simply replacing an existing ceiling light with a ceiling fan you won't need to fiddle around with the switch box.

The cable. The size of the wire required to run the fan circuit depends on the overcurrent protection of the circuit you are tapping into. If you bring power in from a nearby outlet that has 20-amp overcurrent protection (circuit breaker or fuse), run 12-gauge wire within the fan circuit. If the circuit has 15-amp protection use 14-gauge wire. Fan units with no light kit can be installed with two-conductor (black and white) cable. Fan/light units require three-conductor (black, white, red) cable. If you are installing a fan only, but it is prewired to accept a light kit, it's a good idea to go ahead and use three-conductor cable just in case you want to add a light some day. In the meantime, simply bend the red conductor out of the way.

Additional materials. Along with the cable and switch box, you will need one or two switches, some wire caps and some extra wire for making pigtails. For units heavier than 35 pounds, you'll need a mounting kit—check the manufacturer's instructions.

SAFE AND SECURE

The electrical box that supports a ceiling fan must be rated for use with a ceiling fans (see photo) and be properly anchored to the ceiling framing. There are several options for mounting the box, depending on the location of box in relation to the ceiling framing.

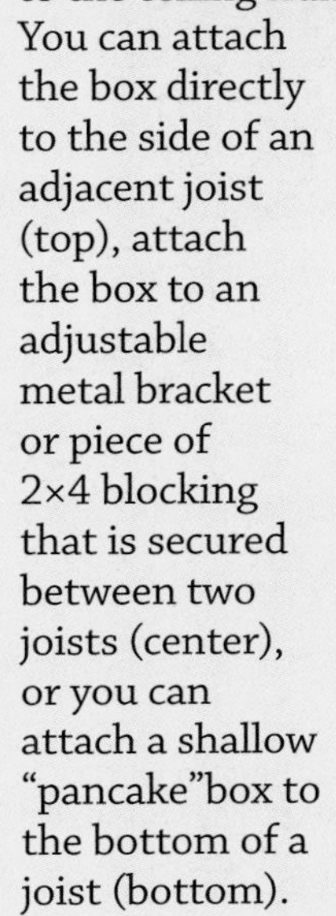

You can attach the box directly to the side of an adjacent joist (top), attach the box to an adjustable metal bracket or piece of 2×4 blocking that is secured between two joists (center), or you can attach a shallow "pancake"box to the bottom of a joist (bottom).

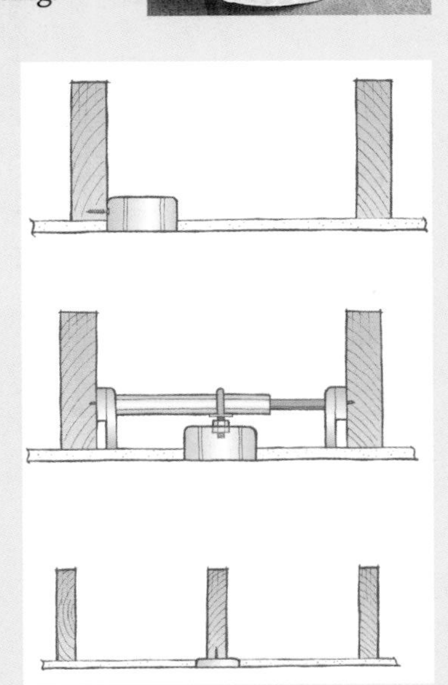

HOW TO INSTALL A CEILING FAN

1 Remove the electricity from the circuit you are working on by turning off the breaker or pulling out the fuse. Verify loss of power with a multimeter at the switch and/or fan outlet.

2 Using three-conductor cable (NM/3), make a run from the switch outlet box to the fan outlet box. This provides two hot wires (black and red): one for the fan and one for the light fixture hanging from the fan. Black is normally used for the fan, red for the light. After removing the knockout, pull about 8 in. of cable into the fan outlet box. Remove sheathing to within less than an inch of where the cable enters into the box. Strip ½ in. of insulation off the ends of all insulated wires. **NOTE:** In some cases, you may be able to use your existing ceiling box and wiring (See Replacing an existing light fixture with a ceiling fan, previous page).

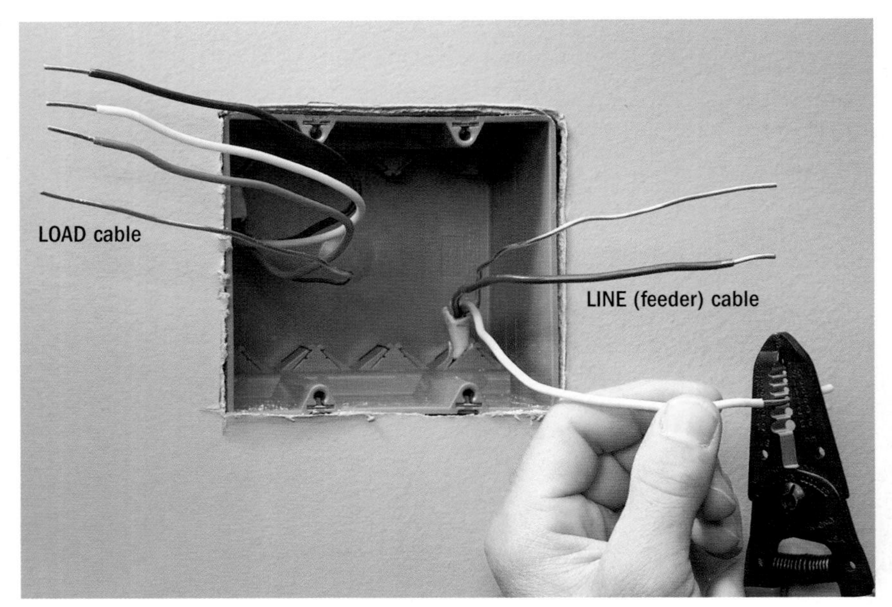

3 At the switch box, remove cable sheathing to within less than 1 in. of the point where the cables enter the box. Strip ½ in. of insulation off of all insulated wires. The feeder cable providing power to the switch box likely includes a black wire, white wire, and ground. The load cable to the fan/light unit should have a black wire, red wire, white wire, and ground wire.

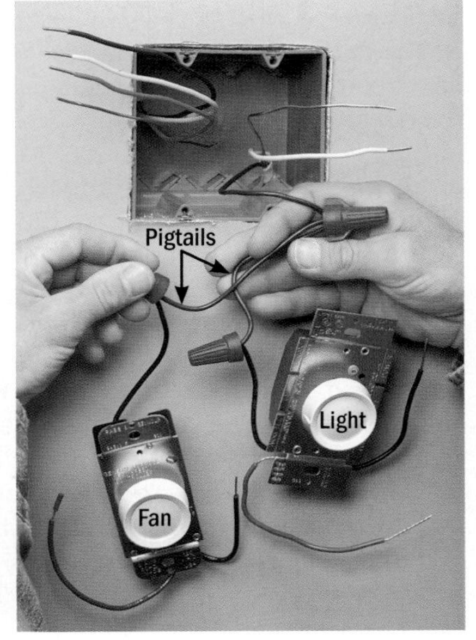

4 At the switch box, twist the black feeder wire in with two black pigtails. Attach one pigtail to one of the black leads on the fan switch and the second pigtail to one of the black leads on the light switch.

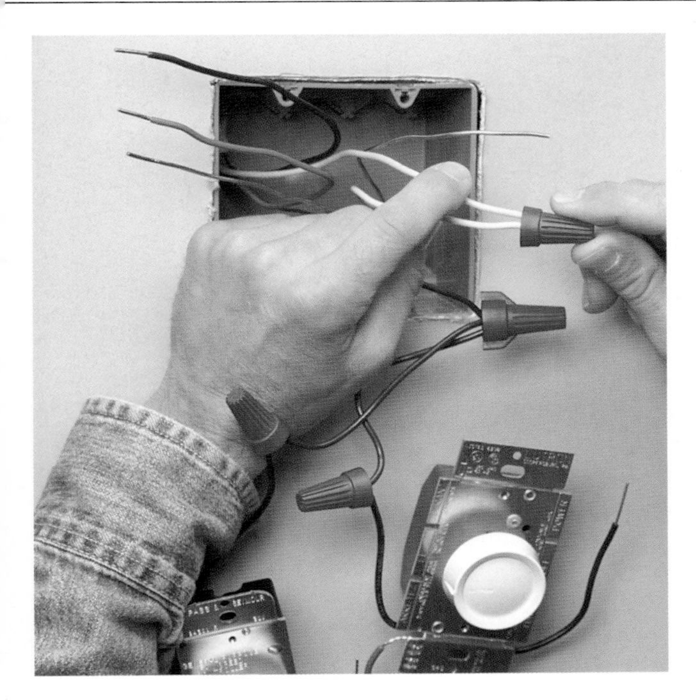

5 Splice the white neutral wires from the incoming and outgoing cables together, securing with a wire cap. You'll now have the incoming neutral of the power cable spliced to the load neutral of the 3-conductor cable.

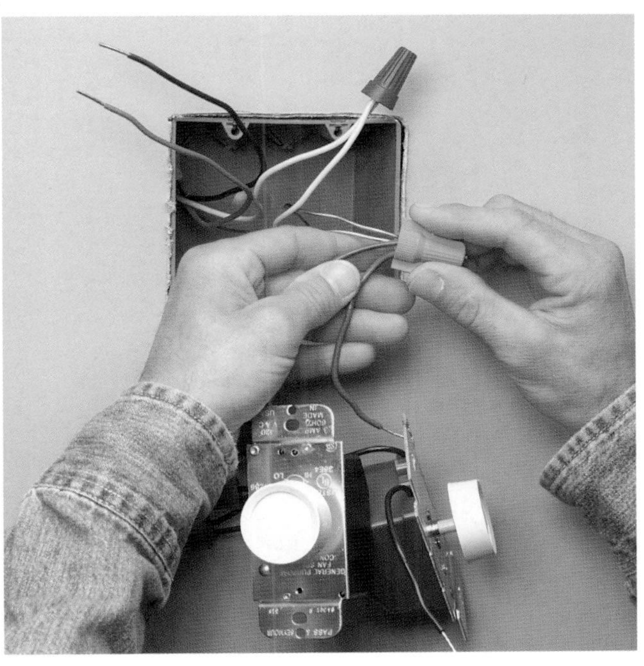

6 Twist the ground wires from the incoming and outgoing cables together and secure with a wire cap.

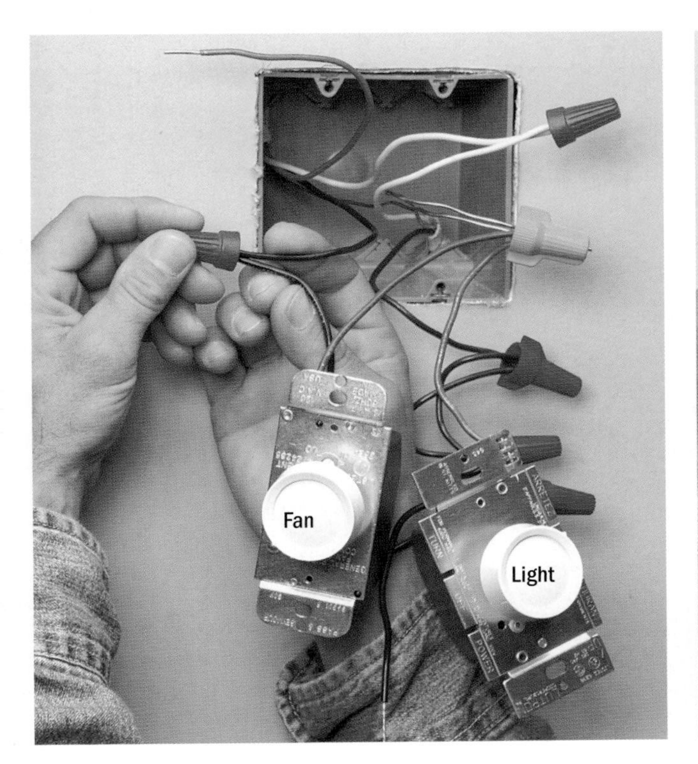

7 Make the connections from the switches to the fan. Attach the stripped black wire from the 3-conductor cable to the fan control switch: if your switch has a preattached black wire, twist it together with the black lead from the cable.

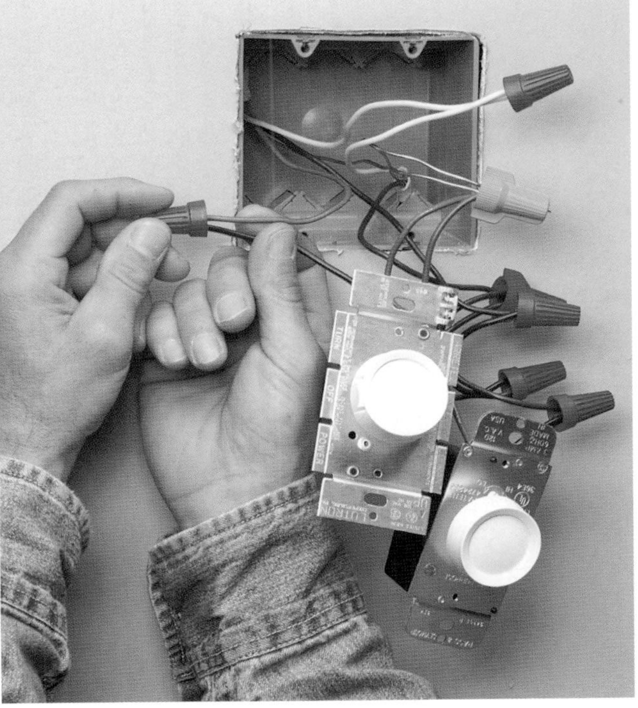

8 Make the switch connection for the light with the red lead from the 3-conductor cable by twisting the wire together with the wire from the switch.

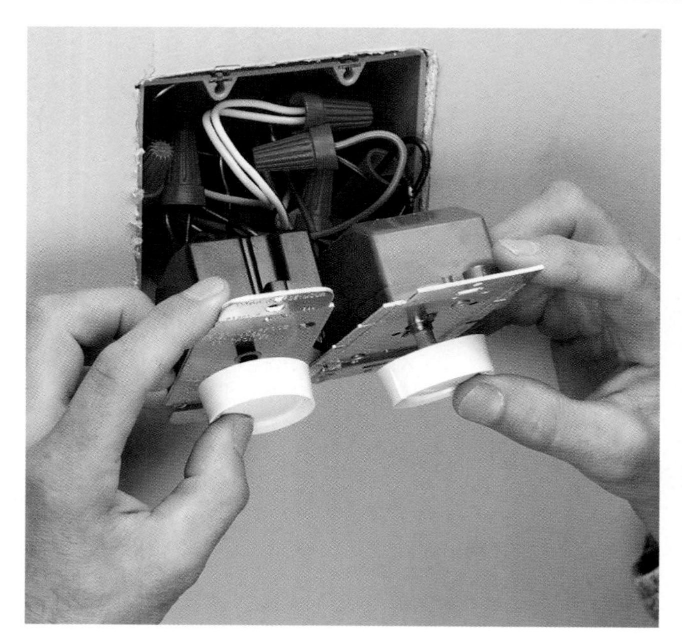

9 Push the wires neatly back into the box with your fingers. First, prebend the wires accordion-style in the direction you want them to fold into the box. If you did it right, the wires should fold neatly back into the box in a "Z" pattern. Press the ground wires in first, followed by the neutral wires, then the hot wires. Dimmer and fan switches have deep bodies, so create as much room as possible.

10 Carefully push both switches back into the box and screw them in with the top and bottom attachment screws that are hanging from the drywall ears. As you tighten the screws clockwise, note that you can reposition each switch slightly to the left or right so you can plumb the switches. Attach the cover plate.

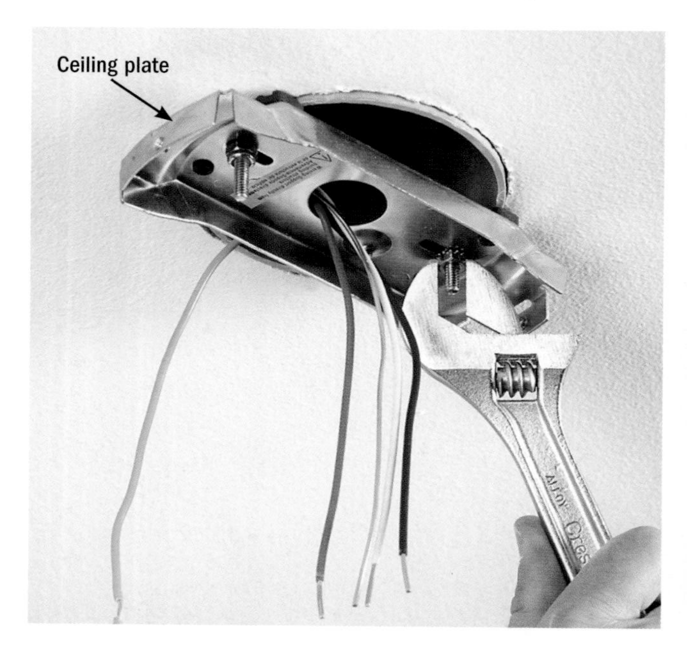

11 Attach the fan mounting hardware. The model being installed in this sequence is mounted to a ceiling plate that attaches to the ceiling outlet box with bolts and nuts.

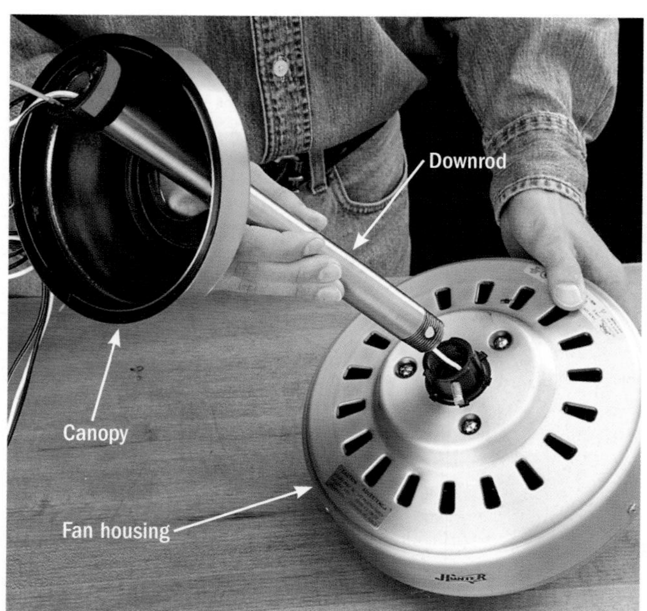

12 Assemble the fan unit, following the manufacturer's instructions. We purchased an extra-long down rod for the fan shown here so the fan would be at the recommended 7 ft. height in the room we installed it in. Thread the fan fixture wires through the down rod and attach the down rod to the fan housing, feeding it through the canopy that fits against the ceiling.

13 Hang the fan unit from the mounting hardware to support it while you make the wire connections. Most manufacturers design their product with some type of system to allow you to hang the fan temporarily.

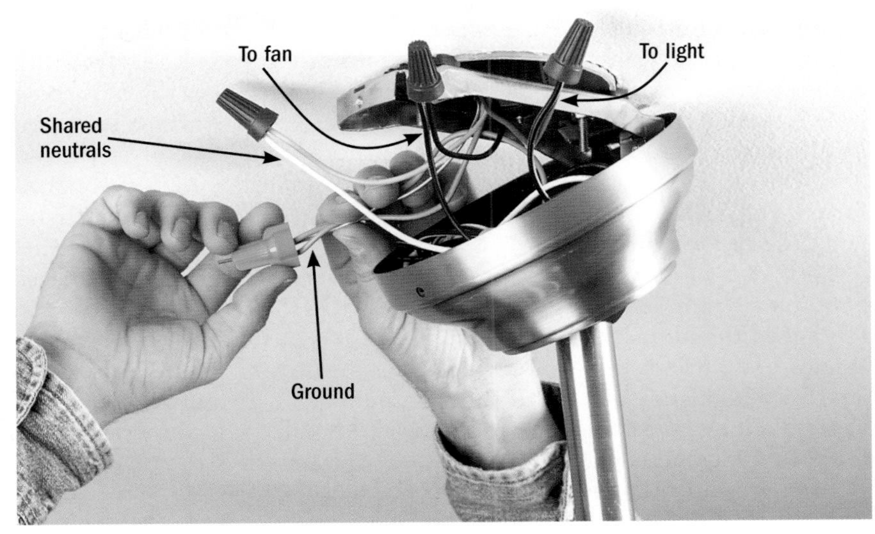

14 Make the wire connections from the outlet box to the fan unit. Splice the red incoming wire from the wall switch to the fan's light wire (normally colored red, blue or yellow). Splice the black incoming wire from the wall switch to the fan's black wire. Splice the white neutral incoming wire from the wall switch outlet box to the fan's white neutral wire. Splice the ground incoming wire from the wall switch outlet box to the fan's green ground wire. Cover all splices with wire caps. Push all splices into the fan outlet box.

15 Swing the housing up against the ceiling and affix it to the ceiling plate according to the manufacturer's instructions. Assemble the fan blades by attaching them to the blade irons with the hardware provided by the manufacturer (inset photo). Attach the irons to the hub at the bottom of the fan assembly.

16 Attach the light fixture (or the switch housing in non-light or single-light models). A connector plug in the switch housing fits into the fan housing unit and distributes the power to the appropriate pull-switches and to the light or lights (inset photo). Apply power at the service panel and test the operation. Most fans include a kit for balancing the fan blade in the event of wobble. Install globes and other decorative accessories.

Installing a Bathroom Vent Fan

No one likes to walk into a bathroom clouded with steam from a hot shower. Besides making you feel sticky, this excess humidity can cause serious problems: Unless it is forced outside, it will end up in the walls, creating the potential for mold and rot.

Although older homes incorporated bathroom windows for ventilation, this passive form is inadequate for preventing moisture problems – a ceiling vent fan will clear the air quickly.

First, determine the right size fan to install. For a room with an 8-ft. ceiling, multiply the square footage of the room by 1.1. For example, a 100-sq.-ft. bathroom will be best served by a vent fan with a rating of at least a 110 cfm. If the bathroom has a vaulted ceiling, add 15 percent for every additional foot of ceiling height.

Another important consideration is the noise a vent fan produces, which is measured in sones. Modern vent fans that are considered quiet produce .3 to 1.5 sones, which is several times quieter than earlier models.

Vent fans are available in a variety of styles, including models that look like traditional ceiling fixtures or even recessed lights. Many also feature built-in lights and heaters.

Select a switch to control the fan. A timer switch is the best choice. This type of switch turns off after a set amount of time (typically 15 to 60 minutes), so the fan will run long enough to clear the air, but you won't waste energy by leaving the fan on longer than is necessary. If your vent fan is also equipped with a light or heater, consider a switch with multiple controls or separate switches to control each function individually.

Install your fan near the source of the humidity. You can install one directly above a tub or shower, but it must be UL-listed for over-the-tub installation and connected to a GFCI circuit. Most new vent fans are approved for such installations.

Once you have selected a location, drill a small hole through the ceiling and push a piece of wire or coat hanger up through the hole.

From the floor above, locate the wire and clear away any insulation surrounding it. Mark the cut lines for the vent fan opening between the joists, following the manufacturer's hole-size specifications. Cut the

VENT FAN OUTLET OPTIONS: CEILING VENT FAN WITH ROOF CAP

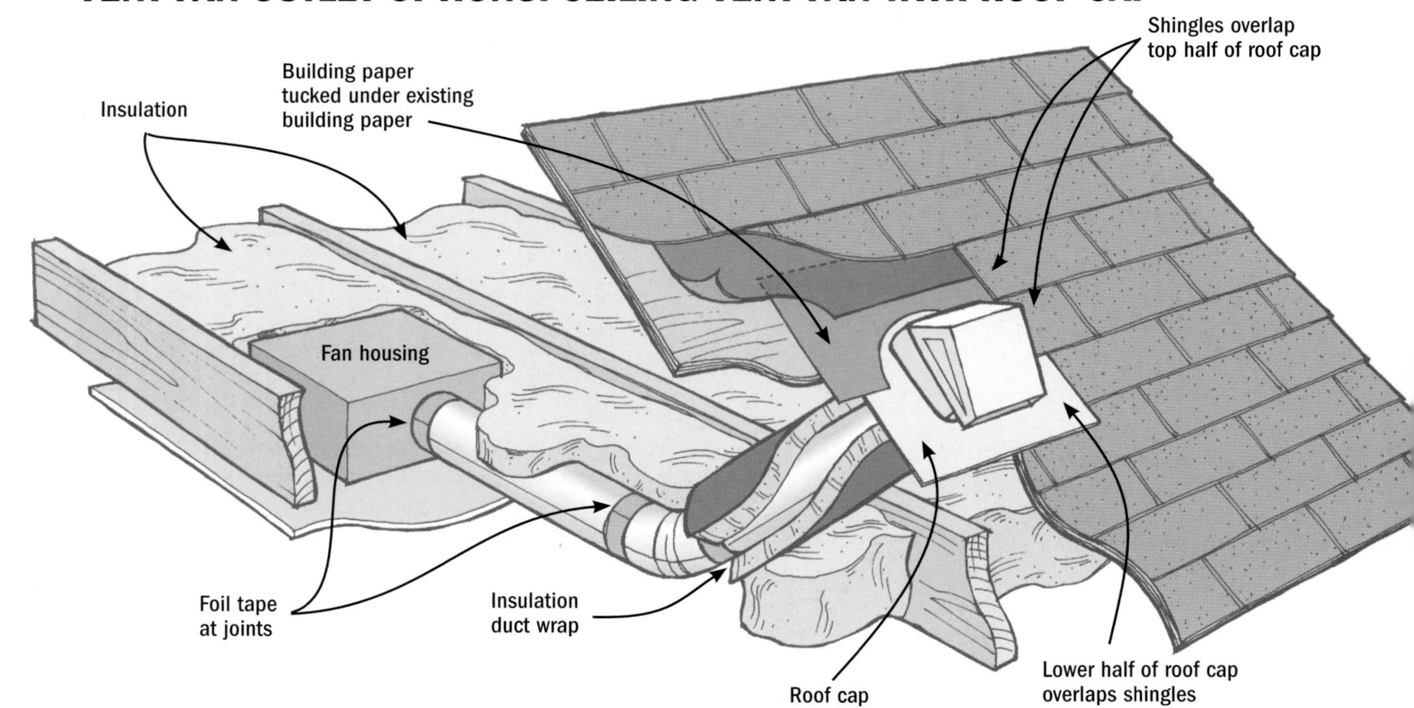

VENT FAN OUTLET OPTIONS: CEILING VENT FAN WITH WALL CAP

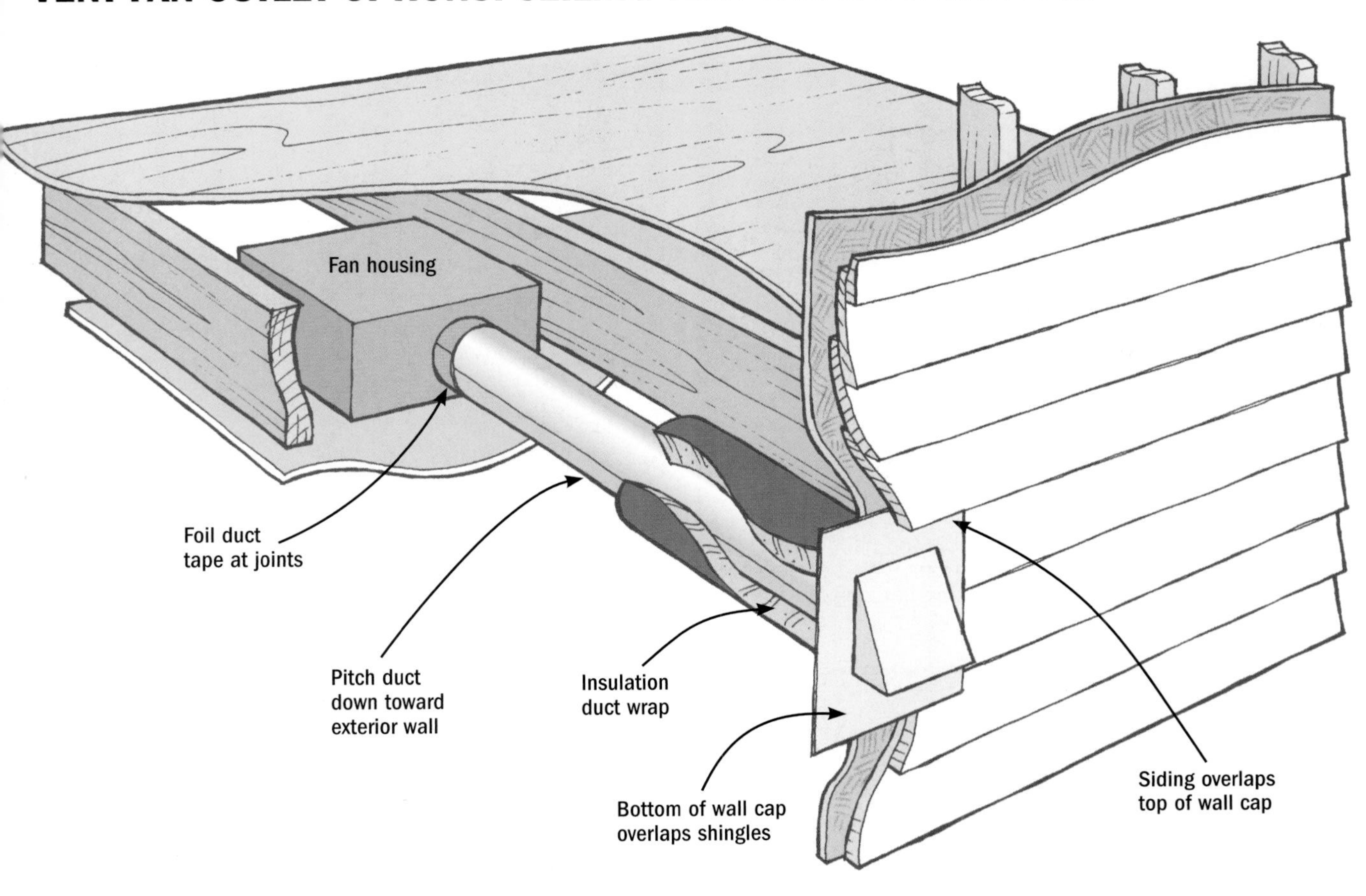

opening with a drywall saw, jigsaw or reciprocating saw. Next, secure the fan housing in the opening.

Bathroom vent fans must exhaust the air to the outside. Choose an exit point for the ductwork. Do not vent the ducts through your soffits because the humid air that is expelled can be sucked back into the attic through nearby soffit vents.

The exit or outlet that the duct connects to is called a wall cap or a roof cap. The advantage of installing a wall cap is that the duct can be pitched toward the outside, allowing possible condensation to drain away from the vent fan. A wall cap also will not be blocked by snow, a potential problem for roof caps. Choose the outlet location that is easiest to install in your house.

To determine the exact outlet location on the roof or wall, drive a 3-in. deck screw through the roof or drill a small hole through the wall.

Next, go outside and locate the protruding screw or hole on the outside of the house. Cut an opening to match the size of the roof cap or wall cap duct connection. Install cap, seal and overlap the shingles or siding and the cap flashing so that water will shed properly over the cap and not enter the house.

Once the wall cap or roof cap is secure, go back inside the house and finish connecting the duct pieces between the fan and the cap. The duct path from the vent fan to the wall or roof cap should be as smooth, short and straight as possible to provide the most efficient airflow and reduce noise. Rigid galvanized duct offers the best performance, but flexible insulated duct is also acceptable for runs that are less than 6 ft. long. Seal all duct connections with foil tape, duct mastic or silicone. When installing rigid duct, use 45-degree elbows to create gradual changes in direction. Also, whenever possible, install at least 2 ft. of straight run before the first elbow to allow the air to build momentum before changing direction. To help prevent condensation in cold climates, cover ducts located in attics with loose insulation or apply duct-wrap insulation.

Run 12-2 NM cable to the vent fan and switch locations. (Use 12-3 NM cable when installing a fan-light combination unit with separate switches or timers.)

INSTALLING A VENT FAN

1 Make the wiring connections in the fan housing and then fasten the housing to a ceiling joist with 1-¼-in. screws. Apply silicone between the fan housing and ceiling to prevent air leaks.

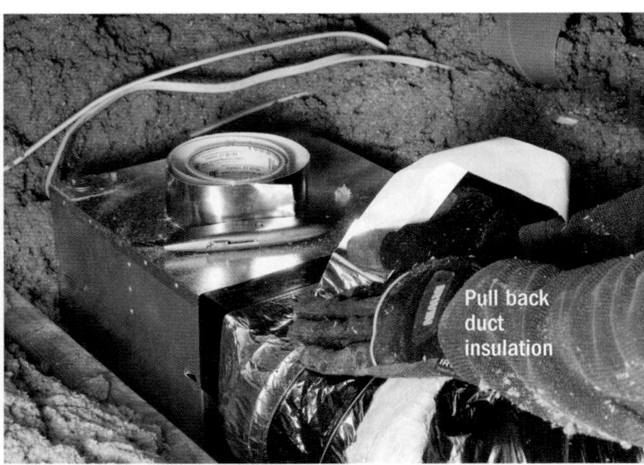

2 Attach the duct to the fan housing with foil tape. Next, rout the duct to the outlet location and drive a 3-in. screw through the ceiling or wall to mark the outlet outside the house.

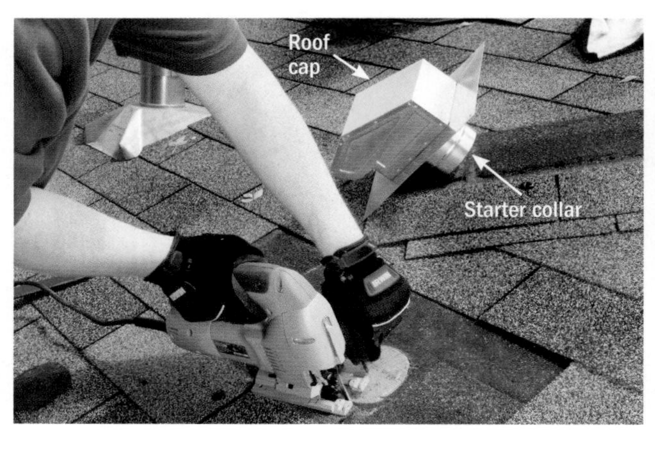

3 Remove the shingles that will be directly under the roof cap installation location and then use a jigsaw or hole saw to cut a hole slightly larger than the roof cap starter collar.

4 Make a cut in the existing building paper just above the top edge of the roof cap, and slide a piece of building paper under the existing paper to flash the top and sides of the roof cap.

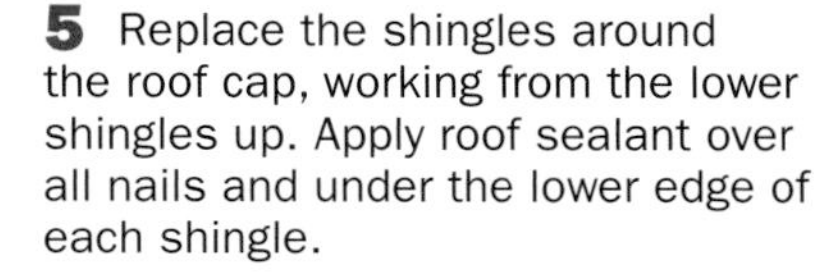

5 Replace the shingles around the roof cap, working from the lower shingles up. Apply roof sealant over all nails and under the lower edge of each shingle.

6 Connect the timer switch. In this case an existing single box containing a GFCI outlet was removed, the opening was cut larger and a new double box was installed to hold both the GFCI and the vent fan timer switch.

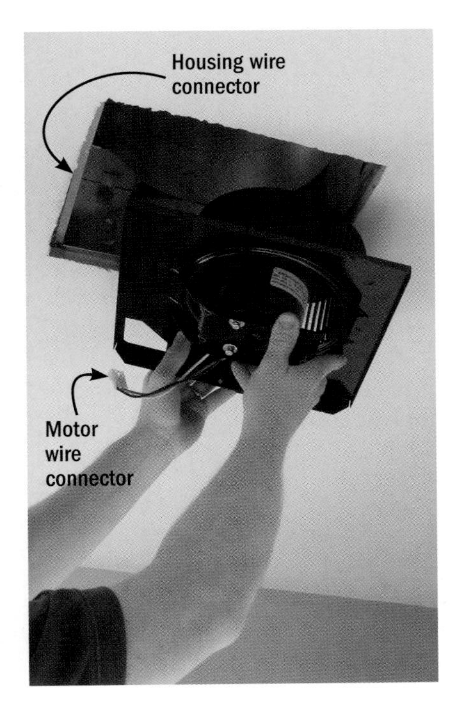

7 Reinstall the motor and blower in the fan housing and plug the motor wire connector into the housing wire connector. Finish the installation by fitting the fan grille over the housing.

VENT FAN WIRING OPTIONS

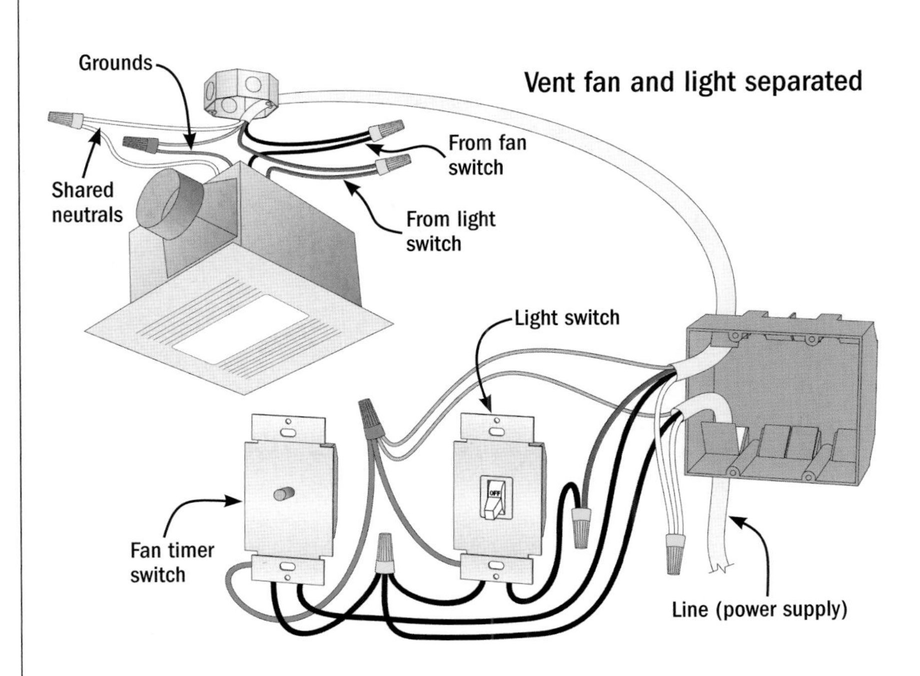

Vent fan only (line to switch)

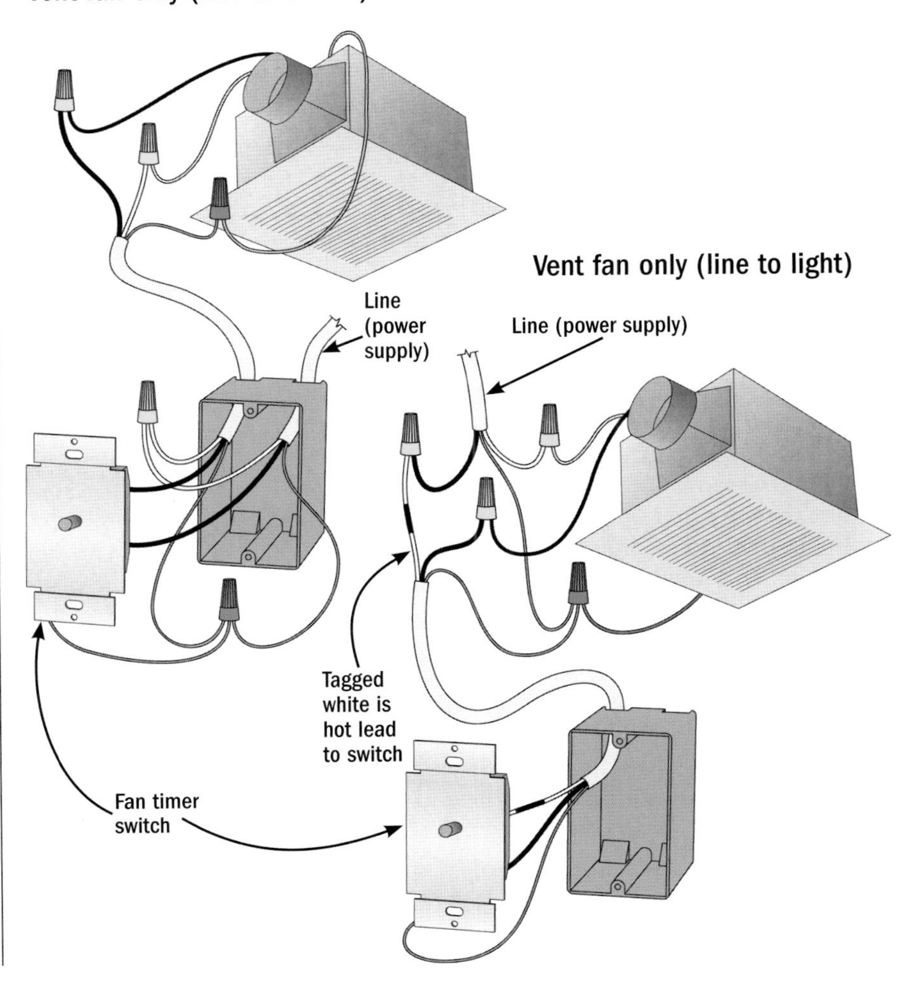

An electric baseboard heater is a clean and quiet source of supplementary heat. Some newer models (not shown here) contain an enclosed fluid system that does not become as hot as a standard metal heating element, reducing the risk of burns from contact.

Installing a Baseboard Heater

Electric baseboard heaters are convenient devices for providing supplementary heat to an area that is underserved by your home heating system. They can also be used as a primary heat source in small additions, instead of going to the effort and expense of expanding the existing heating system. In colder climates where heating demand is high, electric heat is not considered a cost-effective option for the whole house.

Most baseboard heaters require a 240-volt circuit. They come in various lengths and wattages, but they're all wired the same way. If you're installing more than one heater, use a thermostat for each heater. This allows each area of the room to be controlled independently, lowering your electric bill by putting heat only where it is needed.

Before you wire a baseboard heater, choose which end of the heater you want the feeder wire to enter. Both ends of any baseboard heater are designed for wiring, with knockouts for wiring in the back, bottom, and on the side. Pick the end that's closer to the feeder cable or has better access for adjusting the thermostat.

Baseboard heaters normally require their own circuit, most often wired with 12-gauge wire and 20 amps of current. You are allowed 16 ft. of baseboard on one 20-amp circuit. This can be achieved with one unit or several units, as long as the total does not exceed 16 ft. If more than 16 ft. of heater is desired, you can either run another circuit or increase the amperage capacity of the original circuit (as long as the number of feet of heater you're installing does not exceed 80% of the amperage rating—for example, a 30-amp circuit should not supply more than 24 ft. of heater).

Typically, baseboard heaters come equipped with a built-in thermostat that mounts in one of the junction boxes on the ends of the unit. The power feed is wired through the thermostat. If you prefer, you can wire the heater through a wall thermostat, which will be more accessible.

SAFETY TIP

Never install a baseboard heater directly under a wall receptacle. Cords plugged into the receptacle may come in contact with the heater element, which can melt the insulation on the cord and start a fire.

HOW TO INSTALL A BASEBOARD HEATER

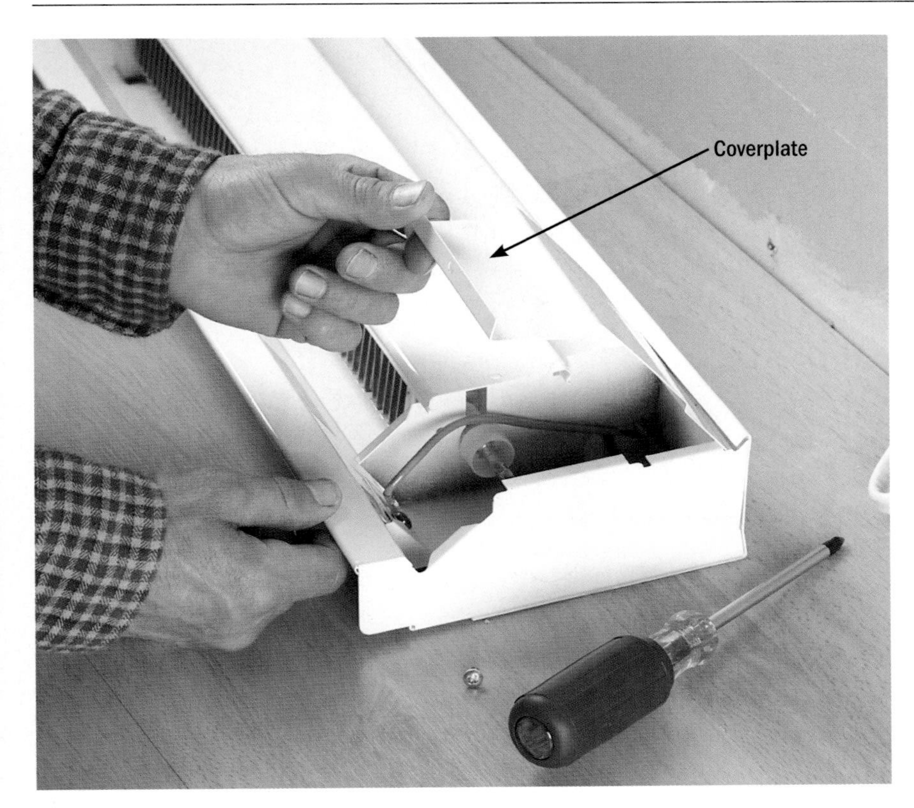

1 Bring power cable to the installation area (See pages 112 to 113). A 20-amp, 240-volt circuit wired with NM 12/2 cable with ground was run for the project shown here. Do not hook up the circuit at the service panel until the heater installation is complete. If you are using an existing circuit, turn off power at the main panel and test to make sure there is no current (See page 27). Determine which end of the heater the cable should enter and remove that coverplate from that end. Using a hammer and screwdriver, knock out a hole for the cable.

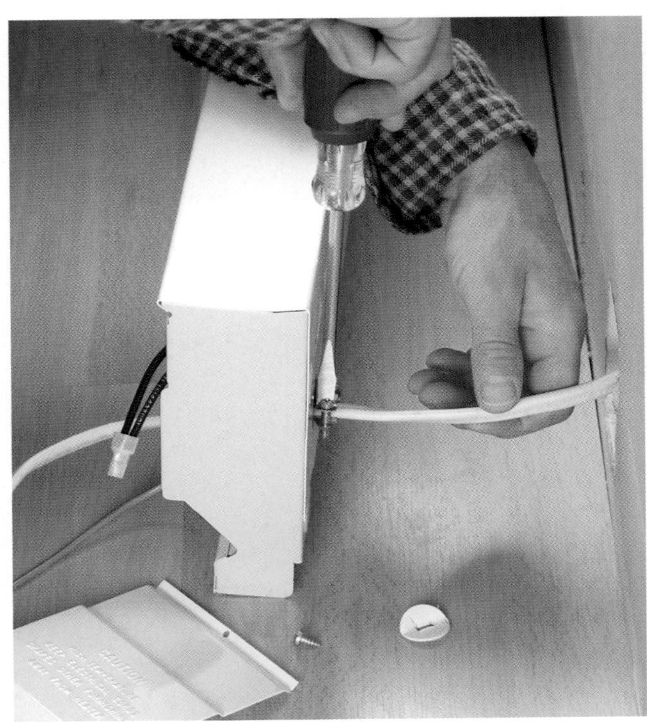

2 Run 6 to 8 in. of sheathed cable into the heater. Secure the cable to the internal junction box in the heater with a cable clamp.

3 Attach the baseboard heater to the wall by driving screws through the back panel at wall stud locations. You'll need to drill guide holes through the metal panels first—check the installation instructions for any restrictions on which parts of the back panel may be drilled.

HOW TO INSTALL A BASEBOARD HEATER (CONTINUED)

4 Strip all but about ½ in. of the sheathing off the cable. Tag the white conductor with black electrical tape to indicate that it's hot.

5 There will be two hot wires coming out of the heater, connected with a removable wire cap. Cut the wires just beneath the cap to separate them.

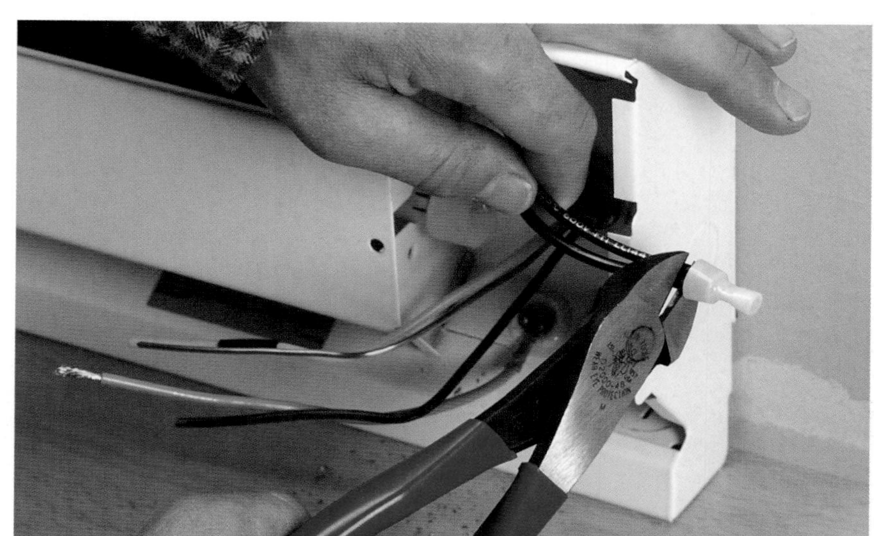

6 Strip ½ in. of insulation from each wire. Begin making the wire connections. The bare ground from the feeder cable should be connected to the ground screw on the frame of the heater, either directly or with the green pigtail wire that is preinstalled on some heaters.

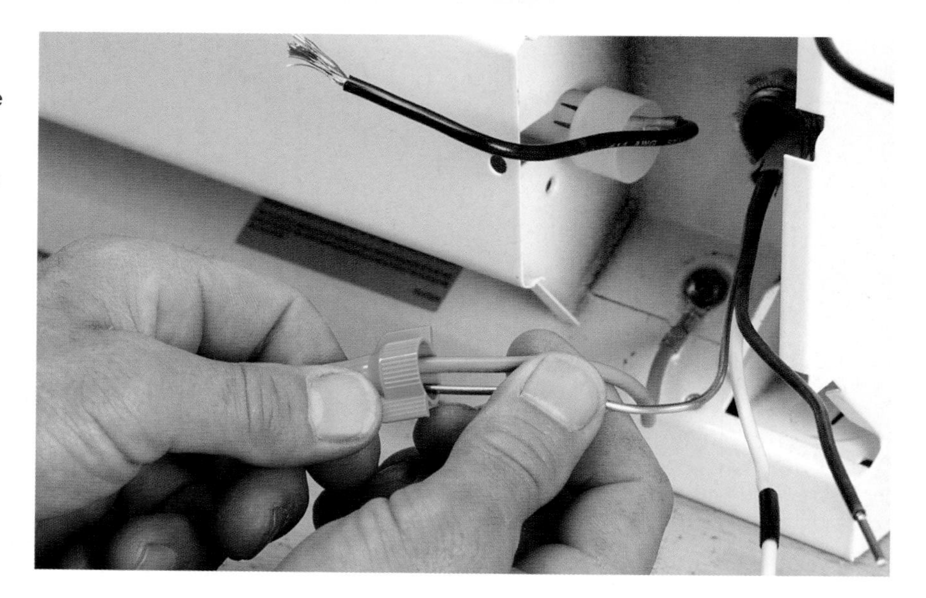

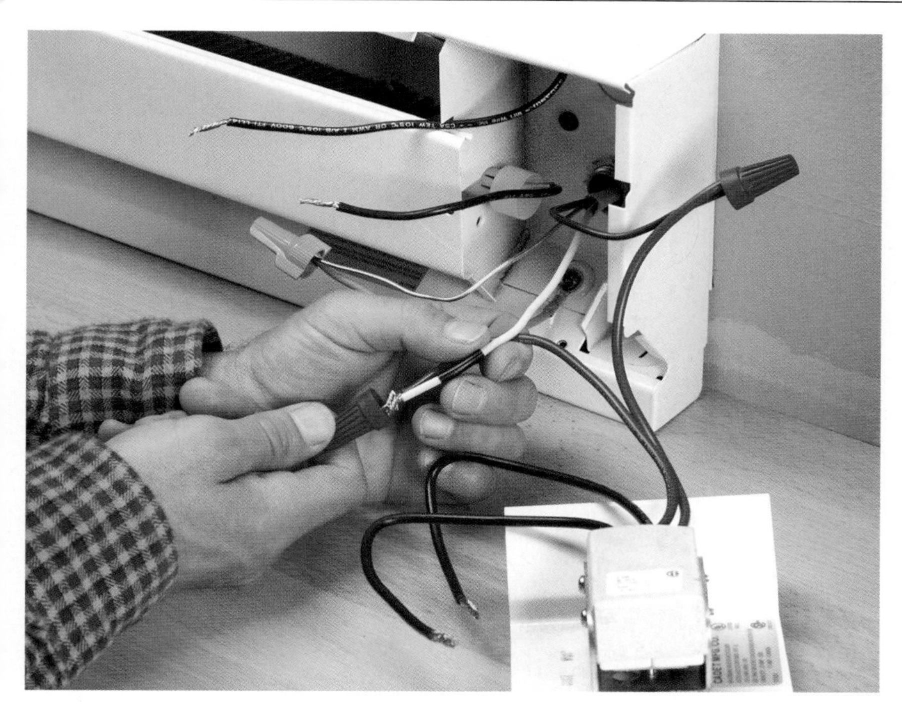

7 Splice the black wire from the feeder cable to one of the red wires from the double-pole thermostat (make sure to read the wiring instructions that come with the heater—some models will have a single-pole thermostat, and in some cases the wiring scheme is different if you choose to make the hookup in the junction box at the left end of the unit). Splice the tagged wire from the feeder cable to the other red wire from the thermostat.

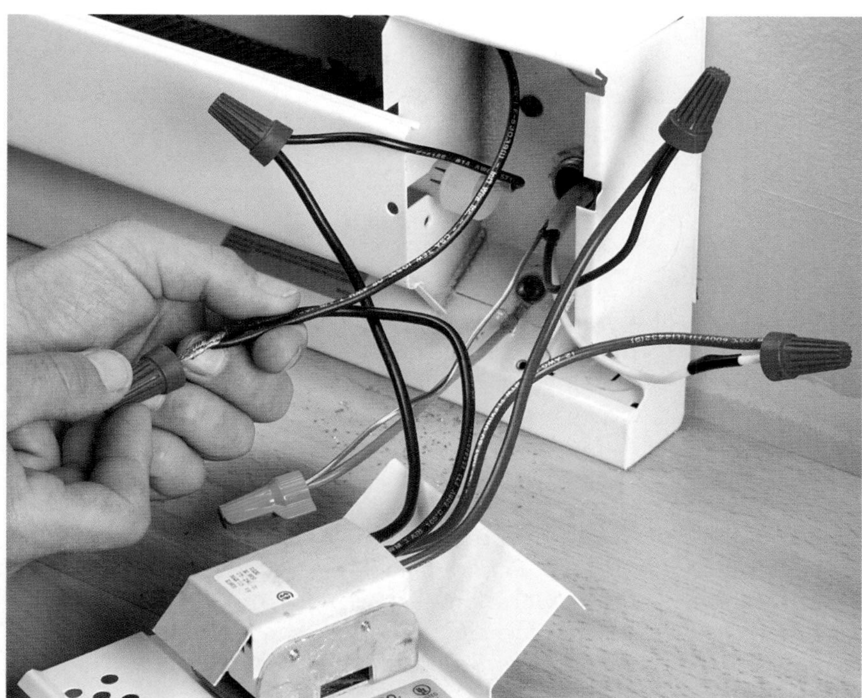

8 Splice each black wire from the thermostat to a black wire from the heater. Carefully fold the wires back into the junction box.

9 Reattach the coverplate to the heater. If you have run a new circuit for the heater, arrange to have the work inspected before supplying power to the circuit. Once the power is available, turn the heater on. Expect there to be some smoke and odor as the paint burns off the heater element—it should subside quickly.

Wall Mounting a TV

Too often the sleek appearance of a wall-mounted television is ruined by a mess of cords dangling underneath. If you're planning to mount a TV on the wall, take some time to consider the installation logistics. Knowing what challenges you'll face and developing a plan that addresses them can make a huge difference in the finished appearance of your home-theater setup.

The most foolproof approach is to purchase the television first and then work on the installation. But as long as you know the screen size, you can buy a bracket and complete most of the installation before you bring home the TV. (TVs within a given screen-size range have very similar weights and dimensions.)

Many wall-mount brackets are available, ranging from models that hold the TV flat and stationary to brackets that extend, tilt and turn so that the TV can be positioned to face almost any area in the room. Low-profile brackets keep the TV close to the wall, but they also leave little room for accessing the cable jacks, which can make connecting cables more difficult.

Choose a bracket that is rated to support your TV's weight and meets your viewing needs. Most brackets include detailed instructions and the necessary hardware to securely attach the bracket and TV to the wall. The bracket should be anchored into at least one wall stud. If you are installing a small bracket that will be attached between two studs, then use a wallboard anchor that is designed and rated to support heavy loads.

For the best viewing angle, a good rule of thumb is to mount the bracket at the eye level from which you'll most often watch TV. However, the design of the room may dictate that you mount the TV in another location, such as over a mantel. And if you have young children or pets, you may want to mount the TV high to keep it out of their reach.

The location of your AV components may also affect where you mount your TV. It's typically easier to rout cables when the components are close to the TV, but don't let their proximity to the TV limit your design. You can always use longer cables to reach the components.

You may choose to store your components in a closet or closed cabinet to keep them out of sight. If you hide your components, then you will need to

OUTLET BOX OPTIONS

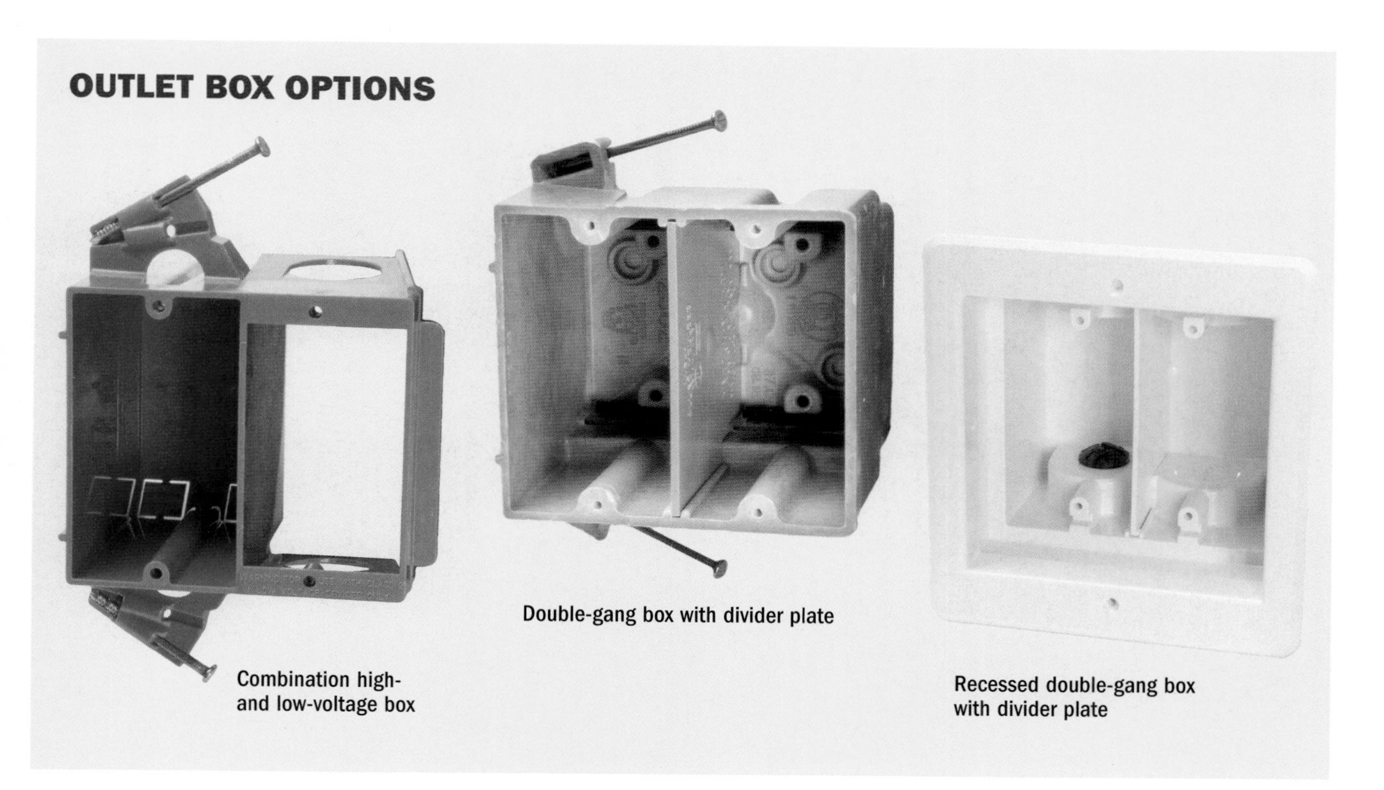

Combination high- and low-voltage box

Double-gang box with divider plate

Recessed double-gang box with divider plate

either install a remote control signal sensor that relays the signal or purchase a radio frequency remote that can send signals through cabinet doors or walls.

Routing cables is typically the most challenging part of a wall-mount installation. Two types of cables connect to the TV: high-voltage (the power cord) and low-voltage (audio, video and data cables). These two types of cables must not share the same space in an outlet box. You can install separate boxes for each type of cable or install a combination box with a divider that keeps the cables separated (see Outlet Box Options).

Professional installers have differing opinions about the best outlet box location. A good general rule is to install the box above the bracket if the TV will be mounted at or above standing eye-level and below the bracket if the TV will be mounted below standing eye-level. If you're not sure on which side of the TV the cables will connect, installing the box near the center of the bracket offers the most flexibility.

WALL TV CONNECTOR PLATE A & B

Connector plate

You may let the low-voltage component cables hang out of the outlet box opening or install a low-voltage connector cover plate. These plates make it easy to connect and disconnect cables and offer a more attractive appearance when the outlet box will not be concealed behind components.

HOW TO INSTALL

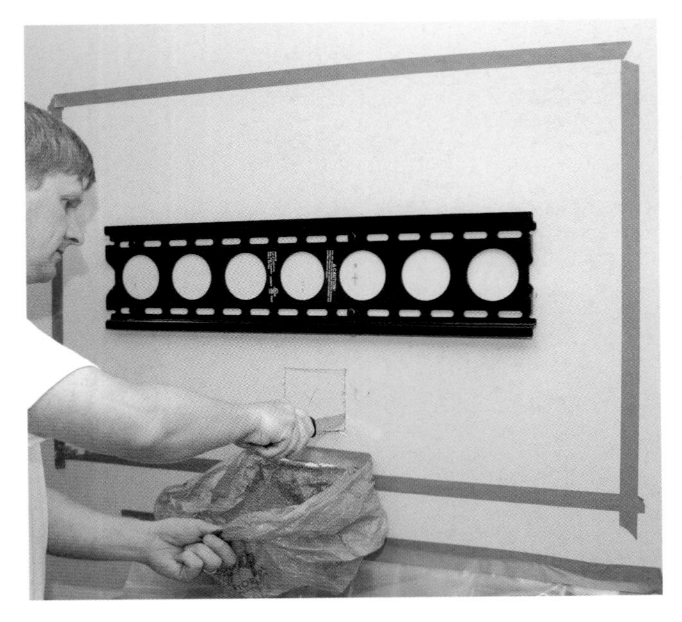

1 Determine the TV location. I used tape to mark the perimeter of the TV. Locate and mark the wall studs. Then install the bracket in the middle of the opening. Next, mark the location of the device box and cut the opening for it.

2 Rout power-supply cables to the device box. Rout audiovisual cables from the device box to the home-theater components. Then feed the ends of the cables into the device box and secure the box in the opening.

3 Connect the power-supply wires to the outlet. To protect the TV from power spikes, install an outlet that features surge protection.

4 Fasten the TV mounts to the back of the TV, and mount the TV on the wall bracket. Carefully follow all mounting instructions provided by the manufacturers of the bracket and the TV. Finally, connect the cables to the TV, wall plug and components.

Installing a Yard Light Post

A dark yard is great if you're a stargazer, but most people prefer a little illumination at night. Besides welcoming guests and helping to ensure a safe walk to your door, good exterior lighting deters prowlers.

Adding a light post is not difficult. If you've installed an interior light fixture, you should have no trouble with this project. Because the wires run underground, you'll have to do some digging, but a rented power trencher makes the job easy.

The wiring connections for a light post are fairly simple. Like any other fixture installed in a potentially wet location, you must protect the light post with a ground fault circuit interrupter (GFCI). You can buy a lantern with a photocell that automatically turns the light on and off or wire a switch to turn the light on and off.

First, determine the location of the light. You can't place a private light in the public right-of-way. Most cities require a minimum distance (2 to 4 ft.) between the street or sidewalk and any fixture that you intend to install. These restrictions will be identified when you apply for a project permit.

Another consideration when choosing a location for the light post is the path back to the power source (usually the location you will tie into the power at your house or garage). The shorter the distance, the less digging is required. Select a location that has the fewest obstructions in the path back to the power source. Avoid crossing under trees to prevent potential damage to root systems.

Next, dig the trench for the power cable.

SAFETY TIP

Before doing any digging, you must apply for a permit and have your property checked for buried utilities. You can dig short runs with a hand shovel, but for long runs or tough conditions it is much more efficient to rent a power trencher.

Use cable or wire and conduit that are approved by your local code for underground burial. Roll out the cable in the trench, leaving enough excess on each end to reach the power source and light post connections plus a couple of extra yards - you can always cut off the excess, but you can't stretch the cable if it's too short.

The cable must be protected by conduit from the point that it emerges from the ground to where it enters the house or garage. Cut a piece of ½-in. rigid nonmetallic conduit long enough to extend 12 in. below grade. Connect the conduit to an L-body fitting if you are going directly into the house or to a threaded male box connector if you are connecting to an exterior receptacle box. Fasten the conduit to the house with conduit straps, and seal any gaps in the house wall with silicone or latex sealant.

Make a frost loop in the trench and then feed the cable through the conduit. A frost loop provides slack for the cable so that connections aren't pulled apart during frost heave.

On the light post end of the trench, the post base must be anchored to a concrete footing. Create a path for the cable through the footing by running ½-in.-dia. conduit through a tubular concrete form. Level the form and backfill a few feet of the trench to hold the form in position. Do not fill the rest of the trench until the project has been inspected and approved.

Fill the form with concrete, keeping the conduit centered in the form. Next, push the anchor bolts attached to the post base into the wet concrete.

Feed the UF cable through the post, leaving 12 in. of cable extending out of the top of the post. Secure the post wiring connections with wire caps, and wrap the caps with electrical tape. Insert the wires back into the post. Secure the lantern to the post and secure the post to the base.

The light post must be protected by a GFCI. You can either tie into a circuit that is protected by a GFCI circuit breaker or install a GFCI receptacle. Make the wiring connections to the power supply in the house.

THE LIGHT POST CABLE'S PATH

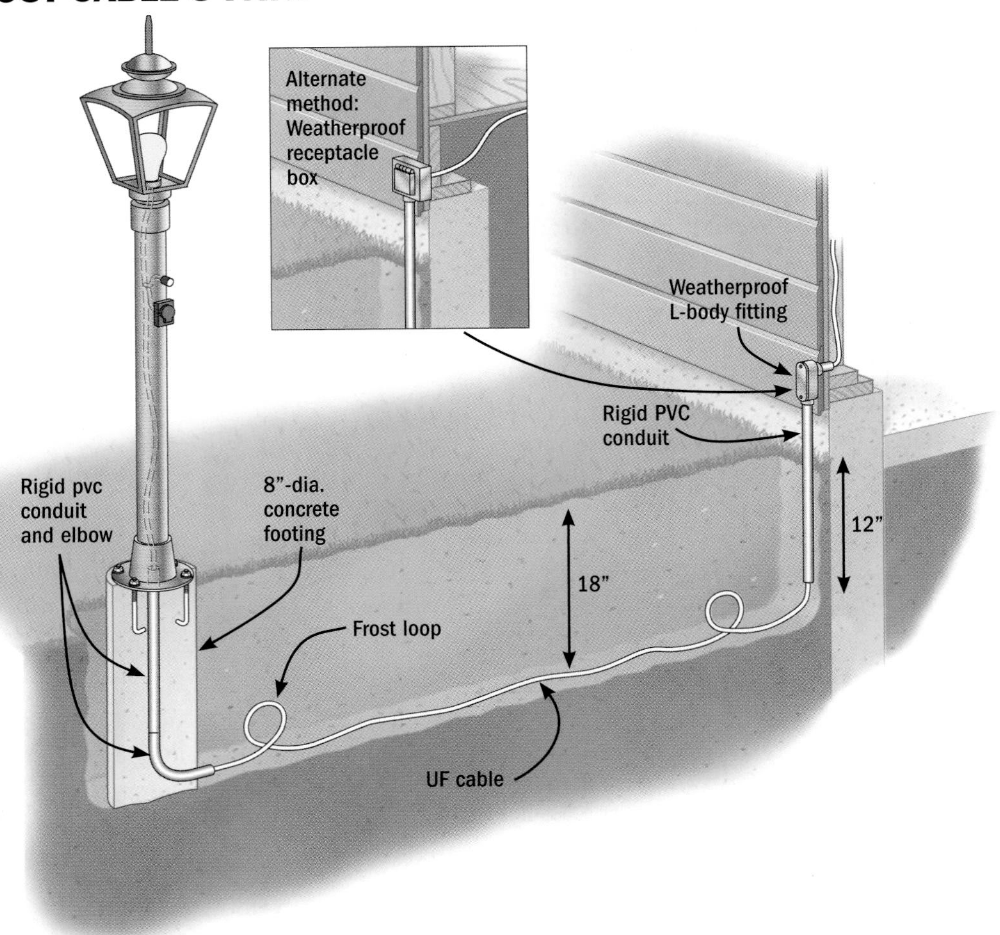

HOW TO INSTALL

1 Fit the short conduit section through the house and fasten the long section of conduit with a conduit strap. Pull the cable from the trench through the conduit and attach the L-body cover plate.

2 Fasten a 90-degree sweep and a 16-in. straight piece of PVC conduit. Fit the conduit through the concrete form and feed the cable from the trench through the conduit, leaving a frost loop in the trench. Backfill a few feet of the trench to hold the form in place.

3 Fill the form with freshly mixed concrete, keeping the conduit centered in the form. Position the post mount over the conduit and set the post mount anchor bolts in the wet concrete.

GFCI RECEPTACLE WIRING

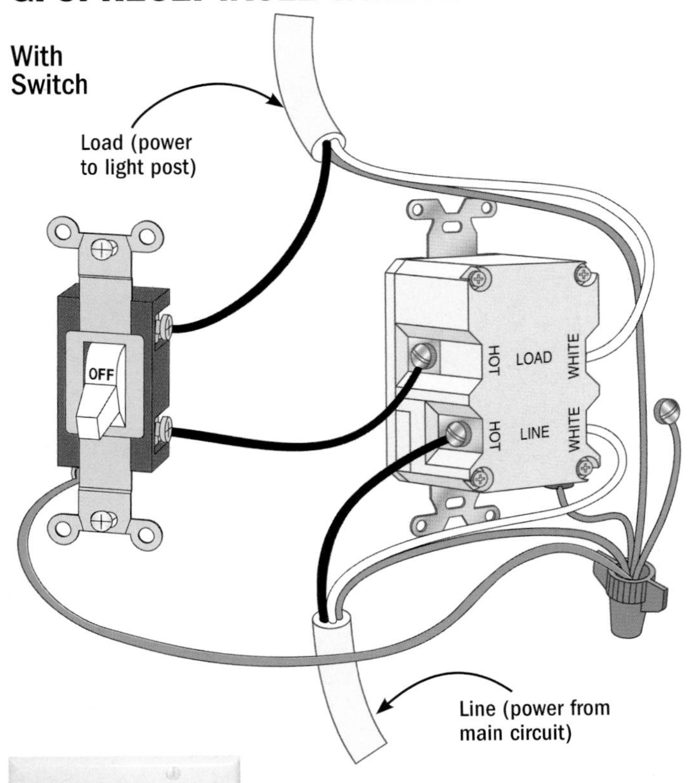

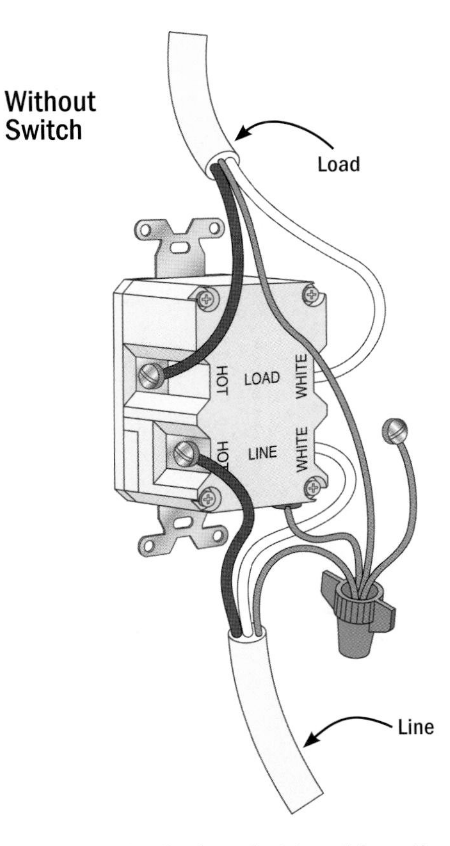

GFCI receptacles are designed to trip or cut off the flow of power when any abnormal current flow is detected. This protection is extended to other fixtures, such as a light post, when they are connected to the circuit after the GFCI. To do this, connect the incoming "line" wires that travel from the power source to the LINE terminals on the receptacle, and connect the outgoing "load" wires that travel to the light post to the LOAD terminals on the receptacle. [1 or 2 drawings – GFCI with a switch and GFCI alone]

4 Connect the line and load cables to the switch and GFCI receptacle terminals (see "GFCI Receptacle Wiring,"). Replace the switch/ receptacle box cover plate when connections are complete (inset).

5 Feed the cable through the post and connect the cable, photocell, receptacle and lantern wires as directed in the light post manufacturer installation instructions. Twist a wire cap on all connections and wrap the cap with electrical tape.

6 After the concrete has cured for at least 24 hours, lower the post into the base. Secure the post with the base set screws. Once the post is secure, test the lantern and GFCI operation.

By providing electrical service from the house, you can make your garage or shed safer and more convenient to use.

Bringing Service to an Outbuilding

Electrical service increases the utility and security of any outbuilding, including garages and sheds. Most codes require that the outbuilding be wired on its own circuit or circuits—be sure to check your local codes to get requirements and permits and to arrange for inspection of the wiring. All circuits servicing outbuildings must be GFCI protected (See pages 98 to 110). The best way to provide protection is to install a GFCI breaker in the service panel (See page 42). Another option (the one used in the shed-wiring project shown here) is to install a GFCI-protected receptacle at the beginning of the run and wire it to protect all devices that follow it on the circuit. Make sure to consider your power needs before beginning your project. If you plan to use power equipment, such as a table saw or air compressor in the outbuilding, make sure the service you provide is adequate (See page 8). Many stationary tools require a dedicated 20-amp circuit.

WIRING DIAGRAM: POWER FROM HOUSE TO OUTBUILDING

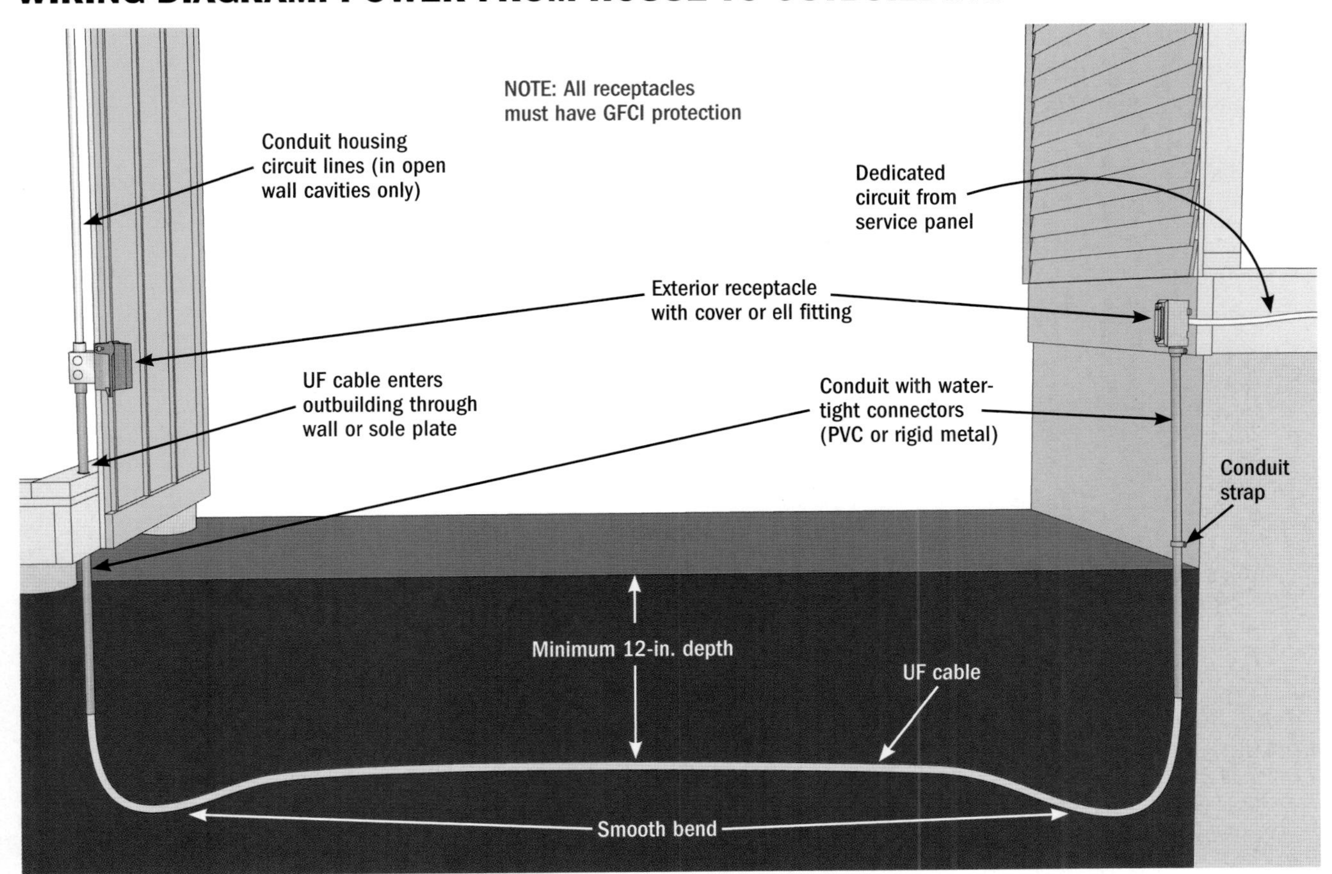

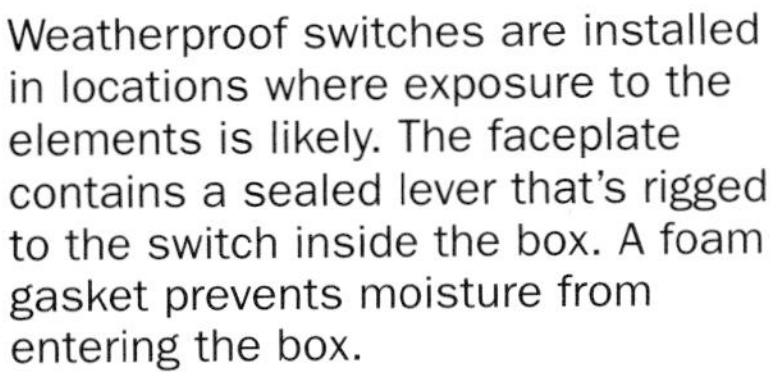

Weatherproof switches are installed in locations where exposure to the elements is likely. The faceplate contains a sealed lever that's rigged to the switch inside the box. A foam gasket prevents moisture from entering the box.

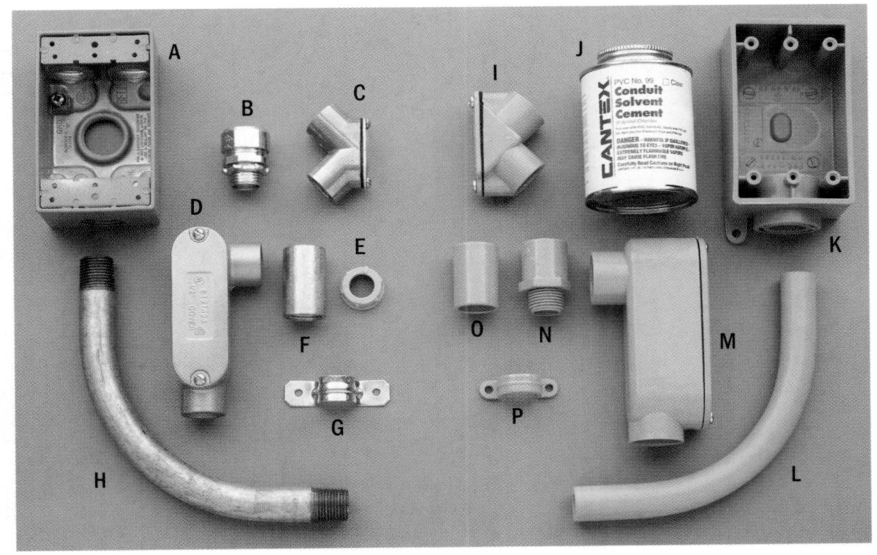

Conduit fittings make bending conduit unnecessary for most exterior wiring jobs. *Common fittings for metal conduit include:* (A) Exterior box; (B) compression coupling; (C) 90° connector; (D) ell fitting; (E) plastic bushing; (F) threaded coupling; (G) pipe strap; (H) 90° sweep. *Common fittings for PVC (plastic) conduit include:* (I) 90° connector; (J) conduit solvent compound (for solvent-welding jowints); (K) exterior box; (L) 90° sweep; (M) ell fitting; (N) threaded coupling; (O) straight coupling; (P) plastic pipe strap.

HOW TO RUN ELECTRICAL SERVICE TO AN OUTBUILDING

1 Provide power (outbuildings usually require a separate circuit; most garages need two 20-amp circuits). Run circuit cable from the panel to the selected exit point on the exterior of your house. Drilling through the rim joist of the house is probably the most expedient spot to feed the new cable through. Use conduit to get from the service panel to the exit point at the foundation wall. See pages 112 to 113 (Tips for running cable), 45 to 46 (Installing a new circuit) and 36 to 37 (Conduit). Do not hook up the circuit at the panel until all the wiring has been completed and inspected. If using an existing circuit, shut off the power or disconnect the circuit before continuing.

2 Dig a trench for the UF (Underground Feeder) cable. If your new circuit will be GFCI-protected (and it should be), you only need to bury the cable 12 in. deep, in most cases. We used a narrow trenching shovel for the job, but for longer runs or runs in very hard soil, you may want to rent a power trenching machine. To reduce the risk of cutting through the buried cable, try to locate the trench in an area where you won't be likely to dig in the future (for example, under a pathway, as seen here).

CAUTION: Contact your public utilities company to have them inspect your site at least three days before you plan to dig. As a free service, they will flag any cables or pipes that are within the general construction area.

3 Cut a length of conduit to fit from the bottom of the exterior box to a point 12 in. below grade at the wall. We used ½-in.-dia. rigid PVC conduit (See photo, previous page). You'll need to excavate an extra 4 in. next to the house so you can run the UF cable out of the conduit and bend it smoothly back up to 12 in. depth. In most cases, a conduit sweep like the ones pictured on the previous page are not required, but make sure to check your local building codes first.

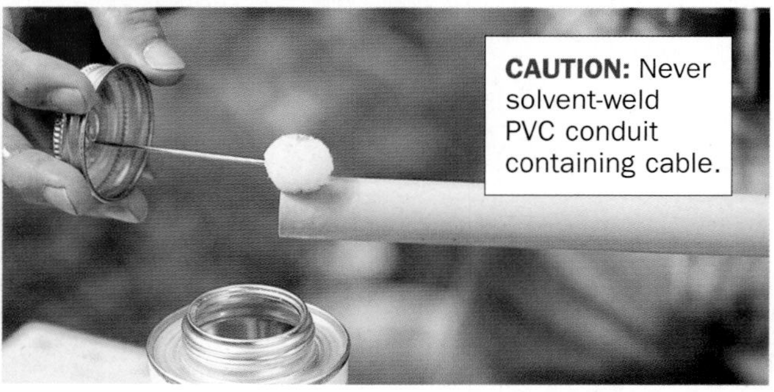

CAUTION: Never solvent-weld PVC conduit containing cable.

4 Cut the conduit section to length: with PVC conduit, use a tubing cutter (top photo); if you're using metal conduit, use a hacksaw. Attach the section of conduit to the receptacle box or junction box you plan to attach to the exterior house wall. Use waterproof connectors for metal conduit and use solvent cement for PVC (bottom photo). In most cases, you'll need to use a connector to transition from the conduit to the box.

5 Anchor the receptacle or junction box to the house wall, then anchor the conduit to the foundation. Use self-tapping masonry screws to attach conduit straps to concrete or block walls. Seal the edges of the box with silicone caulk.

6 Feed one end of the UF cable up through the bottom opening in the conduit and into the box mounted on the house. You'll need at least 12 in. of cable to work with in the box.

7 Strip sheathing and insulation from both cables (See page 34), then install the exterior receptacle or junction box (See pages 65 to 66). We installed a GFCI-protected receptacle and wired it to protect the other outlets downstream (See pages 103 to 105).

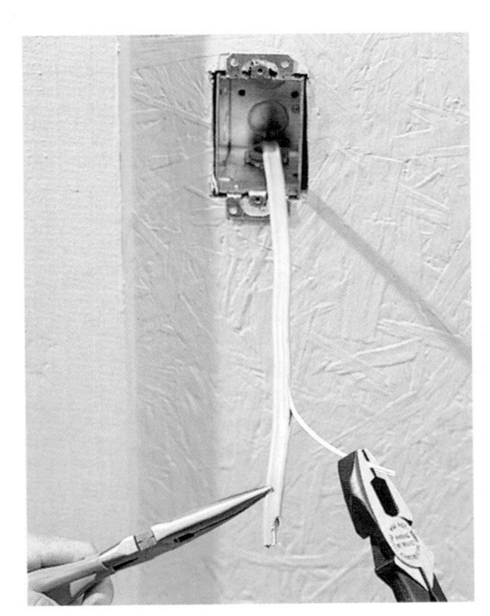

TIP: UF cable sheathing is tougher than ordinary NM thermoplastic sheathing and stripping it can be tricky. Nip the end of the cable to expose the wire ends, and lightly score the sheathing with a knife before pulling. Get a tight grasp on one of the conductors with a pair of pliers, then pull the sheathing with another pair of pliers to separate the wires from the sheathing.

8 Roll out the cable in the trench until you reach the outbuilding. Take care not to kink the cable and be sure to inspect the bottom of the trench for any sharp objects first. Also make sure the bend in the cable is smooth after it exits the conduit. Do not cut the cable to length yet.

9 Drill through the wall or floor of the outbuilding at the selected service entry point. In the shed shown here, we drilled a hole through the soleplate just inside the outer joist location. The hole should be about ⅛ in. larger in diameter than the conduit diameter.

10 Cut out an opening for the exterior outlet box. Generally, it's easier to mount the box inside the outbuilding, with the front edges flush with the exterior walls, than it is to flush-mount an exterior box on the exterior wall then feed the cable in, as you may have done at the house.

11 Attach the conduit to the outlet box at the outbuilding. In the photo above, a male PVC coupling is solvent-welded to the conduit then secured inside the metal box with a cable clamp nut. Secure the conduit to the wall framing members with cable straps. To keep moisture and insects out, seal the entry hole with silicone caulk.

12 Pull the UF cable up through the conduit and into the outlet box, using a fish tape if necessary. Keep enough slack in the cable so you can create a gentle curve toward the house at the point where the cable enters the conduit.

13 Make the wiring connections at the entry outlet in the outbuilding. Protect receptacles with a weatherproof outlet cover (inset photo and page 66). At the house, make sure all connections are properly made. Do not hook up the power until your work has passed an on-site inspection (if you are adding additional new outlets, wait until you've completed that work before arranging for the inspection). After the inspection, turn on the power for the new circuit.

14 After power is supplied, test the circuit with a plug-in analyzer to make sure power is present, polarization is correct and the ground-fault protection is functioning properly.

TIP: For extra protection against cutting through the UF cable with a shovel, lay scraps of exterior-rated wood across the top of the cable after you lay it in the trench.

15 Backfill the trench, making sure there are no sharp objects in the backfill material. Tamp the backfill with a hand tamper. Do not fill the trench until after the work has been inspected. Additional outlets (See pages 156 to 157) on the same circuit should be installed prior to the inspection.

HOW TO RUN ELECTRICAL SERVICE TO AN OUTBUILDING: ADDING ADDITIONAL OUTLETS

NOTE: The following two pages show options for adding additional outlets to the new circuit installed in steps 1 through 15 of this project. Be sure to have all new work inspected before making final electrical hook-ups at the service panel.

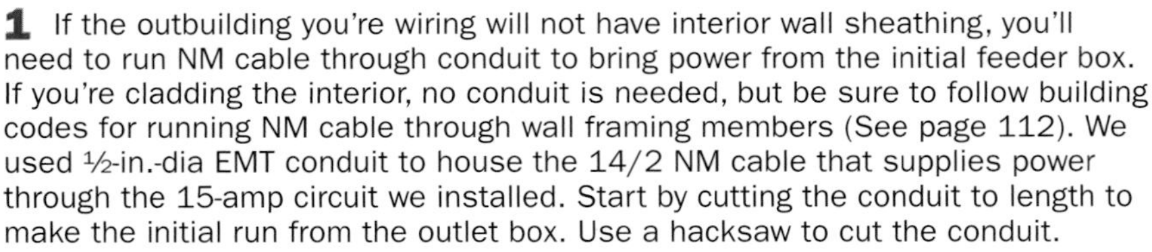

1 If the outbuilding you're wiring will not have interior wall sheathing, you'll need to run NM cable through conduit to bring power from the initial feeder box. If you're cladding the interior, no conduit is needed, but be sure to follow building codes for running NM cable through wall framing members (See page 112). We used ½-in.-dia EMT conduit to house the 14/2 NM cable that supplies power through the 15-amp circuit we installed. Start by cutting the conduit to length to make the initial run from the outlet box. Use a hacksaw to cut the conduit.

2 Connect the conduit to the outlet box with a conduit connector (an offset connector with setscrews is shown here).

3 Use metal straps to secure the conduit to the wall framing members. Most codes specify that you install a strap no further than 3 ft. from any fixture and that a strap be used at intervals no more than 10 ft. apart in straight runs. Also mount a strap near elbows and sweeps in the conduit run.

4 Feed the cable from the outlet box and through the conduit as you make connections. A fish tape can be useful. Also, be sure to deburr the cut ends of conduit before inserting cable. Install the next outlet in line: It's generally not recommended that you combine wall outlets and lights on the same circuit, but for a small outbuilding you may choose to go ahead and do it. In such cases, you'll find it easier to wire the receptacles in series before interrupting with any switches and lights. We installed an interior receptacle (GFCI protection is required) next.

5 If installing more fixtures from the feed line, attach conduit to each box as you work. In the photo shown here, conduit has been run to a light switch location. Attach the cover-plate to the box after making wiring connections.

6 Run power to the cable and conduit to the next box: since it's generally better to bring power for switched fixtures to the switch first, we ran cable up the wall cavity to a double-gang box that houses a switch for the ceiling light and one for the outdoor light. Wire the switches. We ran a separate line from each switch to the fixture it controls. In some cases, you may find it more efficient to run NM/3 cable and pigtail the shared white neutral at the first box before running the feed wire from the second switch to the fixture at the end of the line.

7 Wire and install the first switched fixture: in this case, an interior ceiling light mounted to a ceiling box on the inside of the shed. Be sure to follow all manufacturer's directions for installing and grounding the fixture.

8 Install the remaining fixtures, if any. In the project shown here, an exterior on-at-dusk security light was installed. The box for the light was installed with the outer edges flush with the exterior wall surface. For security reasons, we located the switch inside the shed so the light cannot be turned off from outside. If you prefer to locate the switch so it's accessible from outside, be sure to use a weatherproof switch (See page 151). When you've finished installing all the fixtures, caulk around all moisture entry points on the outlets and fixtures with silicone caulk. Arrange for your final inspection.

Index